PROBLEMS AND SOLUTIONS IN GENERAL PHYSICS

for Science and Engineering Students

PROBLEMS AND SOLUTIONS

SIMON G. G. MacDONALD, University of St. Andrews, Dundee, Scotland

IN GENERAL PHYSICS
for Science and Engineering Students

ADDISON-WESLEY PUBLISHING COMPANY

READING, MASSACHUSETTS · LONDON · PALO ALTO · DON MILLS, ONTARIO

This book is in the
Addison-Wesley series in Physics

Preface

The idea of writing a book of this type has been in the back of my mind for some years. My experience as a university teacher in the United Kingdom and in the West Indies has convinced me that the average student is badly in need of help in tackling the solving of problems in physics. Far less time appears to be spent in choosing and preparing material for recitation classes than in the selection and preparation of lecture notes and demonstrations, though it is arguable that the former is of greater importance and requires greater care.

The necessary resolution to sit down and write the book was acquired in 1964, part of which year I spent in the United States as a visiting professor. There I found the same problem as in Britain. In both countries a student can pick up a reasonable working knowledge of the ideas of physics from formal lectures and textbooks, and spends enough time in the laboratory, under supervision, to acquire the rudiments of an experimental technique. But problem-solving is something that he finds inordinately difficult. Professors have long ago accepted the fact that a student cannot be expected to comprehend the fundamental ideas of physics from lecture sessions alone, and the avalanche of basic texts which pours from the presses each year attests to our desire to give the student the best possible material with which to supplement these lectures. But we still expect him to acquire a knowledge of how to apply his information to practical problems by attending recitation classes with little further supplementary work.

Most textbooks give a few simple examples in the text and then set much more difficult problems, with very few hints for solution, at the end of each chapter. It would therefore appear that a book of carefully thought-out problems, covering the standard groundwork of a basic physics course and worked out in detail with full explanation of the methods used, would fill a gap in the present system and prove helpful to the serious student. There have been conflicting views expressed about the amount of detail required in the solutions in such a book. Too great detail will bore the competent student, besides making the book of inordinate length and excessive price; too few intermediate steps will leave the average student bemused. I have attempted to steer a middle course.

I have tried to brighten up some of the hoary old problems that have been in circulation since physics became a recognized university subject. Other problem situations have been constructed to fill obvious gaps. But the ideas for most of the problems came from the vast field that every conscientious lecturer surveys in making up his notes and recitation class questions: textbooks, problem papers, old examination questions, his own imagination, and the rest. An acknowledgment of indebtedness is therefore not possible in the space available. In some cases the indebtedness is hard to pinpoint, since the same problem appears in identical form in several sources and priority is difficult to assign. I am very grateful to the University of St. Andrews for permission to use problems set for their past degree examination papers; but for the rest, I have accepted ideas only, and have constructed new problems around them. If anyone recognizes in the text that follows some of his own brain children, suitably disguised, I can only extend to him here my grateful thanks for the idea.

It is inevitable in a book of this type that the occasional error will creep in, even although all solutions have been checked independently. I shall be extremely pleased to have these pointed out to me.

My sincere thanks are due to Dr. D. M. Burns for the immense amount of work put in by him in checking the solutions to the problems, and to Dr. Burns and Professor G. D. Preston for their valuable criticisms of the first draft of the book. I should also like to express my appreciation of the helpful advice and criticism given on specific topics by many of my other colleagues in Dundee, and I must express my gratitude to Miss P. M. Mitchell for producing such an excellent typescript from a mass of barely readable material.

Finally, acknowledgment must be made of the understanding and patience shown by my wife, who has endured, for so many evenings while this book was being written, a moody and preoccupied husband and a sadly curtailed social life.

Dundee, Scotland   S.G.G.M.
June 1967

Introduction

This book falls quite naturally into three parts. In the first section an attempt is made to cover the whole basic range of physics with worked examples illustrating all the major manipulations required to apply theory to the solution of everyday problems. In the second section, the reader is given a collection of problems to do for himself to see whether he has absorbed the principles laid down in the previous part of the book. Solutions to all these problems are supplied at the end of this section. And, finally, the third section contains further problems without solutions, although the answers to all these problems are given.

If the book is to succeed in its aim of teaching students how to set about solving problems, and if it is at the same time to be of reasonable length, the interruption of the text with condensed versions of the theory required at any stage is to be avoided. It is for this reason that the layout of the first section of the book has been tied to existing widely used basic texts. This also has the advantage that symbols need not be laboriously explained and that equations can be quoted with little comment. The contents of most basic texts are very similar, although the subjects may be taken in a slightly different order from one book to the next. This should present no great difficulty, as the chapters in this book are clearly titled and a subject index is included at the end.

Section I provides worked examples covering the whole range of topics dealt with in most textbooks of wide circulation.* To solve the problems in any chapter, the reader need know only the theory of the subject matter of that chapter or of a previous one. Diagrams are used freely throughout, since there is no better way of seeing clearly what is happening. British and metric units are used, as in all standard textbooks, but in the electricity and magnetism chapters only the rationalized MKS system of units is employed. This conforms with current practice.

The second section of the book contains just over a hundred problems drawn from all branches of the subject and arranged, as far as possible, in the same order as in Section I. If he has conscientiously worked through to this point, the student should find these problems well within his capabilities. The solutions to the problems are grouped at the end of the section so that the reader will not be tempted, when the method of solution is not immediately apparent, to let his eye stray from question to answer.

The third section is intended to provide the student with further practice in the skills he has acquired and may prove useful to teachers in recitation classes.

A student can replace symbols in a formula by numbers just as easily as a teacher can. The area in which he needs guidance is that of deciding which formula to use, and selecting and tying together the various pieces of knowledge he has acquired at various stages. Problems of the plug-in type are therefore

---

*For example, to name but a few, *University Physics* or *College Physics*, by Sears and Zemansky (Addison-Wesley); *Modern University Physics* or *Modern College Physics* by Richards, Sears, Wehr, and Zemansky (Addison-Wesley); *Physics for Students of Science and Engineering*, by Halliday and Resnick (Wiley); *Elements of Physics* or *Principles of College Physics* by Shortley and Williams (Prentice-Hall); *Elementary Classical Physics* and *Elementary Modern Physics* by Weidner and Sells (Allyn and Bacon); *Physics* by Hazen and Pidd (Addison-Wesley); *Modern College Physics*, by White (Van Nostrand).

avoided as far as possible in the following pages. An attempt has been made instead to use examples in which a little thought and a good understanding of physics will lead to a solution, and it is hoped that students will get the feel of problem-solving from working through the book. All the basic manipulations are represented and it is believed that no major item has been omitted.

The number of significant figures used in the working of any problem has been selected in order to conform both to the number of figures quoted in the given data and also to the accuracy of experimental results obtainable in the branch of physics dealt with in the problem. Thus physical constants such as c, e, or h, which are not quoted in the problem but are required for the solution, and which are listed in the appendix, are given only to the accuracy required. They are therefore quoted with a different number of significant figures in different problems. Note that it simplifies calculation if g is taken as π^2 m $\cdot$ s^{-2} in all problems of simple harmonic motion, since this is an approximation which is correct to better than 1%.

The optical sign convention used in this book is one that has become increasingly popular in recent years. Object distances measured against the oncoming light are taken as positive, and image distances measured with the ongoing light are taken as positive, all distances being measured from the vertex of the optical component. Distances measured to centers of curvature and focal points are positive if measured with the ongoing light, and distances above the axis are also positive. It should be noted that this system is essentially the same as the "real is positive, virtual is negative" system, except that when light strikes a refracting surface, going from a more-dense into a less-dense medium, the sign of the radius of curvature of that surface is reversed.

For the benefit of the student or teacher who wishes to refer back to problems of a particular type, an index is included. All problems which deal with a specific subject are listed there according to chapter and problem number if in Section I, or according to section and problem number if in the other sections.

Although the first section of the book is designed to explain to the reader how to solve typical problems in physics, the more competent student should be able to solve quite a few of them for himself. He should therefore tackle each problem on his own before reading through the solution. In this way he will more readily come to an appreciation of his mistakes and misunderstandings and to a knowledge of how he may correct them.

It should also be stressed to all readers, whether they intend to attempt the problems in Section I themselves or not, that they should study the appropriate theory thoroughly before looking at the problems. Further, they should read carefully through the solution step by step, making sure that they appreciate fully why a given problem has been done in the particular way it has. It does not benefit the reader, or for that matter the author, for the reader to glance through the solution and then raise his eyes to heaven overcome with its simplicity and beauty, if he is then unable to carry out a similar solution himself.

Contents

SECTION II

SECTION III

SECTION I

1

Composition and Resolution of Vectors

PROBLEM 1.1

An army recruit on a training exercise is instructed to walk due west for 5 mi, then in a northeasterly direction for 4 mi, and finally in a southeasterly direction for 3 mi. When he completes his exercise, how far is he from his starting point and how far north and west of it?

Solution. Each portion of the recruit's walk represents a displacement in space and may therefore be represented by a vector, as in the diagram.* The first vector will lie due west and will have a length F_1 cm, where

$$F_1 \text{ cm} = k \text{ cm} \cdot \text{mi}^{-1} \times 5 \text{ mi},$$

and k is a suitable conversion factor to make the vector of reasonable length.

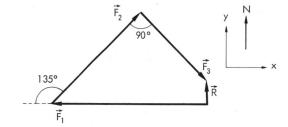

Similarly, the second portion of the walk is represented by a vector of length F_2 cm, where

$$F_2 \text{ cm} = k \text{ cm} \cdot \text{mi}^{-1} \times 4 \text{ mi},$$

and points in the northeasterly direction from the end of the first displacement vector.

Finally, the third part of the walk is represented by a vector of length F_3 cm, where

$$F_3 \text{ cm} = k \text{ cm} \cdot \text{mi}^{-1} \times 3 \text{ mi},$$

and points in the southeasterly direction from the end of the second displacement vector.

A vector **R** is now drawn from the starting point to the end of the third vector; **R** is equal to the sum of the three displacement vectors originally drawn. That is,

$$\mathbf{R} = \mathbf{F}_1 + \mathbf{F}_2 + \mathbf{F}_3.$$

Thus $(R_x; R_y) \equiv (F_{1x} + F_{2x} + F_{3x}; F_{1y} + F_{2y} + F_{3y})$. But

$$R_x = -F_1 + F_2 \cos 45° + F_3 \cos 45° = \left(-5 + 4 \times \frac{1}{\sqrt{2}} + 3 \times \frac{1}{\sqrt{2}}\right) \text{mi}$$

$$= (-5 + 3.5\sqrt{2}) \text{ mi} = -0.051 \text{ mi}$$

and

$$R_y = 0 + F_2 \sin 45° - F_3 \sin 45° = \left(4 \times \frac{1}{\sqrt{2}} - 3 \times \frac{1}{\sqrt{2}}\right) \text{ mi} = 0.707 \text{ mi}.$$

Thus $(R_x; R_y) = (-0.051 \text{ mi}; 0.707 \text{ mi})$. The recruit finishes 0.051 mi west and 0.707 mi north of his starting point.

The vector **R** is one of magnitude $\sqrt{R_x^2 + R_y^2}$ at an angle of $\tan^{-1}(R_y/R_x)$ to the x-axis. Thus **R** has magnitude of 0.709 mi and makes an angle of $94°8'$ with the positive direction of the x-axis.

---

*In all diagrams, a vector is represented by a letter symbol with an arrow above it. In text material, a vector is represented by boldface type.

PROBLEM 1.2

Three forces acting at a point are $\mathbf{F}_1 = 2\mathbf{i} - \mathbf{j} + 3\mathbf{k}$, $\mathbf{F}_2 = -\mathbf{i} + 3\mathbf{j} + 2\mathbf{k}$, and $\mathbf{F}_3 = -\mathbf{i} + 2\mathbf{j} - \mathbf{k}$. Find the directions and magnitudes of $\mathbf{F}_1 + \mathbf{F}_2 + \mathbf{F}_3$, $\mathbf{F}_1 - \mathbf{F}_2 + \mathbf{F}_3$, and $\mathbf{F}_1 + \mathbf{F}_2 - \mathbf{F}_3$.

Solution. When vectors are added (or subtracted), their components in the directions of the unit vectors add (or subtract) algebraically. Thus since

$$\mathbf{F}_1 = 2\mathbf{i} - \mathbf{j} + 3\mathbf{k}, \qquad \mathbf{F}_2 = -\mathbf{i} + 3\mathbf{j} + 2\mathbf{k}, \qquad \mathbf{F}_3 = -\mathbf{i} + 2\mathbf{j} - \mathbf{k},$$

then it follows that

$$\mathbf{F}_1 + \mathbf{F}_2 + \mathbf{F}_3 = 0\mathbf{i} + 4\mathbf{j} + 4\mathbf{k}.$$

Similarly, one may write

$$\mathbf{F}_1 - \mathbf{F}_2 + \mathbf{F}_3 = 2\mathbf{i} - 2\mathbf{j} + 0\mathbf{k} \qquad \text{and} \qquad \mathbf{F}_1 + \mathbf{F}_2 - \mathbf{F}_3 = 2\mathbf{i} + 0\mathbf{j} + 6\mathbf{k}.$$

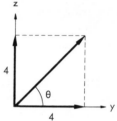

The vector $\mathbf{F}_1 + \mathbf{F}_2 + \mathbf{F}_3$ thus has no component in the x-direction, one of 4 units in the y-direction, and one of 4 units in the z-direction. It therefore has a magnitude of $\sqrt{4^2 + 4^2}$ units $= 4\sqrt{2}$ units $= 5.66$ units, and lies in the $y - z$ plane, making an angle θ with the y-axis, where $\tan \theta = \frac{4}{4} = 1$. Thus $\theta = 45°$.

Similarly, $\mathbf{F}_1 - \mathbf{F}_2 + \mathbf{F}_3$ has a magnitude of $2\sqrt{2}$ units $= 2.82$ units, and lies in the $x - y$ plane, making an angle ϕ with the x-axis, where $\tan \phi = -\frac{2}{2} = -1$. Thus $\phi = 135°$.

Also $\mathbf{F}_1 + \mathbf{F}_2 - \mathbf{F}_3$ has a magnitude of $\sqrt{2^2 + 6^2}$ units $= 2\sqrt{10}$ units $= 6.32$ units, and lies in the $x - z$ plane at an angle χ to the x-axis, where $\tan \chi = \frac{6}{2} = 3$. Thus $\chi = 71°34'$.

PROBLEM 1.3

The pilot of an airplane flying on a straight course knows from his instruments that his airspeed is 300 mph. He also knows that a 60-mph gale is blowing at an angle of 60° to his course. How can he calculate his velocity relative to the ground?

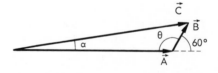

Solution. Relative to an observer on the ground, the airplane has two velocities, one of 300 mph relative to the air and the other of 60 mph at an angle of 60° to the course, due to the fact that it is carried along by the moving air mass.

To obtain the total velocity, it is therefore necessary to add the two components by vector addition. In the diagram, $\mathbf{A}$ represents completely, in magnitude and direction, the velocity of the aircraft relative to the air, and $\mathbf{B}$ the velocity of the air relative to the ground. When they are added in the normal manner of vector addition, $\mathbf{C}$ is their resultant. The magnitude of $\mathbf{C}$ is given by the formula

$$C^2 = A^2 + B^2 - 2AB \cos \theta.$$

But $A = 300$ mph, $B = 60$ mph, and $\theta = (180° - 60°) = 120°$. Therefore

$$C^2 = (300 \text{ mph})^2 + (60 \text{ mph})^2 - 2 \times 300 \text{ mph} \times 60 \text{ mph}(-\tfrac{1}{2}) = 111{,}600 \text{ (mph)}^2;$$
$$\therefore \quad C = 334 \text{ mph}.$$

Also, from the addition formula for vectors, we have

$$\sin \alpha = \frac{B}{C} \sin \theta = \frac{60 \text{ mph}}{334 \text{ mph}} \times \frac{\sqrt{3}}{2} = 0.156.$$
$$\therefore \quad \alpha = 9°.$$

PROBLEM 1.4

One of the holes on the Old Course at St. Andrews, in Scotland, runs due west. When playing on it recently, a golfer sliced his tee shot badly and landed in thick rough 120 yd WNW of the tee. The ball was in such a bad lie that he was forced to blast it SSW onto the fairway, where it came to rest

75 yd from him. A chip shot onto the green, which carried 64 yd, took the ball to a point 6 ft past the hole on a direct line from hole to tee. He sank the putt. What is the length of this hole? (As everyone knows, the Old Course is perfectly flat.)

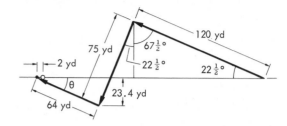

Solution. Since the course is flat, all displacements are in the one horizontal plane. The west and north components of the tee shot are $120 \cos 22\frac{1}{2}° = 110.9$ yd and $120 \sin 22\frac{1}{2}° = 45.9$ yd, respectively.

The west and south components of the second shot are similarly $75 \sin 22\frac{1}{2}° = 28.7$ yd and $75 \cos 22\frac{1}{2}° = 69.3$ yd. The ball after the second shot is thus $(110.9 + 28.7)$ yd $= 139.6$ yd west and $(69.3 - 45.9)$ yd $= 23.4$ yd south of the tee.

The chip shot travels 64 yd and finishes up in a position neither north nor south of the tee. Thus $\sin \theta = 23.4$ yd$/64$ yd, or $\theta = 21.4°$. Hence the westerly component of this shot is $64 \cos \theta$ yd $= 59.6$ yd.

The length of the hole is the sum of the westerly components of the displacements due to each shot. It is

$$(110.9 + 28.7 + 59.6 - 2.0) \text{ yd} = 197 \text{ yd}.$$

PROBLEM 1.5

A yule log is being dragged along an icy horizontal path by two horses. The owner keeps the log on the path by using a guide rope attached to the log at the same point as the traces from the horses. Someone in the adjacent woods fires a shotgun, which causes the horses to bolt to opposite sides of the path. One horse now exerts a pull at an angle of 45°, and the other an equal pull at an angle of 30°, relative to the original direction. What is the minimum force the man has to exert on the rope in order to keep the log moving along the path?

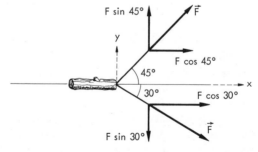

Solution. The diagram shows the forces exerted on the log by the horses at the moment they bolt. These forces can be resolved into components along the path and at right angles to the path. Thus the total forces in the x- and y-directions are

$$P_x = F \cos 45° + F \cos 30°$$

and

$$P_y = F \sin 45° - F \sin 30°.$$

To keep the log on the path the man must counteract the force in the y-direction, P_y, by an equal and opposite force, $-P_y$. Any force he exerted in addition in the x-direction would have to be added vectorially to $-P_y$ and would produce a total force greater in magnitude than $|-P_y|$.

Hence the minimum force he must exert has magnitude

$$P_y = F(\sin 45° - \sin 30°) = F\left(\frac{1}{\sqrt{2}} - \frac{1}{2}\right) = 0.207 \, F,$$

and must be directed in the negative y-direction, i.e., at right angles to the path.

In the above analysis frictional forces have been ignored. The frictional force acting along the path does not affect the solution. The frictional force trying to prevent motion at right angles to the line of the path reduces the magnitude of the force the man need apply. It is, however, assumed that on an icy path this frictional force is small in comparison with F, and its effect is therefore ignored.

PROBLEM 1.6

The owner of a car and a helpful passer-by attempt to pull the former's car from the field into which it has skidded. They attach two ropes to the front of the chassis symmetrically, each rope being 1 ft from the center point, and exert pulls of 200 lb and 150 lb in parallel directions, both at an angle of 30°

to the horizontal. To what point of the chassis must a tractor be attached and what horizontal force must it exert to produce an equivalent effect?

Solution. The resultant force of the two pulls exerted by the men must be **R** of magnitude $(200 + 150)$ lb $= 350$ lb, in the same direction as either of the forces, i.e., at $30°$ to the horizontal. Only the horizontal component of this force is doing useful work in pulling the car from the field. This component has magnitude $R \cos 30 = 350$ lb $\times$ $\sqrt{3}/2 = 303.1$ lb. This is the force that the tractor must exert.

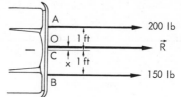

The point of attachment of the tractor must be the point O at which the line of action of the resultant **R** cuts the front of the chassis. But

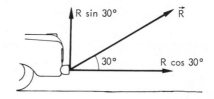

$$\frac{OA}{OB} = \frac{150 \text{ lb}}{200 \text{ lb}} = \frac{3}{4} \quad \text{and} \quad AB = 2 \text{ ft.}$$

$$\therefore \quad \frac{OA}{OA + OB} = \frac{OA}{AB} = \frac{3}{3+4} = \frac{3}{7};$$

$$\therefore \quad OA = \tfrac{3}{7} \times 2 \text{ ft} = \tfrac{6}{7} \text{ ft.}$$

Thus the point of attachment of the tractor is $\frac{6}{7}$ ft from A, that is, $\frac{1}{7}$ ft from the center point of the front of the chassis.

PROBLEM 1.7

The crew of a spacecraft, which is out in space with the rocket motors switched off, experience no weight and can therefore glide through the air inside the craft.

The cabin of such a spaceship is a cube of side 15 ft. An astronaut working in one corner requires a tool which is in a cupboard in the diametrically opposite corner of the cabin. What is the minimum distance which he has to glide and at what angle to the floor must he launch himself?

If he decides instead to put on boots with magnetic soles which allow him to remain fixed to the metal of the cabin, and thus enable him to walk along the floor and, in the absence of gravitational effects, up the walls and across the ceiling, what is the minimum distance he needs to get to the cupboard?

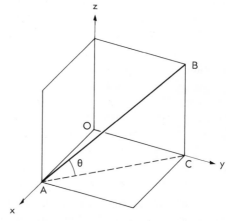

Solution. The first diagram shows the cabin with two of the walls and the roof removed. Axes have been set up with the $x, y,$ and z directions coinciding with the length, breadth, and height of the room. The astronaut must get from point A to point B. Point A has coordinates $(15$ ft, $0, 0)$. Point B has coordinates $(0, 15$ ft, 15 ft$)$. The vector **AB** thus has components $(15$ ft; 15 ft; 15 ft$)$ and its length is $\sqrt{15^2 + 15^2 + 15^2}$ ft $= 15\sqrt{3}$ ft $= 26$ ft. This is the distance the astronaut must glide.

The angle to the floor at which he launches himself is θ, where $\tan \theta = BC/AC$. Point C has coordinates $(0, 15$ ft, $0)$. Thus BC has length 15 ft and AC has length $\sqrt{15^2 + 15^2}$ ft $= 15\sqrt{2}$ ft $= 21.2$ ft.

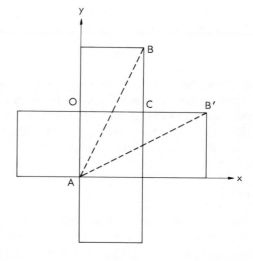

$$\therefore \quad \tan \theta = \frac{15 \text{ ft}}{15\sqrt{2} \text{ ft}} = \frac{1}{\sqrt{2}} = 0.707 \quad \text{or} \quad \theta = 35.25°.$$

The second figure shows the cabin minus the roof in an exploded diagram; points *A, B,* and *C* are again marked in. For convenience a new set of coordinate axes has been chosen. The astronaut walks the same distance from *A* to *B* by any particular route whether the walls are upright or flat as in the exploded diagram. But in the diagram it is much easier to see that the minimum distance from *A* to *B* is the straight-line path between the two points. The vector **AB** has components 15 ft in the *x*-direction and 30 ft in the *y*-direction. Distance *AB* therefore equals $\sqrt{15^2 + 30^2}$ ft $= 33$ ft $6\frac{1}{2}$ in.

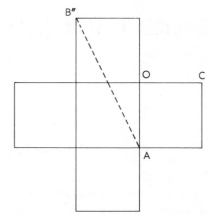

Note that *B′* is the same point as *B* in the exploded diagram; *AB′* is thus an alternative route. There is a further alternative route *AB″* which can be seen most clearly in the third figure, in which one of the walls has been removed and the cabin exploded in a different way.

In the first route, the astronaut crosses the floor and climbs a "breadth" wall; in the second, he crosses the floor and climbs a "length" wall; and in the third he crosses neither floor nor ceiling, but climbs two different walls. In this particular problem, since the cabin is cubical, all these routes are of the same length. In a problem in which the length *l,* breadth *b,* and height *h* are all different, the three routes correspond to vectors having components $(l; b + h)$, $(b; l + h)$, and $(h; l + b)$. The shortest of these will be the one in which the *x*-component is the longest dimension and the *y*-component the sum of the other two.

2

Equilibrium of a Particle and a Rigid Body

PROBLEM 2.1

A window cleaner is using a uniform ladder of weight 75 lb, one end of which is leaning against a smooth vertical wall, the other end resting on the sidewalk. It is prevented from slipping by rubber suction pads rigidly attached to the feet of the ladder and stuck firmly to the concrete. If the man of weight 150 lb is standing symmetrically three-quarters of the way up the ladder, and if the normal force exerted by the wall on each side of the ladder is 43.3 lb, what is the force exerted on the ladder by each suction pad?

Solution. The ladder is uniform and thus its weight acts at its center. The man is symmetrically placed on the ladder. Hence, by symmetry, the normal forces exerted by the wall on the two sides of the ladder are equal, as are the forces exerted by the two suction pads.

Let the force exerted by either suction pad on the ladder be resolved into component forces **x** and **y** along the sidewalk and normal to it, respectively. The complete force system acting on the ladder is as shown, the man exerting a force equal to his weight on the ladder. The ladder, of course, exerts an equal and opposite force on him, since he is in equilibrium.

The whole system is in equilibrium. It follows that

$$2x = 2N \quad \text{and} \quad 2y = W + W'.$$

Hence

$$x = 43.3 \text{ lb}, \quad y = \frac{75 \text{ lb} + 150 \text{ lb}}{2} = 112\tfrac{1}{2} \text{ lb}.$$

The total force exerted by each suction pad on the ladder thus has magnitude

$$F = \sqrt{x^2 + y^2} = \sqrt{43.3^2 + 112.5^2} \text{ lb} = 120.6 \text{ lb},$$

and it acts at an angle θ to the horizontal, where

$$\tan \theta = \frac{y}{x} = \frac{112\tfrac{1}{2} \text{ lb}}{43.3 \text{ lb}} = 2.60, \quad \theta = 69°.$$

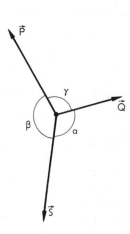

PROBLEM 2.2

Three forces acting on a particle and keeping it in equilibrium must be coplanar and concurrent. Show that the vectors representing the forces, when added in order, form a closed triangle; and further show that the magnitude of any force divided by the sine of the angle between the lines of action of the other two is a constant quantity.

Solution. Let the three forces be **P**, **Q**, and **S** at angles α, β, and γ to one another as shown in the diagram. In order that the three forces shall be in equilibrium, the resultant **R** of **P** and **Q** must be equal and opposite to **S**.

6

The vectors **P**, **Q**, and **S** are concurrent and, since the vector **R** is in the same plane as **P** and **Q**, they are coplanar.

But the resultant of **P** and **Q** is obtained by vector addition, as in the second diagram. That is, **R** is the third side of the triangle formed by **P** + **Q**. The force **S** is equal and opposite to **R** and thus will occupy the same space as **R**, the third side of the triangle, but will be opposite in direction to **R**. Thus **P** + **Q** + **S** taken in order form a closed triangle and their sum is of necessity zero. By the sine law,

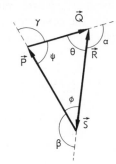

$$\frac{P}{\sin \theta} = \frac{Q}{\sin \phi} = \frac{S}{\sin \psi}.$$

$$\therefore \quad \frac{P}{\sin (180 - \alpha)} = \frac{Q}{\sin (180 - \beta)} = \frac{S}{\sin (180 - \gamma)}.$$

$$\therefore \quad \frac{P}{\sin \alpha} = \frac{Q}{\sin \beta} = \frac{S}{\sin \gamma} = \text{const.}$$

PROBLEM 2.3

The uniform drawbridge of a castle has a weight of 3600 lb and is 20 ft long. It is hinged at one end and a chain is attached to the center of the other end. The drawbridge is lowered by letting out the chain over a pulley which is located in the castle wall 34.6 ft above the hinge. When the drawbridge is horizontal but has not yet touched the ground on the other side of the moat, what is the force acting on it at the hinge? (Use the result of the preceding problem.)

Solution. In the position stated in the problem, three forces are acting on the drawbridge: the weight acting downward, the tension in the chain, and the reaction at the hinge. The direction of **W** is as shown in the diagram, and must act through the center point of the draw-bridge, since the drawbridge is uniform. The tension **T** acts in a direction θ, in which $\tan \theta = 34.6/20$. Thus $\theta = 60°$.

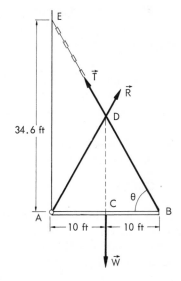

Since the three forces are in equilibrium, **R** must be coplanar and concurrent with **T** and **W**. Thus **R** acts from one end of the drawbridge to the point at which the lines of action of **W** and **T** meet. Comparing triangles ACD and DCB, we see that **R** acts at 60° to the drawbridge also.

In the preceding problem it was shown that the vectors representing the three forces in equilibrium must form a closed triangle if taken in order. But in triangle EAD the three sides are in the directions of the forces acting on the drawbridge. Any triangle formed of the three vectors must be similar to this one, and in similar triangles the lengths of the sides always maintain the same ratio. Thus

$$W : R : T = EA : AD : DE.$$

But triangle DAB is an equilateral triangle, since all the angles measure 60°. Thus $AD = AB = 20$ ft.

$$\therefore \quad \frac{R}{3600 \text{ lb}} = \frac{20 \text{ ft}}{34.6 \text{ ft}} \quad \text{or} \quad R = 2081 \text{ lb.}$$

Therefore **R** has a magnitude of 2081 lb and acts at 60° to the drawbridge.

PROBLEM 2.4

A small boy is amusing himself by dragging a box up and down a sidewalk which slopes at 15° to the horizontal. An onlooker notices that, to get the box started up the slope, the boy needs to exert six times the force that he needs to exert to get it started down the slope. Given that the boy always pushes or pulls the box with a force parallel to the sidewalk, what is the coefficient of static friction between the box and the concrete?

Solution. When the box is about to slide down the slope, the forces acting on it are as shown in the first diagram. The weight of the box acts vertically downward, the frictional force which attempts to prevent the motion acts up the slope, and the concrete exerts a normal force at right angles to the slope. In addition the boy is exerting a force **P** down the slope. When the box is just on the point of moving, $F = \mu_s N$, where μ_s is the coefficient of static friction required.

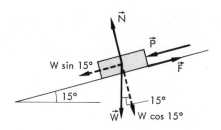

Let us resolve the force **W** into its components along, and at right angles to, the slope. Since the angle between the slope and the horizontal is 15°, this is also the angle between the normal to the slope and the normal to the horizontal (i.e., the vertical). Thus **W** has components $W \cos 15°$ at right angles to the plane and $W \sin 15°$ down the plane.

The box is just in equilibrium. From the conditions for equilibrium, we know that

$$N = W \cos 15°$$

and

$$P + W \sin 15° = F = \mu_s N = \mu_s W \cos 15°.$$
$$\therefore \quad P = \mu_s W \cos 15 - W \sin 15°.$$

The second diagram shows that, when the box is about to slide up the slope, the situation is very similar. But now the boy exerts a force **P′** up the slope and the frictional force, since it is still attempting to prevent the motion, must now act down the slope. The box is just in equilibrium once more, so that

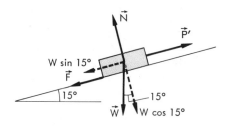

$$N = W \cos 15° \quad \text{and} \quad P' = W \sin 15° + F = W \sin 15° + \mu_s N = W \sin 15° + \mu_s W \cos 15°.$$

But we know that the force $P' = 6P$.

$$\therefore \quad W \sin 15° + \mu_s W \cos 15° = 6(\mu_s W \cos 15° - W \sin 15°).$$
$$\therefore \quad 5\mu_s W \cos 15° = 7W \sin 15°.$$
$$\therefore \quad \mu_s = \tfrac{7}{5} \tan 15° = \tfrac{7}{5} \times 0.268 = 0.375.$$

PROBLEM 2.5

A gymnast hangs from the midpoint of a rope 1 m long, the ends of which are tied to two light rings which are free to move on a horizontal rod. What is the maximum possible separation of the rings when the gymnast is hanging in equilibrium, if the relevant coefficient of static friction is 0.35?

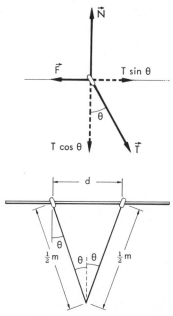

Solution. Since the gymnast hangs from the midpoint of the rope, by symmetry the tensions in the two portions of the rope must be equal and have magnitude T, and each portion will be inclined at the same angle θ to the vertical. Thus the system of forces acting on each ring will be the same.

Now consider one of the rings. Three forces are acting on it: the tensional pull on the ring due to the rope, the normal force exerted upward by the rod, and the frictional force attempting to prevent motion of the ring toward its fellow. Since the ring is light, its weight may be ignored. If the ring is too far out, slipping will occur. At the maximum distance apart, each ring is just on the point of slipping. Hence $F = \mu_s N$.

When we resolve **T** into its horizontal and vertical components, the equations for equilibrium become

$$N = T \cos \theta \quad \text{and} \quad F = \mu_s N = T \sin \theta.$$
$$\therefore \quad \tan \theta = \mu_s = 0.35 \quad \text{or} \quad \theta = 19.6°.$$

But $(d/2)/\frac{1}{2}m = \sin \theta = 0.33$. Therefore $d = 0.33\,m$, which is the maximum separation permissible. Note that θ and d do not depend on T and therefore the ring separation is not dependent on what it is that is hanging from the midpoint of the rope.

PROBLEM 2.6

A boy is sledding on a snowy slope and looks very weary as he drags his sled up again after each run down. A helpful physics student who is passing by, and who knows that the coefficient of kinetic friction between a sled and snow is around 0.10, points out to the boy that he is exerting pull on the tow rope at an incorrect angle to the ground for minimum effort. At what angle to the slope should the pull be exerted?

Solution. There are four forces acting on the sled, as shown in the diagram: the weight **W**, the normal force **N** exerted by the slope, the frictional force **F** exerted by the snow down the slope opposing the motion, and the upward pull **P** exerted by the boy at an angle θ to the slope. The sled is moving with uniform velocity up the hill and thus the forces are in equilibrium and $F = \mu_k N$, where μ_k is the coefficient of kinetic friction.

Let us resolve all forces into components along, and at right angles to, the slope. From the conditions for equilibrium, we have

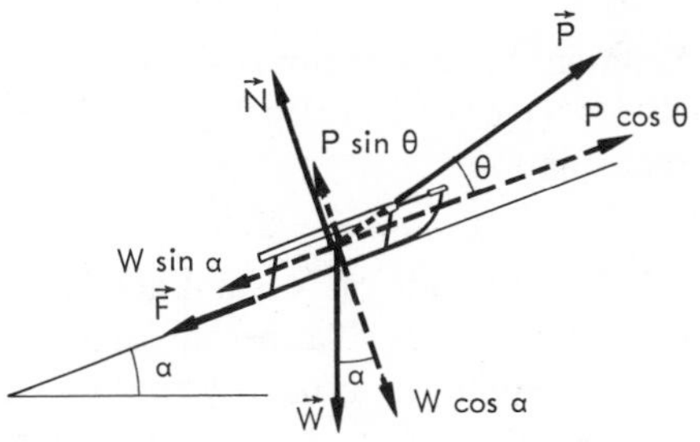

$$W \cos \alpha = N + P \sin \theta,$$

$$P \cos \theta = W \sin \alpha + F$$
$$= W \sin \alpha + \mu_k(W \cos \alpha - P \sin \theta).$$

$$\therefore \quad P = \frac{W \sin \alpha + \mu_k W \cos \alpha}{\cos \theta + \mu_k \sin \theta} = \frac{C}{\cos \theta + \mu_k \sin \theta},$$

where C is a constant. For minimum force to be exerted by the boy,

$$\frac{dP}{d\theta} = \frac{C}{(\cos \theta + \mu_k \sin \theta)^2}(-\sin \theta + \mu_k \cos \theta) = 0.$$

$$\therefore \quad \sin \theta = \mu_k \cos \theta \quad \text{or} \quad \tan \theta = \mu_k = 0.10.$$

Thus the boy should drag his sled up in such a way that the rope makes an angle of 5.7° with the slope.

It might have seemed at first sight that a force parallel to the slope would be most efficient. It is now clear that this is not so. Any component of the pull **P** at right angles to the slope decreases the normal force **N** and thus the frictional force **F**. The best compromise between maximum forward force and least frictional force is achieved at the angle 5.7°.

3

Equilibrium. Moment of a Force

PROBLEM 3.1

Repeat Problem 2.1 for a case in which the normal force exerted by the wall is unknown, as it would be in practice, but given that the ladder is inclined at an angle of 60° to the horizontal.

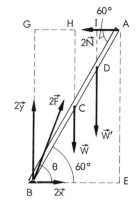

Solution. The diagram is similar to the diagram for Problem 2.1, but various points have been labeled. By the same argument as in Problem 2.1, we obtain the equations

$$2x = 2N, \qquad 2y = W + W'.$$

The magnitude of **N** is unknown, so that x is not immediately obtainable, but y equals $112\frac{1}{2}$ lb as before. In order to obtain x, we use the second condition of equilibrium, namely that the sum of the moments of the forces about any point in their plane must be zero. In order to eliminate N, we choose A as the point about which moments are to be calculated. Thus

$$2x \times AE + W \times AH + W' \times AI - 2y \times AG - 2N \times 0 = 0.$$
$$\therefore \quad 2x \times AB \sin 60° = 2y \times AB \cos 60° - W \times AC \cos 60° - W' \times AD \cos 60°.$$

We divide throughout by AB. And thus we obtain

$$2x \sin 60° = 2y \cos 60° - W \times \tfrac{1}{2} \cos 60° - W' \times \tfrac{1}{4} \cos 60°.$$
$$\therefore \quad x = \frac{(2y - \tfrac{1}{2}W - \tfrac{1}{4}W') \cos 60°}{2 \sin 60°} = \frac{(225 \text{ lb} - 37\tfrac{1}{2} \text{ lb} - 37\tfrac{1}{2} \text{ lb})\tfrac{1}{2}}{2(\sqrt{3}/2)} = \frac{150 \text{ lb}}{2\sqrt{3}} = 43.3 \text{ lb}.$$

Since we know x, the completion of the problem is the same as in Problem 2.1, and we find that **F** is 120.6 lb at an angle of 69° to the horizontal.

PROBLEM 3.2

A uniform wooden beam, of length 20 ft and weight 200 lb, is lying on a horizontal floor. A carpenter raises one end of it until the beam is inclined at 30° to the horizontal. He maintains it in this position by exerting a force at right angles to the beam while he waits for his mate to arrive to lift the other end. What is the magnitude of the force he exerts?

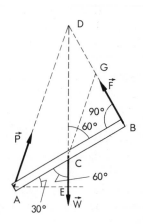

Solution. It will be instructive to solve this problem by three methods to show the different ways one can tackle it.

Consult the first diagram: AB is the beam and C its midpoint. The weight **W** acts through C, since the beam is uniform and the two other forces

10

acting on the beam are the force **F** exerted by the carpenter at B at right angles to AB and a total force **P** exerted by the floor at A in an unspecified direction.

Since the beam is acted on by three forces which maintain it in equilibrium, the lines of action of the three forces must be concurrent. Thus the direction of force **P** is from A to the point D at which **F** and **W** meet. Draw CG parallel to AD.

(a) The angle between the directions of **F** and **W** is

$$180° - \angle CDB = \angle DCB + \angle DBC = 60° + 90° = 150°.$$

The angle between the direction of **F** and **P** is angle ADB. But angle DCB is 60° and angle DBC is a right angle. Thus $DB/CB = \tan 60°$ or $DB = \sqrt{3}\ CB = (\sqrt{3}/2)AB$.

$$\therefore \quad \tan \angle DAB = \frac{DB}{AB} = \frac{\sqrt{3}}{2} = 0.866, \quad \angle DAB = 40.9°, \quad \text{or} \quad \angle ADB = 90° - 40.9° = 49.1°.$$

But from Problem 2.2 it follows that

$$\frac{P}{\sin 150°} = \frac{W}{\sin 49.1°} = \frac{F}{\sin(360° - 150° - 49.1°)}.$$

$$\therefore \quad F = W\frac{\sin 160.9°}{\sin 49.1°} = 200 \text{ lb} \times \frac{0.3272}{0.7558} = 86.6 \text{ lb}.$$

(b) In Problem 2.2 it was proved that the three forces taken in order form a closed triangle. Such a triangle is DCG. The lengths of the sides of all similar triangles have the same ratio. Hence

$$W:P:F = DC:CG:GD.$$

In the similar triangles BCG and BAD,

$$\frac{BG}{BD} = \frac{BC}{BA} = \frac{1}{2}; \quad \therefore \quad BG = GD = \frac{1}{2} BD.$$

Thus

$$\frac{F}{W} = \frac{GD}{DC} = \frac{1}{2}\frac{BD}{DC} = \frac{1}{2} \sin 60° = \frac{\sqrt{3}}{4}. \quad \therefore \quad F = 86.6 \text{ lb}.$$

(c) Take moments about A. Then, since the forces are in equilibrium,

$$P \times 0 + F \times AB - W \times AE = 0.$$

$$\therefore \quad F = W\frac{AE}{AB} = W\frac{AC \cos 30}{AB} = \frac{1}{2} W \cos 30 = \frac{\sqrt{3}}{4} W. \quad \therefore \quad F = 86.6 \text{ lb}.$$

It will be seen that taking moments about one point is by far the easiest method in this case. This, though not invariably so, is generally true.

PROBLEM 3.3

A loose-fitting specimen drawer has a depth from back to front of 8 in. The coefficient of friction involved when the drawer jams is 0.6. Show that the drawer cannot be opened by its owner when he applies a pull to the drawer at right angles to its length more than 6.7 in. from its center.

Solution. Consider the diagram, in which the drawer is seen from above. A horizontal force **F** at right angles to CD and at a distance x from the center line of the drawer is being applied in an attempt to open it. If the force is applied noncentrally, it will tend to produce not only forward motion but also a clockwise rotational motion about the center of the drawer. Since the drawer is loose-fitting, this means that corners B and D will make contact with the sides of the case and sticking will occur at these points. But the rotational movement that occurs is so small that its effect on the direction

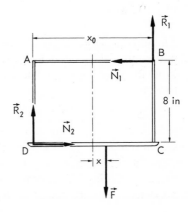

of the forces brought into play at B and D may be neglected. These forces acting on the drawer at B and D will be (a) normal forces exerted by the sides, $\mathbf{N}_1$ and $\mathbf{N}_2$, and (b) frictional forces, $\mathbf{R}_1$ and $\mathbf{R}_2$, tending to prevent the motion. When the force $\mathbf{F}$ is applied in such a way that the drawer is just on the point of sticking, from the laws of friction, $R_1 = \mu N_1$ and $R_2 = \mu N_2$, where μ is the coefficient of static friction between drawer and side.

When the drawer just sticks, the system is in equilibrium, and thus

$$F = R_1 + R_2 = \mu N_1 + \mu N_2 \qquad \text{and} \qquad N_1 = N_2.$$

Further, taking moments about D, and then about B, we have

$$N_1 \times 8 \text{ in.} + R_1 \times x_0 - F \times \left(x + \frac{x_0}{2}\right) - R_2 \times 0 - N_2 \times 0 = 0$$

and

$$N_2 \times 8 \text{ in.} + F \times \left(\frac{x_0}{2} - x\right) - R_2 \times x_0 - R_1 \times 0 - N_1 \times 0 = 0.$$

Thus

$$F\left(\frac{x_0}{2} + x\right) = 8N_1 \text{ in.} + x_0 R_1 = (8 \text{ in.} + \mu x_0)N_1$$

and

$$F\left(\frac{x_0}{2} - x\right) = -8N_2 \text{ in.} + x_0 R_2 = (\mu x_0 - 8 \text{ in.})N_1.$$

$$\therefore \quad \frac{(x_0/2) + x}{(x_0/2) - x} = \frac{\mu x_0 + 8 \text{ in.}}{\mu x_0 - 8 \text{ in.}}.$$

$$\therefore \quad \frac{x_0}{2x} = \frac{\mu x_0}{8 \text{ in.}} \qquad \text{and} \qquad x = \frac{4 \text{ in.}}{\mu} = 6.7 \text{ in.}$$

If in the above argument R_1 is set equal to αN, and R_2 to αN_2, the final equation obtained is

$$x = \frac{4 \text{ in.}}{\alpha} \qquad \text{or} \qquad \alpha = \frac{4 \text{ in.}}{x}.$$

If $x < 6.7$ in., then $\alpha > \mu$, which is impossible; but if $x > 6.7$ in., then $\alpha < \mu$, which means that the frictional force opposing the motion has not yet reached its limiting value.

Thus if the man applies the force closer to the center line than 6.7 in., he can pull the drawer out, since the frictional forces brought into play are not large enough to overcome the applied force. But if he applies the force further from the center than 6.7 in., the frictional forces are adequate and the drawer sticks.

PROBLEM 3.4

The quadrilateral $ABCD$ is a square of side 1 ft which can rotate about the fixed point O, which is the midpoint of the diagonals. Forces of 2, 3, 2, and 1 lb act along sides AB, BC, CD, and DA, respectively. Find the magnitude and line of action of a single force which would produce the same effect as these four forces.

Solution. At first sight this may not appear to be a problem in equilibrium, but the easiest method of solution is obtained when it is changed into one.

Add a fifth force $\mathbf{E}$, the force necessary to produce equilibrium. This force (see diagram) acts at the angle θ to AB, at a distance of x from A. The resultant required in the problem must be equal and opposite to $\mathbf{E}$, since the single force equivalent to the four given forces must, with $\mathbf{E}$, produce equilibrium.

Resolve the five forces parallel to AB and at right angles to AB. Since the forces are in equilibrium,

$$2 \text{ lb} - 2 \text{ lb} - E \cos \theta = 0 \quad \text{and} \quad 1 \text{ lb} - 3 \text{ lb} + E \sin \theta = 0.$$

$$\therefore \quad E \cos \theta = 0 \quad \text{and} \quad E \sin \theta = 2 \text{ lb}.$$

$$\therefore \quad \theta = 90° \quad \text{and} \quad E = 2 \text{ lb}.$$

Taking moments about O and using the condition for equilibrium, one obtains

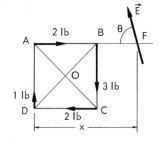

$$-2 \text{ lb} \times \tfrac{1}{2} \text{ft} - 3 \text{ lb} \times \tfrac{1}{2} \text{ft} - 2 \text{ lb} \times \tfrac{1}{2} \text{ft} - 1 \text{ lb} \times \tfrac{1}{2} \text{ft} + E(x - \tfrac{1}{2} \text{ft}) = 0.$$

$$\therefore \quad E(x - \tfrac{1}{2} \text{ft}) = 4 \text{ ft} \cdot \text{lb}.$$

$$\therefore \quad x - \tfrac{1}{2} \text{ft} = \frac{4 \text{ ft} \cdot \text{lb}}{2 \text{ lb}} = 2 \text{ ft} \quad \text{or} \quad x = 2\tfrac{1}{2} \text{ ft}.$$

Thus the equilibrant has a magnitude of 2 lb and acts at right angles to AB in a direction away from O, along a line passing through a point at a distance of $2\frac{1}{2}$ ft from A. The resultant required has thus the same magnitude and position but acts at right angles to AB toward O.

PROBLEM 3.5

The carpenter's mate in Problem 3.2 arrives and lifts the other end of the beam onto his shoulder. Both men are of the same height so that the beam is carried horizontally, but the carpenter is much the stronger of the two and wishes to bear 50% more of the weight than his mate. How far from the end of the beam should he put his shoulder?

Solution. The beam exerts downward forces on the shoulders of the carpenter and his mate. By Newton's third law, the carpenter and his mate must be exerting equal and opposite forces R_C and R_M upward on the beam, the former at distance x from one end and the latter at the other end.

Since the beam is uniform the weight acts through the center. Since the three forces acting on the beam are in equilibrium, $R_M + R_C = 200$ lb. But $R_C = 150/100 \, R_M$.

$$\therefore \quad \tfrac{2}{3} R_C + R_C = 200 \text{ lb} \quad \text{or} \quad R_C = \tfrac{3}{5} \times 200 \text{ lb} = 120 \text{ lb}.$$

Taking moments about A, one obtains

$$R_M \times 0 + R_C(20 \text{ ft} - x) - 200 \text{ lb} \times 10 \text{ ft} = 0.$$

$$\therefore \quad 20 \text{ ft} - x = \frac{2000 \text{ ft} \cdot \text{lb}}{R_C} \quad \text{or} \quad x = 20 \text{ ft} - \frac{2000 \text{ ft} \cdot \text{lb}}{120 \text{ lb}} = 20 \text{ ft} - 16\tfrac{2}{3} \text{ ft} = 3\tfrac{1}{3} \text{ ft}.$$

PROBLEM 3.6

A uniform eccentric drive wheel is circular and of radius 4 in. It has a circular hole cut in it, of radius $\frac{1}{2}$ in., for the drive shaft. The center of the hole is $\frac{1}{2}$ in. from the center of the wheel. What is the location of the center of gravity of the drive wheel?

Solution. By symmetry the center of gravity must lie on the diameter AB which passes through O and X, the centers of the circular wheel and circular hole. Set AB horizontal and let Y, which is a distance x from O, be the location of the center of gravity of the drive wheel. Weights acting vertically are now at right angles to AB.

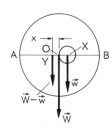

If the circular piece removed to form the hole were replaced, the resultant of the weight $W - w$ of the drive wheel plus the weight w of the piece replaced would have to be the weight **W** of the whole circle which acts at O. But the moment of the resultant weight about any point in the plane of the wheel must be equal to the sum of the moments about the same point of the individual forces making up the resultant. For simplicity let the point chosen be O.

The weight of the circle replaced must act at X. Further the weights of the wheel, the replaced portion, and the full circle are proportional to their masses and thus, since the wheel is uniform, proportional to their areas.

The moment of the resultant weight about O is zero. Hence $(W - w)x - w \times \frac{1}{2}$ in. $= 0$.

$$\therefore \quad x = \frac{1}{2} \text{ in.} \times \frac{w}{W - w} = \frac{1}{2} \text{ in.} \times \frac{k\pi \times \frac{1}{2}^2 \text{ in}^2}{k\pi \times 4^2 \text{ in}^2 - k\pi \times \frac{1}{2}^2 \text{ in}^2},$$

where k is the proportionality constant between weight and area.

$$\therefore \quad x = \frac{1}{2} \times \frac{\frac{1}{2}^2}{4^2 - \frac{1}{2}^2} \text{ in.} = \frac{1}{8} \times \frac{1}{\frac{9}{2} \cdot \frac{7}{2}} \text{ in.} = \frac{1}{126} \text{ in.}$$

4

Rectilinear Motion

PROBLEM 4.1

On a long straight road a car accelerates uniformly from rest, reaching a speed of 45 mph in 11 s. It has to maintain that speed for $1\frac{1}{2}$ mi behind a truck until a suitable opportunity for passing the truck arises. The car then accelerates uniformly to 75 mph in a further 11 s. After maintaining that speed for 3 min, the car is brought to a halt by a uniform deceleration of 11 ft·s^{-2}.

Illustrate the motion on a suitable diagram, and calculate (a) the total distance traveled, (b) the total time taken, (c) the average speed, and (d) the average acceleration in the first 142 s.

Solution. A velocity-time diagram should be drawn. During the first 11 s the car accelerates uniformly to a speed of 45 mph = 66 ft·s^{-1}. This part of the diagram is therefore a straight line OA inclined to the t-axis at an angle whose tangent is 66/11. The distance traveled, s_1, is the area under this portion of the graph. Thus

$$s_1 = \tfrac{1}{2} \times 11 \text{ s} \times 66 \text{ ft·s}^{-1} = 363 \text{ ft}.$$

In the second portion of the motion, the car travels for $1\frac{1}{2}$ mi at a constant speed of 45 mph. This part of the graph, AB, is a straight line parallel to the t-axis, its length being

$$t_2 = \frac{1\frac{1}{2}\,\text{mi}}{45\,\text{mi·hr}^{-1}} \times 60 \text{ min·hr}^{-1} \times 60 \text{ s·min}^{-1} = 120 \text{ s}.$$

In the third portion of the motion, the car increases its speed by 30 mph = 44 ft·s^{-1} at uniform acceleration in 11s. This part of the graph is thus a straight line BC of slope $\frac{44}{11}$. The distance traveled in this 11 s, s_3, is the area under this part of the graph, i.e., the shaded portion.

$$\therefore \quad s_3 = \tfrac{1}{2} \times 11 \text{ s} \times 44 \text{ ft·s}^{-1} + 11 \text{ s} \times 66 \text{ ft·s}^{-1} = 968 \text{ ft}.$$

The next portion of the graph is again a straight line parallel to the t-axis. The time t_4 is 3 min = 180 s, and thus

$$s_4 = 75 \text{ mi·hr}^{-1} \times \frac{3}{60} \text{ hr} = 3.75 \text{ mi}.$$

In the final part of the motion, the car is brought to rest from a speed of 110 ft·s^{-1} by a uniform deceleration of 11 ft·s^{-2}. This portion of the graph, DE, is thus a straight line with a negative slope of $\frac{110}{11}$. The time taken to come to rest, t_5, and the distance traversed, s_5, are

$$t_5 = \frac{110 \text{ ft·s}^{-1}}{11 \text{ ft·s}^{-2}} = 10 \text{ s} \quad \text{and} \quad s_5 = \frac{1}{2} \times 10 \text{ s} \times 110 \text{ ft·s}^{-1} = 550 \text{ ft}.$$

15

(a) The total distance traveled is

$$s = s_1 + s_2 + s_3 + s_4 + s_5 = 363 \text{ ft} + 1\tfrac{1}{2} \text{ mi} + 968 \text{ ft} + 3\tfrac{3}{4} \text{ mi} + 550 \text{ ft}$$

$$= 5\tfrac{1}{4} \text{ mi} + 1881 \text{ ft} = 5 \text{ mi } 3201 \text{ ft} = 5 \text{ mi } 1067 \text{ yd.}$$

(b) The total time taken is

$$t = t_1 + t_2 + t_3 + t_4 + t_5 = (11 + 120 + 11 + 180 + 10) \text{ s} = 332 \text{ s} = 5 \text{ min } 32 \text{ s.}$$

(c) The average speed, $\bar{v}$, is the total distance traveled divided by the total time taken. Thus

$$\bar{v} = \frac{5 \text{ mi } 1067 \text{ yd}}{332 \text{ s}} = \frac{29{,}601}{332} \text{ ft} \cdot \text{s}^{-1} = 89.16 \text{ ft} \cdot \text{s}^{-1} \times \frac{60 \text{ mph}}{88 \text{ ft} \cdot \text{s}^{-1}} = 60.8 \text{ mph.}$$

(d) The average acceleration in the first 142 s, $\bar{a}$, is the final speed achieved divided by the total time taken. Thus

$$\bar{a} = \frac{110 \text{ ft} \cdot \text{s}^{-1}}{142 \text{ s}} = 0.78 \text{ ft} \cdot \text{s}^{-2}.$$

PROBLEM 4.2

A Formula I racing car can reach 120 mph from a standing start and come to rest again, all in 30 s. The coefficient of static friction between tires and road, which is exploited to the limit in braking, is $\tfrac{11}{14}$. Assuming uniform acceleration throughout, find the total distance covered in the process, and the acceleration during the time that the velocity is increasing.

Solution. At time $t = 0$, the car starts from rest. At $t = 30$ s, the car has come to rest once more. During the second part of the motion, the magnitude of the decelerating force **F** due to friction is equal to the coefficient of static friction μ between tires and road times the normal force exerted by the road on the car. But the car has no motion in the vertical direction, and thus the normal force must be equal and opposite to the weight of the car, **W**. Hence $F = \mu W$, or the deceleration a_2 is given by $a_2 = F/m = \mu g$.

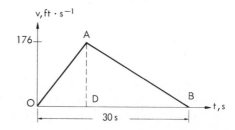

Construct a velocity-time diagram in the following manner. During the second portion of the motion the car has uniform deceleration, coming to rest at $t = 30$ s. The uniform deceleration should be represented as a straight line in the velocity-time diagram cutting the t-axis at 30 s and having a slope of, $-\mu g$. Draw such a line AB from B, A being the point which has a v-coordinate of 120 mph $= [120 \times (88/60)] \text{ ft} \cdot \text{s}^{-1} = 176 \text{ ft} \cdot \text{s}^{-1}$. The straight line OA must then be the representation of the first portion of the travel, since the acceleration is uniform and O and A represent the initial and final points of this part of the motion.

The total distance traveled is the area under the graph, s. If AD is the perpendicular from A to the t-axis,

$$s = \tfrac{1}{2}AD \cdot OD + \tfrac{1}{2}AD \cdot DB = \tfrac{1}{2}AD(OD + DB) = \tfrac{1}{2} \times 176 \text{ ft} \cdot \text{s}^{-1} \times 30 \text{ s} = 2640 \text{ ft} = \tfrac{1}{2} \text{ mi.}$$

The acceleration as the speed increases is the slope of the portion of the graph OA. That is, $a_1 = AD/OD$. But

$$a_2 = \frac{AD}{DB} = \frac{176 \text{ ft} \cdot \text{s}^{-1}}{DB}.$$

$$\therefore \quad DB = \frac{176 \text{ ft} \cdot \text{s}^{-1}}{a_2} = \frac{176 \text{ ft} \cdot \text{s}^{-1}}{\mu g} = \frac{176 \text{ ft} \cdot \text{s}^{-1}}{\tfrac{11}{14} \times 32 \text{ ft} \cdot \text{s}^{-1}} = 7 \text{ s.}$$

$$\therefore \quad a_1 = \frac{AD}{(30 - 7) \text{ s}} = \frac{176 \text{ ft} \cdot \text{s}^{-1}}{23 \text{ s}} = 7.65 \text{ ft} \cdot \text{s}^{-2}.$$

PROBLEM 4.3

A skier is filmed by a motion-picture photographer who notices him traveling down a ski run. The skier travels 36 ft during the fourth second of the filming and 48 ft during the sixth second. What distance did he cover during the eight seconds of filming? Assume that the acceleration is uniform throughout.

Solution. Time $t = 0$ is taken as the instant at which filming starts and x_r and v_r denote the distance traveled and speed acquired after r seconds. Applying the equation of uniformly accelerated motion $x_{r+t} - x_r = v_r + \frac{1}{2}at^2$ to the given data, we find that $36 \text{ ft} = x_4 - x_3 = v_3 \times 1 \text{ s} + \frac{1}{2}a \times (1 \text{ s})^2$, where a is the acceleration of the skier. Similarly, $48 \text{ ft} = x_6 - x_5 = v_5 \times 1 \text{ s} + \frac{1}{2}a \times (1 \text{ s})^2$.

$$\therefore \quad (48 - 36) \text{ ft} = 12 \text{ ft} = (v_5 - v_3) \times 1 \text{ s}.$$

But applying a further equation, $v_{r+t} = v_r + at$, to this situation, we obtain $v_5 - v_3 = a \times 2 \text{ s}$.

$$\therefore \quad 12 \text{ ft·s}^{-1} = a \times 2 \text{ s} \quad \text{or} \quad a = 6 \text{ ft·s}^{-2}.$$

By similar reasoning, we have $x_1 - x_0 = v_0 \times 1 \text{ s} + \frac{1}{2}a \times 1 \text{ s}^2$.

$$\therefore \quad (x_4 - x_3) - (x_1 - x_0) = (v_3 - v_0) \times 1 \text{ s} = a \times 3 \text{ s}^2.$$

$$\therefore \quad 36 \text{ ft} - (x_1 - x_0) = 18 \text{ ft}; \quad \therefore \quad x_1 - x_0 = 18 \text{ ft}.$$

Hence

$$v_0 = \frac{18 \text{ ft} - 3 \text{ ft}}{1 \text{ s}} = 15 \text{ ft·s}^{-1}.$$

Thus the distance traveled in 8 s of filming is

$$x_8 - x_0 = v_0 \times 8 \text{ s} + \frac{1}{2}a \times 64 \text{ s}^2 = 120 \text{ ft} + 192 \text{ ft} = 312 \text{ ft}.$$

The problem may also be solved by using a velocity-time diagram. Since the acceleration is uniform, the motion is represented in the diagram by a straight line inclined at an unknown angle to the two axes and cutting the v-axis at an unknown point, not the origin.

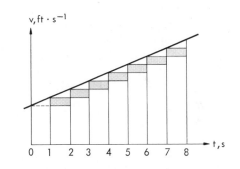

The distance traveled in any second is the area under the curve between the two time ordinates. One can easily see from the diagram that the difference in the distances traveled in successive seconds is always the same; it is the area represented by one of the shaded rectangles shown. Since it is known that the distances gone in the fourth and sixth seconds of filming were 36 ft and 48 ft, respectively, it follows immediately that the area of each of these shaded rectangles is $(48 - 36)/2 \text{ ft} = 6 \text{ ft}$. Working from the two areas known, one finds that the distances gone in successive seconds were 18 ft, 24 ft, 30 ft, 36 ft, 42 ft, 48 ft, 54 ft, and 60 ft. The total distance traveled in the whole eight seconds of filming is thus the sum of these distances, that is, 312 ft.

PROBLEM 4.4

The owner of a car backs it from his driveway into a narrow street and into the path of two cars which are traveling along the street, one behind the other, at 45 mph. The driver of the first oncoming car applies his brakes when he is $76\frac{1}{2}$ ft away. The second oncoming driver takes 1 s to react after the brake lights of the first car go on. Each driver applies the maximum deceleration of 27 ft·s^{-2}. Does the first man crash into the backing car? What is the minimum distance necessary between the two oncoming cars so that the second does not run into the back of the first? Assume that the first car stops dead if it crashes.

If the owner of the backing car looks down the road at the instant the first driver applies his brakes, how long does he have to do something about the situation?

Solution. It is necessary to calculate the distance s required for either of the cars to come to rest under full braking. The appropriate equation of motion is $v^2 = v_0^2 + 2a(x - x_0)$. Here $v_0 = 45$ mph $= 66$ ft·s^{-1}, $v = 0$, and $a = -27$ ft·s^{-2}.

$$\therefore \quad 0 = (66 \text{ ft·s}^{-1})^2 - 2 \times 27 \text{ ft·s}^{-2} \times s \quad \text{and} \quad s = \frac{66 \times 66 \text{ ft}^2 \cdot \text{s}^{-2}}{54 \text{ ft·s}^{-2}} = 80\tfrac{2}{3} \text{ ft.}$$

The first man is only $76\tfrac{1}{2}$ ft from the stationary car and must therefore crash, since he needs $80\tfrac{2}{3}$ ft in which to come to a full stop.

If the second car is distance x behind the first, it travels for 1 s, that is, for 66 ft, at a speed of 66 ft·s^{-1}, before the driver applies his brakes, and a further $80\tfrac{2}{3}$ ft before stopping. If he is to avoid a crash,

$$66 \text{ ft} + 80\tfrac{2}{3} \text{ ft} \le 76\tfrac{1}{2} \text{ ft} + x. \quad \therefore \quad x \ge 70\tfrac{1}{6} \text{ ft.}$$

Thus the second car would have to be at least $70\tfrac{1}{6}$ ft behind the rear of the first.

The time necessary for the first car to decelerate $76\tfrac{1}{2}$ ft is obtained from the equation $x - x_0 = v_0 t - \tfrac{1}{2}at^2$. That is, $76\tfrac{1}{2}$ ft $= (66 \text{ ft·s}^{-1}) \times t - \tfrac{1}{2} \times (27 \text{ ft·s}^{-2}) \times t^2$.

$$\therefore \quad 27t^2 - 132t \text{ s} + 153 \text{ s}^2 = 0 \quad \text{or} \quad 9t^2 - 44t \text{ s} + 51 \text{ s}^2 = 0 \quad \text{or} \quad (t - 3 \text{ s})(9t - 17 \text{ s}) = 0.$$

$$\therefore \quad t = \tfrac{17}{9} \text{ s} \quad \text{or} \quad t = 3 \text{ s.}$$

The first answer is the one required. The second is the time it would take the car to pass the point $76\tfrac{1}{2}$ ft away, continue decelerating to rest, and then accelerate back to the point $76\tfrac{1}{2}$ ft away from the starting position. This is not a physically admissible solution to the present problem.

The driver of the backing car thus has less than 2 sec to do something, far too short a time for him to avoid the crash even if he has a very fast reaction time.

PROBLEM 4.5

At the National Physical Laboratory in London, g has been measured accurately by projecting a ball up an evacuated tube and electronically timing the passage of the ball in its upward and downward flight through two light beams an accurately known distance s apart. If the successive times of passage through the beams are t_0, t_1, t_2, and t_3, show that

$$g = 2s/(t_1 - t_0)(t_2 - t_0) = 2s/(t_3 - t_1)(t_1 - t_0).$$

Solution. Take x_0 as any position on the flight path shown in the diagram, in which the upward and downward portions have been shown separated for clarity. Let the upward velocity at that position be v_0 and let x be the position a time t later. Then

$$x - x_0 = v_0 t - \tfrac{1}{2} gt^2$$

or

$$t^2 - \frac{2v_0}{g} t + \frac{2(x - x_0)}{g} = 0.$$

This equation will have two solutions, t' and t''. Thus

$$(t - t')(t - t'') = 0$$

or

$$t^2 - t(t' + t'') + t' t'' = 0.$$

Thus the product of the solutions, comparing the two equations, is

$$t' t'' = \frac{2(x - x_0)}{g} \quad \text{or} \quad g = \frac{2(x - x_0)}{t't''}.$$

In particular, if x_0 is the position of the lower light beam and x is the position of the upper one, then

$$x - x_0 = s, \quad t' = t_1 - t_0, \quad t'' = t_2 - t_0.$$

$$\therefore \quad g = 2s/(t_2 - t_0)(t_1 - t_0).$$

Alternatively, if x_0 is the position of the upper light beam and x is the position of the lower one, then

$$x - x_0 = -s, \qquad t' = t_0 - t_1, \qquad t'' = t_3 - t_1.$$
$$\therefore \qquad g = 2s/(t_3 - t_1)(t_1 - t_0).$$

PROBLEM 4.6

A boy leaning over a railway bridge 49 ft high sees a train approaching with uniform speed and attempts to drop a stone down the funnel. He releases the stone when the engine is 80 ft away from the bridge and sees the stone hit the ground 3 ft in front of the engine. What is the speed of the train?

Solution. Applying the equation applicable to uniform acceleration, $x - x_0 = v_0 t + \frac{1}{2}at^2$, to the dropping of the stone 49 ft from rest under the action of gravity, we have $49 \text{ ft} = 0 + \frac{1}{2} \times 32 \text{ ft} \cdot \text{s}^{-2} \times t^2$.

$$\therefore \qquad t = \sqrt{\frac{2 \times 49 \text{ ft}}{32 \text{ ft} \cdot \text{s}^{-2}}} = \frac{7}{4} \text{ s}.$$

In the time of $\frac{7}{4}$ s it takes the stone to drop, the engine has moved with uniform speed u a distance of $(80 - 3)$ ft.

$$\therefore \qquad u = \frac{77 \text{ ft}}{\frac{7}{4} \text{ s}} = 44 \text{ ft} \cdot \text{s}^{-1} = 30 \text{ mph}.$$

PROBLEM 4.7

An elevator is descending with an acceleration of $5 \text{ ft} \cdot \text{s}^{-2}$. The shade on the ceiling light falls to the floor of the elevator, 9 ft below. At the instant that it falls, one of the passengers sees it, and realizes that the shade will hit his foot. How long does he have to get his foot out of the way?

Solution. At the instant that the light shade becomes detached, it has a downward speed of v_0, and it will drop freely under the action of gravity. Suppose that there is an observer outside the elevator. By the time the shade strikes the (moving) floor of the elevator, it will have been seen by the observer to have dropped a distance s in a time t.

$$\therefore \qquad s = v_0 t + \frac{1}{2}gt^2.$$

In the same time t, the elevator floor will have traveled $s - 9$ ft with the acceleration of $5 \text{ ft} \cdot \text{s}^{-2}$, having started with the same downward speed v_0.

$$\therefore \qquad s - 9 \text{ ft} = v_0 t + \frac{1}{2} \times 5 \text{ ft} \cdot \text{s}^{-2} \times t^2.$$

Subtract one equation from the other. Thus $9 \text{ ft} = \frac{1}{2}(g - 5 \text{ ft} \cdot \text{s}^{-2})t^2 = \frac{1}{2} \times 27 \text{ ft} \cdot \text{s}^{-2} \times t^2$.

This equation could have been obtained more easily by considering the motion of the shade relative to the elevator in an accelerated frame of reference. For, relative to the elevator, the light shade starts off with zero velocity and has an acceleration of $g - 5 \text{ ft} \cdot \text{s}^{-2}$. Thus, applying the same equation of motion as before, we find that the shade drops 9 ft relative to the elevator in a time t, and

$$9 \text{ ft} = 0 \times t + \frac{1}{2}(g - 5 \text{ ft} \cdot \text{s}^{-2})t^2. \qquad \therefore \qquad t = \sqrt{\frac{2 \times 9 \text{ ft}}{27 \text{ ft} \cdot \text{s}^{-2}}} = \sqrt{\frac{2 \text{ s}^2}{3}} = 0.82 \text{ s}.$$

The passenger has therefore less than 1 s to get his foot out of the way, and must react rapidly. In the above solution, the thickness of the passenger's foot is ignored, since it will affect the result only negligibly.

PROBLEM 4.8

An interstellar spaceship powered by rockets is heading for Sirius at a speed of 25,000 mph when the radar scanner picks up a large meteorite 500 mi away at an angle of 45° to the ship's direction of motion. The meteorite is traveling at a speed of 17,700 mph at 90° to the line of sight in such a way that the two directions of motion are concurrent. Should the captain of the ship take evasive action? If so, how much time is available for the maneuver?

Solution. The velocity of the meteorite relative to the space through which it is traveling, v_{MS}, is 17,700 mph at an angle of 90° to the line of sighting, i.e., at 45° to the line of flight of the rocket ship. The velocity of the rocket ship relative to space, v_{RS}, is 25,000 mph toward Sirius. The velocity of space relative to the rocket ship, v_{SR}, is the opposite of this. The velocity of the meteorite relative to the rocket is v_{MR}, where $v_{MR} = v_{MS} + v_{SR}$. The diagram shows the vector addition of v_{MS} and v_{SR} to give v_{MR}. Thus

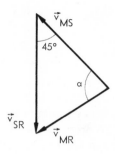

$$v_{MR}^2 = v_{MS}^2 + v_{SR}^2 - 2v_{MS}v_{SR}\cos 45°$$

$$= (25,000^2 + 17,700^2 - \sqrt{2} \times 25,000 \times 17,700)\ \text{mi}^2 \cdot \text{hr}^{-2}$$

$$= 313 \times 10^6\ \text{mi}^2 \cdot \text{hr}^{-2}.$$

$$\therefore \quad v_{MR} = 17,700\ \text{mph} \quad \text{and} \quad \sin \alpha = \frac{25,000}{17,700} \sin 45 = 1. \quad \therefore \quad \alpha = 90°.$$

Thus v_{MR} is directly toward the ship and evasive action must be taken. The time available is

$$t = \frac{500\ \text{mi}}{v_{MR}} = \frac{500\ \text{mi}}{17,700\ \text{mi} \cdot \text{hr}^{-1}} = \frac{500 \times 60}{17,700}\ \text{min} = 1.7\ \text{min}.$$

PROBLEM 4.9

Two children are playing the ridiculous and dangerous game of "chicken," in which they see how long they can delay before dashing across the road in front of an automobile. Show that, if one of the children can run at half the speed of an approaching furniture van, he must start off no later than the moment when he sees the front of the van at an angle of 30° to the sidewalk, and must head across the road in a direction at right angles to this line of sight.

Solution. If the van is moving from right to left, then its velocity with respect to the road, v_{VR}, is in that direction also. The velocity of the road relative to an observer in the van, v_{RV}, is equal and opposite. The velocity of the child with respect to the road is v_{CR}. This is a vector half the length of v_{RV} oriented in any direction within a semicircle, depending on the direction in which the child runs across the road. Now

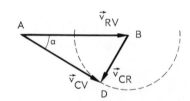

$$v_{CV} = v_{CR} + v_{RV} = v_{RV} + v_{CR}.$$

The vector v_{RV} is represented by AB, v_{CR} is represented by a vector from B to any point D on the dashed semicircle, and v_{CV}, represented by AD, is the velocity of the child relative to the furniture van. To an observer in the van who considers himself stationary, the child would therefore appear to move in the direction EF of the second diagram as long as he stood at the curb, and then in the direction FG when he was in motion. If the path FG is just not to hit the (allegedly) stationary van, G must be a point on the front of the van. When the child is at F on the curb, about to start running, G appears to him to be at an angle α to the curb.

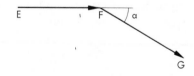

Depending on where D is on the dashed semicircle of the first diagram, α varies in magnitude. It is maximal when AD is tangent to the semicircle, at which point angle ADB is a right angle and

$$\sin \alpha = BD/AB = \tfrac{1}{2}. \quad \text{That is,} \quad \alpha = 30°.$$

The point G is nearest to F when α is greatest. Thus the child, if he is to avoid an accident, can no longer delay running after he sees the front of the van at an angle of 30° to the curb.

The line AD is the direction in which the child runs relative to the furniture van, and BD is the direction in which he runs relative to the road. Angle ABD is obviously 60°. The child looks to the left at 30° to the curb and runs to the right at 60° to the curb. The angle between these two directions is

$$180° - 60° - 30° = 90°.$$

PROBLEM 4.10

The earth acts on any body with a gravitational force inversely proportional to the square of the distance of the body from the center of the earth. Calculate the escape velocity from the earth, i.e., the speed with which a vertically moving body must leave the earth's surface in order to coast along without being pulled back to the earth. Also find the time it takes for a rocket projected upward with this escape velocity to attain a height above the earth's surface equal to its radius. In both cases ignore the effect of any other heavenly bodies and take the earth's radius as 6.38×10^6 m.

Solution. At all times the earth is exerting a force on the rocket inversely proportional to r^2, where r is the distance of the rocket from the center of the earth. The deceleration on the rocket is thus k/r^2, where k is a constant to be determined. Given that a is the acceleration away from the earth, then

$$a = \frac{dv}{dt} = \frac{dv}{dr} \times \frac{dr}{dt} = v \frac{dv}{dr} = -\frac{k}{r^2}.$$

If the escape velocity is V, this initial velocity enables the rocket to reach an infinite distance from the earth before its upward velocity has been reduced to zero. (Otherwise it would start accelerating back toward the earth.)

$$\therefore \qquad \int_V^0 v \, dv = -k \int_R^\infty \frac{dr}{r^2},$$

where R is the radius of the earth. Hence

$$\left[\frac{1}{2} v^2\right]_V^0 = \left[\frac{k}{r}\right]_R^\infty. \qquad \therefore \qquad \frac{V^2}{2} = \frac{k}{R}.$$

But when $r = R$, then $a = -g$. Therefore $-g = -k/R^2$ or $k = gR^2$.

$$\therefore \qquad V = \sqrt{2gR} = \sqrt{2 \times 9.81 \text{ m·s}^{-2} \times 6.38 \times 10^6 \text{ m}} = 11.2 \times 10^3 \text{ m·s}^{-1}.$$

For the second part of the problem, we can rewrite the integral equation above to determine the velocity v of the rocket at any arbitrary distance r. Thus

$$\int_V^v v \, dv = -k \int_R^r \frac{dr}{r^2} \qquad \text{or} \qquad \left[\frac{1}{2} v^2\right]_V^v = \left[\frac{k}{r}\right]_R^r.$$

$$\therefore \qquad \frac{1}{2} v^2 - \frac{1}{2} V^2 = \frac{k}{r} - \frac{k}{R}. \qquad \text{But} \qquad \frac{1}{2} V^2 = \frac{k}{R}.$$

$$\therefore \qquad v^2 = \frac{2k}{r} = \frac{2gR^2}{r} \qquad \text{or} \qquad v = \frac{dr}{dt} = \sqrt{\frac{2gR^2}{r}}.$$

$$\therefore \qquad \int_R^{2R} r^{1/2} \, dr = \sqrt{2gR^2} \int_0^T dt,$$

where the rocket reaches a height R above the surface, i.e., a distance $2R$ from the center of the earth, at time T after takeoff.

$$\therefore \qquad \left[\frac{2}{3} r^{3/2}\right]_R^{2R} = \sqrt{2gR^2} \left[t\right]_0^T. \qquad \therefore \qquad \frac{2}{3}\left[(2R)^{3/2} - R^{3/2}\right] = \sqrt{2gR^2}\, T,$$

or

$$T = \frac{2R^{3/2}(2\sqrt{2} - 1)}{3\sqrt{2gR^2}} = \frac{1}{3}\sqrt{\frac{2R}{g}}(2\sqrt{2} - 1)$$

$$= \frac{1}{3}\sqrt{\frac{12.76 \times 10^6 \text{ m}}{9.81 \text{ m·s}^{-2}}}(2.828 - 1)/60 \text{ s·min}^{-1} = 11.6 \text{ min}.$$

5

Newton's Second Law. Gravitation

PROBLEM 5.1

An observation balloon has a volume of 300 m³ and is filled with hydrogen of density 0.1 g·liter⁻¹. The basket and passengers have a total mass of 350 kg. Find the initial acceleration when the balloon is released, assuming that the air resistance is zero when the velocity is zero. The density of air is 1.3 g·liter⁻¹ and the upward force on the balloon is equal to the weight of air displaced by the balloon.

Solution. The density of hydrogen is $0.1 \text{ g·liter}^{-1} = 100 \text{ g·m}^{-3} = 0.1 \text{ kg·m}^{-3}$. Similarly the density of air is 1.3 kg·m^{-3}. The total mass of hydrogen is thus $0.1 \text{ kg·m}^{-3} \times 300 \text{ m}^3 = 30 \text{ kg}$, and the mass of air displaced is 390 kg. The upward force U on the balloon equals the weight of the air displaced.

$$\therefore \qquad U = 390 \text{ kg} \times 9.8 \text{ m·s}^{-2} = 3822 \text{ newtons (N)}.$$

The total downward force W equals the weight of hydrogen, basket, and passengers.

$$\therefore \qquad W = (350 + 30) \text{ kg} \times 9.8 \text{ m·s}^{-2} = 3724 \text{ N}.$$

When the balloon is released, the net force $U - W$ accelerates the mass of 380 kg upward with acceleration a.

$$\therefore \qquad 3822 \text{ N} - 3724 \text{ N} = 380 \text{ kg} \times a. \qquad \therefore \qquad a = \frac{98 \text{ N}}{380 \text{ kg}} = 0.258 \text{ m·s}^{-2}.$$

PROBLEM 5.2

A curling stone of mass 1 slug is sent off along the ice and comes to rest after 100 ft. If the force of kinetic friction between stone and ice is $\frac{1}{2}$ lb, with what velocity did the stone start, and how long did it take to come to rest?

Solution. The force decelerating the stone is $\frac{1}{2}$ lb and the stone has a mass of 1 slug. Using the equation $F = ma$, the deceleration is $a = -\frac{1}{2} \text{ ft·s}^{-2}$. Applying to the motion of the stone the equation of uniform motion, $v_0^2 + 2a(x - x_0) = v$, where $v = 0$ and $x - x_0 = 100 \text{ ft}$, we obtain $v_0^2 = 2 \times \frac{1}{2} \text{ ft·s}^{-2} \times 100 \text{ ft}$.

$$\therefore \qquad v_0 = 10 \text{ ft·s}^{-1},$$

which is the initial velocity of the stone.

If we now apply the further equation $v = v_0 + at$, the time of motion is

$$t = -\frac{v_0}{a} = \frac{10 \text{ ft·s}^{-1}}{\frac{1}{2} \text{ ft·s}^{-2}} = 20 \text{ s}.$$

PROBLEM 5.3

Starting from rest, an engine at full throttle pulls a freight train of mass 4200 slugs along a level track. After 5 min, the train reaches a speed of 5 mph. After it has picked up more freight cars, it takes 10 min to acquire a speed of 7 mph. What was the mass of the added freight cars? Assume that no slipping occurs and that frictional forces are the same in both cases.

Solution. In the first case the train acquires a speed of 5 mph in 5 min $= \frac{1}{12}$ hr. When one applies the formula $v_1 = v_0 + a_1 t_1$, where $v_0 = 0$, then

$$a_1 = 5 \text{ mph}/\tfrac{1}{12} \text{ hr} = 60 \text{ mi} \cdot \text{hr}^{-2}.$$

In the second case the train acquires a speed of 7 mph in 10 min $= \frac{1}{6}$ hr. When one applies the formula $v_2 = v_0 + a_2 t_2$, then $a_2 = 7 \text{ mph}/\frac{1}{6} \text{ hr} = 42 \text{ mi} \cdot \text{hr}^{-2}$.

In both cases the engine is at full throttle and is thus applying the same net force F to the train: In the first case it is applying it to a mass of 4200 slugs and in the second case to a mass of $M + 4200$ slugs. Thus

$$F = 4200 \text{ slugs} \times a_1 = (4200 \text{ slugs} + M) \times a_2.$$

$$\therefore \quad M = 4200 \left(\frac{a_1}{a_2} - 1\right) \text{ slugs} = 4200 \left(\frac{60 \text{ mi} \cdot \text{hr}^{-2}}{42 \text{ mi} \cdot \text{hr}^{-2}} - 1\right) \text{ slugs} = 4200 \times \frac{3}{7} \text{ slugs} = 1800 \text{ slugs}.$$

Note that although it is not normal to measure acceleration in $\text{mi} \cdot \text{hr}^{-2}$, it is a mistake to convert to more familiar units unless and until it is found to be necessary. In this case the units of acceleration cancel out and no conversion is ever necessary.

PROBLEM 5.4

A ball whose mass is 0.1 slug is falling freely at a given instant with a speed of $100 \text{ ft} \cdot \text{s}^{-1}$. What constant force must be applied to stop the ball in (a) 5 s, and (b) 5 ft?

Solution. In either case two forces will be acting on the ball: the applied force **F**, acting upward, and the weight **W**, acting downward. If m is the mass of the ball, the deceleration a will be given by $a = (F - W)/m$.

(a) Apply the formula $v = v_0 - at$, where $v = 0$, $v_0 = 100 \text{ ft} \cdot \text{s}^{-1}$, and $t = 5$ s. Then

$$\frac{F - W}{m} = a = \frac{v_0}{t} = \frac{100 \text{ ft} \cdot \text{s}^{-1}}{5 \text{ s}} = 20 \text{ ft} \cdot \text{s}^{-2}.$$

$$\therefore \quad F - 0.1 \text{ slug} \times 32 \text{ ft} \cdot \text{s}^{-2} = 0.1 \text{ slug} \times 20 \text{ ft} \cdot \text{s}^{-2}.$$

$$\therefore \quad F = 5.2 \text{ lb}.$$

(b) Apply the formula $v^2 = v_0^2 - 2(x - x_0)$, where $v = 0$, $v_0 = 100 \text{ ft} \cdot \text{s}^{-1}$, and $(x - x_0) = 5$ ft. Then

$$\frac{F - W}{m} = a = \frac{v_0^2}{2(x - x_0)} = \frac{10^4 \text{ ft} \cdot \text{s}^{-2}}{10 \text{ ft}} = 1000 \text{ ft} \cdot \text{s}^{-2}.$$

$$\therefore \quad F - 0.1 \text{ slug} \times 32 \text{ ft} \cdot \text{s}^{-2} = 0.1 \text{ slug} \times 1000 \text{ ft} \cdot \text{s}^{-2}. \quad \therefore \quad F = 103.2 \text{ lb}.$$

PROBLEM 5.5

A Martian performs an experiment to determine the Martian g with the local type of Atwood's machine. He hangs two equal weights of mass 0.02 slug over a frictionless pulley and adds a rider of mass 0.002 slug to one side. When the heavier side has descended 2 ft the rider is removed and the system travels 4 ft in the next 3.5 s. What value does he obtain for g?

Solution. Let **W** be the weight of the large mass M, **w** the weight of the rider of mass m, and **T** the tension in the string. Then, during the accelerated part of the motion,

$$W + w - T = (M + m)a$$

and

$$T - W = Ma.$$

$$\therefore \quad w = (2M + m)a. \quad \therefore \quad g = \frac{2M + m}{m} a.$$

When the rider is removed, w is zero and the acceleration is thus zero also. The motion continues at constant speed v. But the system travels 4 ft in the next 3.5 s.

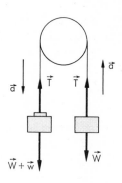

$$\therefore \qquad v = \frac{4 \text{ ft}}{3.5 \text{ s}} = \frac{8}{7} \text{ ft} \cdot \text{s}^{-1}.$$

During the acceleration the speed increases from 0 to $\frac{8}{7}$ ft·s^{-1} in a distance of travel of 2 ft. Apply the equation $v^2 = v_0^2 + 2a(x - x_0)$. Then $\frac{64}{49}$ ft^2·s^{-2} $= 0 + 2 \text{ ft} \times 2a$.

$$\therefore \qquad a = \frac{16}{49} \text{ ft} \cdot \text{s}^{-2}. \qquad \therefore \qquad g = \frac{0.042 \text{ slug}}{0.002 \text{ slug}} \times \frac{16}{49} \text{ ft} \cdot \text{s}^{-2} = 6.86 \text{ ft} \cdot \text{s}^{-2}.$$

PROBLEM 5.6

An astronaut, in his space suit and fully equipped, can jump 2 ft vertically on earth using maximum effort. How high can he jump on the moon if the diameter of the moon is one-quarter that of the earth and its density is two-thirds that of the earth?

Solution.   On the earth's surface,

$$g_e = \frac{GM_e}{R_e^2} = \frac{4}{3} \frac{\pi G R_e^3 \rho_e}{R_e^2} = \frac{4}{3} \pi \rho_e G R_e,$$

where the symbols have their usual significance.
    On the surface of the moon,

$$g_m = \frac{GM_m}{R_m^2} = \frac{4}{3} \pi \rho_m G R_m.$$

$$\therefore \qquad \frac{g_e}{g_m} = \frac{\rho_e}{\rho_m} \frac{R_e}{R_m} = \frac{3}{2} \times \frac{4}{1} = 6; \qquad \text{that is,} \qquad g_m = \frac{1}{6} g_e.$$

When he jumps at maximum effort, the astronaut can launch himself upward with an initial velocity v_0. On earth, when $v = 0$, then $0 = v_0^2 - 2g_e \times 2 \text{ ft}$.

$$\therefore \qquad v_0^2 = 2g_e \times 2 \text{ ft} = 12\, g_m \times 2 \text{ ft}.$$

Therefore, on the moon, when he starts with the same initial velocity, he jumps the distance y vertically, where $0 = v_0^2 - 2g_m \times y$.

$$\therefore \qquad y = \frac{v_0^2}{2g_m} = \frac{24 g_m}{2 g_m} \text{ ft} = 12 \text{ ft}.$$

PROBLEM 5.7

A spaceship from earth enters a circular orbit 22,000 km above the surface of Mars at the equator, which allows it to rotate at the same speed as Mars and thus to stay always above the same point on the planet's surface. The Martians set up a guided missile directly beneath it and fire it vertically upward in an attempt to destroy the intruder. With what minimum velocity must the missile leave the surface in order to succeed in its mission? Mars is a sphere of radius 3400 km and of mean density 4120 kg·m^{-3}.

Solution.   The mass of Mars is its volume times its density.

$$\therefore \qquad M_m = \tfrac{4}{3}\pi R_m^3 \times \rho_m = \tfrac{4}{3}\pi \times (3.4 \times 10^6 \text{ m})^3 \times 4120 \text{ kg} \cdot \text{m}^{-3} = 0.678 \times 10^{24} \text{ kg}.$$

As the guided missile rises, it has a retarding force acting on it at all times due to the gravitational attraction of the planet. At the time when the missile's velocity is v and it is at distance r from the center of the planet, the retarding force is given by $F = GM_m m/r^2$, where G is the universal gravitational constant and m is the mass of the missile. Since $F = ma$, the retardation a on the missile is in the opposite direction to r and its magnitude is

$$a = \frac{GM_m}{r^2}; \quad \text{that is,} \quad v\frac{dv}{dr} = -\frac{GM_m}{r^2}.$$

$$\therefore \quad v\,dv = -GM_m\frac{dr}{r^2}.$$

The minimum velocity, V, with which the missile can be sent off is that which will allow it to attain a distance of 22,000 km above the surface—i.e., a distance of 25,400 km from the center of Mars—before its upward velocity is reduced to zero. Hence

$$\int_V^0 v\,dv = -GM_m \int_{R_1}^{R_2} \frac{dr}{r^2},$$

where $R_1 = 3400$ km and $R_2 = 25,400$ km. Thus

$$\tfrac{1}{2}V^2 = GM_m(1/R_1 - 1/R_2)$$

or

$$V^2 = 2 \times 6.67 \times 10^{-11}\,\text{N·m}^2\text{·kg}^{-2} \times 0.678 \times 10^{24}\,\text{kg} \left(\frac{1}{3.4 \times 10^6\,\text{m}} - \frac{1}{25.4 \times 10^6\,\text{m}}\right)$$

$$= 2.30 \times 10^7\,\text{m}^2\text{·s}^{-2}.$$

$$\therefore \quad V = 4.8\,\text{km·s}^{-1}.$$

See Problem 9.14 for further consideration of this problem.

PROBLEM 5.8

Two rough planes A and B, inclined, respectively, at 30° and 60° to the horizontal and of the same vertical height, are placed back to back. A smooth pulley is fixed to the top of the planes and a string passed over it connecting two masses, the first of 0.2 slug resting on plane A and the other of mass 0.6 slug resting on plane B. The coefficient of kinetic friction on both planes is $1/\sqrt{3}$. Find the acceleration of the system.

Solution. There are four forces acting on each of the two masses: the weight acting downward, the normal force exerted by the plane at right angles to the plane, and the two forces acting along the plane, the tension in the string and the retarding force due to kinetic friction.

In each case resolve the weight into components along the plane and at right angles to it, as shown in the diagram. Since there is no tendency for either mass to rise from the plane, the normal force and the component of the weight at right angles to the plane must be equal and opposite. Further, if μ is the coefficient of kinetic friction between mass and plane, the frictional force in each case is μ times the normal force.

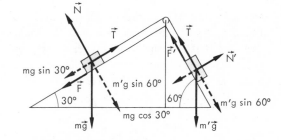

The larger mass on the steeper plane will descend. The frictional force is opposite to the motion, i.e., up the plane, and therefore

$$m'g \sin 60° - T - F' = m'g \sin 60° - T - \mu m'g \cos 60° = m'a.$$

Since the pulley is smooth, the tension is the same at all points in the string. For the other mass, motion is up the plane and thus the frictional force acts down the plane. Thus

$$T - mg \sin 30° - F = T - mg \sin 30° - \mu mg \cos 30° = ma.$$

Adding the two equations obtained, one has

$$m'g \sin 60° - mg \sin 30° - \mu(m'g \cos 60° + mg \cos 30°) = (m + m')a.$$

Therefore one can write, for the acceleration of the system,

$$a = \frac{[0.6 \text{ slug} \times (\sqrt{3}/2) - 0.2 \text{ slug} \times \frac{1}{2}] - (1/\sqrt{3})[0.6 \text{ slug} \times \frac{1}{2} + 0.2 \text{ slug} \times (\sqrt{3}/2)]}{0.8 \text{ slug}} g$$

$$= \frac{(2\sqrt{3}/10) - 0.2}{0.8} \times 32 \text{ ft} \cdot \text{s}^{-2} = 5.9 \text{ ft} \cdot \text{s}^{-2}.$$

PROBLEM 5.9

An Eskimo is about to push along a horizontal snowfield a sled of mass 1.8 slugs carrying a baby seal weighing 70 lb which he has killed while hunting. The coefficient of static friction between sled and seal is 0.8 and the coefficient of kinetic friction between sled and snow is 0.1. Show that the maximum horizontal force that the Eskimo can apply to the sled without losing the seal is 114.8 lb. Calculate the acceleration of the sled when this maximum horizontal force is applied.

Solution. The diagram has been split into two parts, the top part showing the forces acting on the seal and the bottom part the forces acting on the sled.

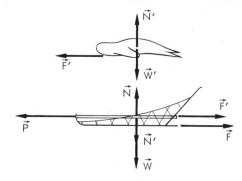

The horizontal force **P** being applied to the sled is assumed to be the maximum permissible one, under which circumstance the static frictional force, **F′**, between seal and sled must be the limiting force of friction, and it is thus equal in magnitude to the relevant coefficient of static friction, μ', times the normal force, N', acting at the interface. At this interface any force exerted on the sled by the seal must be equal and opposite to the reaction exerted on the seal by the sled. Since the frictional force on the sled acts opposite to the direction of **P**, trying to prevent motion of the sled, an opposite force **F′** of magnitude $\mu'N'$ acts on the seal, giving it the necessary acceleration to stay on the sled. Similarly the force **N′** exerted on the sled appears in the opposite direction in the diagram to the normal force acting on the seal.

Considering the seal, one can write

$$N' = W' = M'g \quad \text{and} \quad \mu'N' = \mu'M'g = M'a,$$

where W' and M' are the weight and mass of the seal, respectively, and a is the common acceleration of sled and seal under the action of the maximum possible force **P**.

Assume that **N** is the normal force exerted by the snow on the sled, **W** and M are the weight and mass of the sled, respectively, **F** is the frictional force exerted on the sled by the snow, and μ is the relevant coefficient of kinetic friction. Then, from the bottom half of the diagram, one can write

$$N = N' + W = W' + W = (M + M')g$$

and

$$P - F - F' = P - \mu N - \mu'N' = P - \mu(M + M')g - \mu'M'g = Ma.$$

But from the previous set of equations, $a = \mu'g$. The acceleration under maximum force is thus $0.8g = 25.6 \text{ ft} \cdot \text{s}^{-2}$, and

$$P = M \times \mu'g + \mu(M + M')g + \mu'M'g = (\mu + \mu')(M + M')g$$

$$= 0.9[(1.8 \text{ slugs} + 32 \text{ ft} \cdot \text{s}^{-2}) + 70 \text{ lb}] = 114.8 \text{ lb}.$$

PROBLEM 5.10

The distance between the reception area and the top floor of a skyscraper is 98 m. A passenger in an elevator does not experience any discomfort unless his apparent weight increases by more than 15%, or decreases by more than 10%. What is the shortest time it takes to transport him comfortably from reception area to top floor?

The conditions for the freight elevator are that the articles must remain in contact with the floor and the elevator cable can safely support a load equal to five times the combined weight of the elevator car and the passenger's luggage. How long will his luggage be waiting for him on the top floor if both elevators start off at the same time?

Solution. The apparent weight, W', of a passenger in an elevator moving with acceleration a upward is given by the expression $W' = W + Ma$, where W and M are the weight and mass of the passenger, respectively. Thus the apparent weight experienced by the passenger is greater than the normal weight if the elevator is accelerating upward, and less if the elevator is accelerating downward. Thus if $W' = \frac{115}{100}W$, then

$$a = \frac{15}{100}\frac{W}{M} = \frac{15}{100}g = \frac{3}{20}g; \quad \text{and if} \quad W'' = \frac{90}{100}\frac{W}{M}, \quad \text{then} \quad a' = -\frac{g}{10}.$$

Draw a velocity-time diagram of the motion. The portion illustrating the upward acceleration is given by a straight line of slope a which has a t-component of t_1 and a v-component of V. The deceleration is given by a further straight portion from the end of the first line to the t-axis with slope a'. The t- and v-components are t_2 and V, respectively. Now $V = at_1 = -a't_2$.

$$\therefore \quad \frac{t_1}{t_2} = -\frac{a'}{a} = \frac{2}{3}$$

or

$$t_1 = \tfrac{2}{5}(t_1 + t_2) = \tfrac{2}{5}T$$

and

$$t_2 = \tfrac{3}{5}T.$$

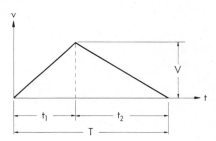

Also the distance covered, s, is given by

$$s = \tfrac{1}{2}at_1^2 - \tfrac{1}{2}a't_2^2 = \tfrac{1}{2}g(\tfrac{3}{20} \times \tfrac{4}{25}T^2 + \tfrac{1}{10} \times \tfrac{9}{25}T^2).$$

$$\therefore \quad T^2 = \frac{2s}{g(\frac{12}{500} + \frac{18}{500})} = \frac{2 \times 98 \text{ m} \times 50}{9.8 \text{ m}\cdot\text{s}^{-2} \times 3} = 333 \text{ s}^2 \quad \text{and} \quad T = 18.25 \text{ s},$$

which is the shortest time of ascent of the passenger elevator.

In the freight elevator, while it is accelerating upward at maximum acceleration, the tension in the cable is $5mg$, where m is the mass of elevator and luggage. Thus $5mg - mg = ma''$ or $a'' = 4g$.

In the deceleration period $a''' = -g$, if the luggage is to stay in contact with the floor. Applying the same technique as before, one obtains

$$\frac{t_1'}{t_2'} = \frac{1}{4} \quad \text{or} \quad t_1' = \frac{1}{5}T' \quad \text{and} \quad t_2' = \frac{4}{5}T'.$$

Hence one obtains, for the freight elevator,

$$T'^2 = \frac{2s}{g(4 \times \frac{1}{25} + \frac{16}{25})} = \frac{2 \times 98 \text{ m} \times 25}{9.8 \text{ m}\cdot\text{s}^{-2} \times 20} = 25 \text{ s}^2 \quad \text{and} \quad T' = 5 \text{ s}.$$

The luggage arrives at the top floor 13.25 s before the passenger.

PROBLEM 5.11

In a car which is accelerating, a plumb line hanging from the roof maintains a constant angle of 30° with the vertical. What can one say about the acceleration and what is its value?

Solution. Since the plumb line maintains a constant angle, the acceleration of the car must be constant.

There are only two forces acting on the bob of the plumb line, the weight $\mathbf{W} = m\mathbf{g}$ acting downward, and the tension $\mathbf{T}$ in the string. Splitting $\mathbf{T}$ into its vertical and horizontal components, one obtains

$$T \cos 30° = mg,$$

since the vertical forces must balance, and

$$T \sin 30° = ma,$$

since the horizontal force must produce acceleration a to match the motion of the car.

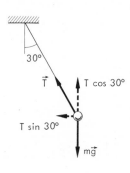

$$\therefore \quad \tan 30° = \frac{a}{g};$$

and

$$\therefore \quad a = g \tan 30° = \frac{g}{\sqrt{3}} = 18.47 \text{ ft} \cdot \text{s}^{-2}.$$

PROBLEM 5.12

A ball bearing is released from rest and drops through a viscous medium. The retarding force acting on the ball bearing has magnitude kv, where k is a constant depending on the radius of the ball and the viscosity of the medium. Find the terminal velocity acquired by the ball bearing and the time it takes to reach a speed of half the terminal velocity.

Solution. In the medium the forces acting on the ball bearing are the weight $m\mathbf{g}$ acting downward and the retarding force opposing the motion acting upward. Thus

$$mg - kv = ma,$$

where a is the acceleration produced at any time. The initial value of a is g, since at the moment of release $v = 0$. As the value of v increases, the acceleration decreases until, when $v = v_0$, the terminal velocity, $a = 0$. Thus $mg - kv_0 = 0$. Therefore $v_0 = (m/k)g$.

At any time t, it will be found that $mg - kv = ma = m(dv/dt)$.

$$\therefore \quad dt = \frac{dv}{g - (k/m)v}; \quad \text{and} \quad \therefore \quad \int_0^t dt = \int_0^v \frac{dv}{g - (k/m)v}.$$

$$\therefore \quad t = \left[-\frac{m}{k} \ln\left(g - \frac{k}{m}v\right) \right]_0^v = -\frac{m}{k}\left[\ln\left(g - \frac{k}{m}v\right) - \ln g \right] = -\frac{m}{k} \ln\left(1 - \frac{k}{mg}v\right).$$

The time to acquire half the terminal velocity, T, is thus

$$T = -\frac{m}{k} \ln\left(1 - \frac{k}{mg} \cdot \frac{mg}{2k}\right) = -\frac{m}{k} \ln\left(\frac{1}{2}\right) = +\frac{m}{k} \ln(2) = 0.69 \frac{m}{k}.$$

6

Motion in a Plane

PROBLEM 6.1

An airplane is traveling horizontally at 480 mph at a height of 6400 ft. The airplane drops a bomb aimed at a stationary target on the ground. To an observer on the aircraft, what angle must the target make with the vertical, when the bomb is dropped, if the bomb is to hit the target?

Suppose that the target is a ship which is steaming at 20 mph away from the aircraft along its line of flight. What alterations would need to be made to the previous calculations?

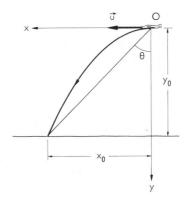

Solution. At the moment of release of the bomb, time $t = 0$, the airplane is at the point which is taken as the origin of the coordinate system, traveling in the positive x-direction with a speed u of 480 mph = 704 ft·s^{-1}. The bomb has, of course, the same initial speed.

There is no acceleration in the x-direction and thus, after time t, when the bomb strikes the target, the distance traveled by the bomb in this direction is $x_0 = ut$.

The airplane and bomb have no initial speed in the y-direction, but the acceleration g acts in this direction. After time t, the downward distance traveled by the released bomb will be $y_0 = \frac{1}{2}gt^2$. But $y_0 = 6400$ ft in this problem, and thus

$$t = \sqrt{\frac{2y_0}{g}} = \sqrt{\frac{2 \times 6400 \text{ ft}}{32 \text{ ft·s}^{-2}}} = 20 \text{ s}.$$

Thus in the same time

$$x_0 = ut = 704 \text{ ft·s}^{-1} \times 20 \text{ s} = 14{,}080 \text{ ft}$$

and

$$\tan \theta = \frac{x_0}{y_0} = \frac{14{,}080 \text{ ft}}{6400 \text{ ft}} = 2.2 \quad \text{or} \quad \theta = 65.5°.$$

The bomb should be released when the target is seen at an angle of 65.6° to the vertical.

If the target is moving, the relative velocity between plane and ship is the important velocity. For, relative to the ship, the bomb has an initial velocity $\mathbf{v}_{BS} = \mathbf{v}_{BW} + \mathbf{v}_{WS}$, where $\mathbf{v}_{BW}$ is the initial velocity of the bomb relative to the water, and $\mathbf{v}_{WS}$ the velocity of the water relative to the ship. Thus

$$v_{BS} = (480 - 20) \text{ mph} = 460 \text{ mph} = 674\tfrac{2}{3} \text{ ft·s}^{-1}.$$

The foregoing analysis can thus be carried out once more, with v_{BS} in place of u. Thus

$$\tan \theta' = \frac{674\tfrac{2}{3} \text{ ft·s}^{-1} \times 20 \text{ s}}{6400 \text{ ft}} = 2.1,$$

and the bomb should now be released when the target is seen at an angle $\theta' = 64.5°$ to the vertical.

PROBLEM 6.2

The total speed of a projectile at its greatest height is $\sqrt{\tfrac{6}{7}}$ of its total speed when it is at half its greatest height. Show that the angle of projection is 30°.

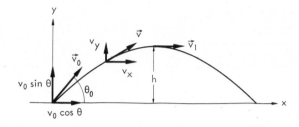

Solution. When a particle is projected as shown in the diagram, the component of the velocity in the x-direction stays at all times the same, $v_x = v_0 \cos \theta_0$, since there is no acceleration in that direction.

In the y-direction, the upward velocity starts at the value $v_0 \sin \theta_0$ and gradually decreases, due to the acceleration g acting downward. At its greatest height h, the upward velocity is reduced to zero. Hence we have

$$0 = (v_0 \sin \theta_0)^2 - 2gh \quad \text{or} \quad h = \frac{(v_0 \sin \theta_0)^2}{2g}.$$

The total velocity at the highest point is thus the x-component only. That is, $v_1 = v_0 \cos \theta_0$. At half the greatest height, $h/2 = (v_0 \sin \theta_0)^2/4g$, the velocity in the y-direction, v_y, is obtained from the equation

$$v_y^2 = (v_0 \sin \theta_0)^2 - 2g\frac{h}{2} = (v_0 \sin \theta_0)^2 - \tfrac{1}{2}(v_0 \sin \theta_0)^2 = \tfrac{1}{2}(v_0 \sin \theta_0)^2.$$

In addition there is also the ever-present x-component of the velocity $v_0 \cos \theta_0$. Hence the total velocity at this point is obtained from

$$v_2^2 = v_x^2 + v_y^2 = (v_0 \cos \theta_0)^2 + \tfrac{1}{2}(v_0 \sin \theta_0)^2 = (v_0 \cos \theta_0)^2 + \tfrac{1}{2}v_0^2(1 - \cos^2 \theta_0) = \tfrac{1}{2}v_0^2 + \tfrac{1}{2}(v_0 \cos \theta_0)^2.$$

However, one also has $v_1^2/v_2^2 = \tfrac{6}{7}$.

$$\therefore \quad \frac{(v_0 \cos \theta_0)^2}{\tfrac{1}{2}v_0^2 + \tfrac{1}{2}(v_0 \cos \theta_0)^2} = \frac{6}{7}; \quad \text{or} \quad 7(v_0 \cos \theta_0)^2 = 3v_0^2 + 3(v_0 \cos \theta_0)^2,$$

or $4 \cos^2 \theta_0 = 3$. One can therefore say that

$$\cos \theta_0 = \frac{\sqrt{3}}{2} \quad \text{or} \quad \theta_0 = 30°.$$

PROBLEM 6.3

A workman sitting on top of the roof of a house drops his hammer. The roof is smooth and slopes at an angle of 30° to the horizontal. It is 32 ft long and its lowest point is 32 ft from the ground. How far from the house wall is the hammer when it hits the ground?

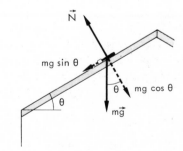

Solution. The first diagram illustrates the first part of the motion. Two forces are acting on the hammer as it slides down the roof: the weight mg acting downward, one component of which, mg cos θ, balances the second force, the normal force exerted by the roof. At the same time the component at right angles, mg sin θ, is unbalanced and produces the acceleration on the hammer.

Apply Newton's second law, and we obtain mg sin θ = ma. Thus the hammer accelerates down the roof with acceleration $a = g \sin \theta$. In this case $\sin \theta = \sin 30° = \tfrac{1}{2}$. But $v^2 = v_0^2 + 2as$, and the hammer travels 32 ft from rest. Hence v, the velocity with which it leaves the roof, is obtained from

$$v^2 = 2 \times \frac{32}{2} \text{ ft·s}^{-2} \times 32 \text{ ft}; \quad \text{that is,} \quad v = 32 \text{ ft·s}^{-1}.$$

In the second stage of the fall, the hammer undergoes projectile motion. It drops 32 ft in time t while traveling a distance x horizontally. Now, with the positive direction of y taken as downward, one obtains $x = v \cos \theta\, t$ and $y = v \sin \theta\, t + \frac{1}{2} g t^2$.

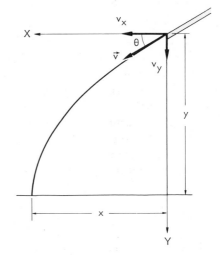

$$\therefore \quad y = v \sin \theta\, \frac{x}{v \cos \theta} + \frac{g}{2} \times \frac{x^2}{v^2 \cos^2 \theta}.$$

$$\therefore \quad \frac{x^2 \times 32 \text{ ft} \cdot \text{s}^{-2}}{2 \times (32 \text{ ft} \cdot \text{s}^{-1})^2 \times \frac{3}{4}} + \frac{x}{\sqrt{3}} - 32 \text{ ft} = 0.$$

or

$$x^2 + 16\sqrt{3}\, x \text{ ft} - 1536 \text{ ft}^2 = 0.$$

$$\therefore \quad (x + 32\sqrt{3} \text{ ft})(x - 16\sqrt{3} \text{ ft}) = 0.$$

$$\therefore \quad x = -32\sqrt{3} \text{ ft} \quad \text{or} \quad +16\sqrt{3} \text{ ft}.$$

The negative answer is clearly inadmissible. It is the answer that would result if the direction of projection were reversed. Hence the correct answer is

$$x = 16\sqrt{3} \text{ ft} = 27.7 \text{ ft from the house.}$$

PROBLEM 6.4

A fort is set up on the moon and is armed with guns which have a maximum range of $\frac{1}{2}$ mi on the earth. If the moon monsters have a weapon which can throw flame a distance of 3 mi on the moon, will the fort be able to survive?

Radius of moon/radius of earth $= \frac{1}{4}$; density of moon $= 3.4$ g$\cdot$cm^{-3}; density of earth $= 5.5$ g$\cdot$cm^{-3}.

Solution. The general expression for the range of a projectile in the usual notation is $R = v_0^2 \sin 2\theta_0/g$. This is a maximum when $\sin 2\theta_0 = 1$. The maximum range on the earth is thus $R_E = v_0^2/g_E$, and on the moon the maximum range is thus $R_M = v_0^2/g_M$. Therefore $R_M/R_E = g_E/g_M$. But

$$g_E = G \frac{m_E}{r_E^2} = G \frac{\frac{4}{3}\pi\, r_E^3\, \rho_E}{r_E^2} = \frac{4}{3}\, \pi G r_E\, \rho_E,$$

where m_E, r_E, and ρ_E are the mass, radius, and density of the earth. With similar notation applying to the moon, $g_M = \frac{4}{3}\pi\, G r_M \rho_M$.

$$\therefore \quad \frac{g_E}{g_M} = \frac{r_E \rho_E}{r_M \rho_M} = 4 \times \frac{5.5 \text{ g} \cdot \text{cm}^{-3}}{3.4 \text{ g} \cdot \text{cm}^{-3}} = 6.47.$$

Thus $R_M = 6.47\, R_E = 3.235$ mi. The earthmen can therefore keep the moon monsters at bay, since the flame throwers cannot get within firing distance.

PROBLEM 6.5

A 2-ft-long string which can just support a weight of 16 lb is fixed at one end to a peg on a smooth horizontal surface. The other end is fixed to a mass of $\frac{1}{2}$ slug. With what maximum constant speed can the mass rotate about the peg?

Solution. If the tension in the string exceeds 16 lb, the string will break. Thus the maximum centripetal force that can be exerted on the mass is 16 lb. But if the mass is circling the peg with a velocity v, the centripetal force necessary to keep it in the circle is mv^2/R, where m is $\frac{1}{2}$ slug and R is the length of the string, 2 ft. Thus

$$16 \text{ lb} = T_{\max} = \frac{mv_{\max}^2}{R} = \frac{\frac{1}{2} \text{ slug} \times v_{\max}^2}{2 \text{ ft}}.$$

$$\therefore \quad v_{\max}^2 = 64 \text{ ft} \cdot \text{lb} \cdot \text{slug}^{-1} = 64 \text{ ft}^2 \cdot \text{s}^{-2} \quad \text{or} \quad v_{\max} = 8 \text{ ft} \cdot \text{s}^{-1}.$$

PROBLEM 6.6

What is the maximum speed at which a car can safely round a circular curve of radius 160 ft on a horizontal road if the coefficient of static friction between tires and road is 0.8? The width between the wheels is 5 ft and the center of gravity of the car is 2 ft above the road. Will the car overturn or skid if it just exceeds this speed?

Solution. The magnitude of the maximum frictional force that can be brought into play between tires and road is $F = \mu N$, where **N** is the normal force exerted by the road on the car and μ is the appropriate coefficient of static friction. But since there is no upward movement of the car, **N** just balances the third force acting on the car, the weight $m\mathbf{g}$. Hence $F = \mu mg$.

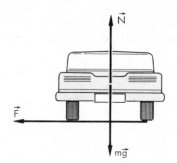

This must provide the centripetal force necessary to keep the car in the curve of radius r when it is moving with the maximum permissible speed v.

$$\therefore \qquad \mu mg = \frac{mv^2}{r}.$$

$$\therefore \qquad v = \sqrt{\mu rg} = \sqrt{0.8 \times 160 \text{ ft} \times 32 \text{ ft} \cdot \text{s}^{-2}}$$

$$= 64 \text{ ft} \cdot \text{s}^{-1} = 43.6 \text{ mph.}$$

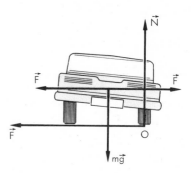

The frictional force **F** acts in the plane of the road surface and not through the center of mass of the car. In addition to providing the centripetal force necessary to keep the car in the curve, the frictional force must therefore produce a rotational motion about the center of mass. To see this effect most clearly, the following stratagem may be employed. Add equal and opposite forces of magnitude $F = \mu N = mv^2/r$ at the center of mass acting parallel to the road surface, as shown in the second diagram. The net effect of these forces is zero, and they do not affect the motion of the car. But it is now seen that the frictional force is equivalent to an equal force through the center of mass plus a couple of moment $\mu N = mv^2/r$ multiplied by the height of the center of mass above the road surface. The force acting through the center of mass can produce only translational motion, and provides the centripetal force necessary to keep the car moving in the curve. But the couple attempts to produce a clockwise rotational motion about the center of the car which would overturn the car if no other couple were brought into play.

But a counterclockwise couple is brought into play as soon as the car begins to tilt. The only point of contact between car and road will then be at O in the second diagram. Therefore **N** must act through this point; but the weight of the car of magnitude $mg = N$ still acts through the center of gravity. These two parallel but displaced forces form a couple of positive moment, tending to restore all car wheels to the road and to prevent the overturning.

The moment of the clockwise negative couple is $-\mu N = -mv^2/r$ multiplied by the height of the center of mass above the road. Thus $M_1 = -\mu N \times 2 \text{ ft} = -\mu mg \times 2 \text{ ft.}$

Assuming that the center of gravity of the car is centrally located, the moment of the positive couple is $N = mg$, multiplied by half the width between the wheels. Thus $M_2 = mg \times 2.5 \text{ ft.}$

$$\therefore \qquad M_2 + M_1 = mg \times 2.5 \text{ ft} - 0.8 \times mg \times 2 \text{ ft} = mg \times 0.9 \text{ ft.}$$

Since this is positive, $|M_2| > |M_1|$.

The restoring couple is therefore greater than the overturning couple at the maximum speed. If this speed is just exceeded, the car does not overturn. It skids, since the centripetal force is not now great enough to provide the acceleration necessary to keep it going round the curve, and the overturning couple is less than the restoring couple.

PROBLEM 6.7

The string of a conical pendulum is 10 ft long and the bob has a mass of $\frac{1}{2}$ slug. The pendulum is rotating at $\frac{1}{2}$ rev·s^{-1}. Find the angle the string makes with the vertical, and also the tension in the string.

Solution. Let r be the radius of the horizontal circle traversed by the bob of mass m, l be the length of the string, and $\mathbf{T}$ be the tension which the string exerts on the mass. The forces acting on the bob are the weight mg downward and the tension $\mathbf{T}$ at an angle θ to the vertical. Resolve $\mathbf{T}$ into horizontal and vertical components. Hence $T \sin \theta$ provides the centripetal force necessary to keep the bob in the circle. Thus $T \sin \theta = mv^2/r$, where v is the velocity of the bob. But v is the distance traveled in 1 s. That is, $v = n \times 2\pi r = 2\pi rn$, where n is the angular speed in rev·s^{-1}. Also $\sin \theta = r/l$.

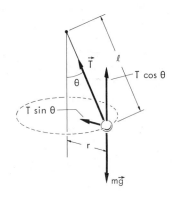

$$\therefore \quad T = \frac{4\pi^2 rmn^2}{r/l} = 4\pi^2 mln^2 = 4\pi^2 \times \tfrac{1}{2} \text{ slug} \times 10 \text{ ft} \times (\tfrac{1}{2} \text{ s}^{-1})^2$$

$$= 49 \text{ lb.}$$

The bob stays in the same horizontal plane, so that the vertical forces must balance. Thus $T \cos \theta = mg$.

$$\therefore \quad \cos \theta = \frac{mg}{4\pi^2 mln^2} = \frac{32}{4\pi^2 \times 10 \text{ ft} \times (\tfrac{1}{2} \text{ s}^{-1})^2} = 0.327; \quad \therefore \quad \theta = 71°.$$

PROBLEM 6.8

A car on a country road in Scotland passes over an old-fashioned hump-backed bridge. The center of gravity of the car follows the arc of a circle of radius 88 ft. Assuming that the car has a weight of 2 tons, find the force exerted by the car on the road at the highest point of the bridge if the car is traveling at 30 mph. At what speed will the car lose contact with the road?

Solution. The forces acting on the car at the highest point of the bridge are its weight $\mathbf{W} = mg$ downward and the normal force $\mathbf{N}$ exerted by the bridge upward. These cannot be equal, since there must be a net downward force to provide the acceleration necessary to keep the car traveling in a circle. Thus $mg - N = mv^2/r$.

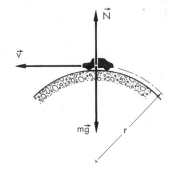

$$\therefore \quad N = m\left(g - \frac{v^2}{r}\right) = \frac{W}{g}\left(g - \frac{v^2}{r}\right) = W\left(1 - \frac{v^2}{rg}\right).$$

Here $v = 30$ mph $= 44$ ft·s^{-1}.

$$\therefore \quad N = 2 \text{ tons} \left(1 - \frac{44^2 \text{ ft}^2 \cdot \text{s}^{-2}}{88 \times 32 \text{ ft} \cdot \text{s}^{-2}}\right) = 2\left(1 - \frac{11}{16}\right) \text{ ton} = \frac{5}{8} \text{ ton.}$$

But action and reaction are equal and opposite. Thus, if the road exerts a force of $\frac{5}{8}$ ton on the car, the car exerts the same force on the road.

The car loses contact with the road when $N = 0$, that is, when $v^2 = rg$. Thus the speed required is

$$v = \sqrt{rg} = \sqrt{88 \text{ ft} \times 32 \text{ ft} \cdot \text{s}^{-2}} = 16\sqrt{11} \text{ ft} \cdot \text{s}^{-1} = 53.1 \text{ ft} \cdot \text{s}^{-1} = 36 \text{ mph.}$$

PROBLEM 6.9

What would be the period of rotation of the earth about its axis if its rotation speed increased until an object at the equator became weightless?

Solution. The two forces acting on a body at the equator are the force exerted on it due to the gravitational attraction of the earth, $m\mathbf{g}_0$, where $\mathbf{g}_0$ is the free-fall acceleration at the equator and acts toward the center, and the normal force exerted by the surface of the earth on the body, $\mathbf{N}$. This latter force acts upward. On a nonrotating earth, or at the poles, these forces are equal. At the equator the forces are unequal, and their difference $mg_0 - N$ provides the centripetal force necessary to keep the body traveling in a circle. Therefore $mg_0 - N = mv^2/R$, where v is the speed of the body and R is the radius of the earth. But the distance traveled in one period of rotation, T, is $2\pi R$. Therefore $T = 2\pi R/v$.

$$\therefore \quad N = mg_0 - \frac{mv^2}{R} = mg_0 - \frac{4\pi^2 mR}{T^2} = m\left(g_0 - \frac{4\pi^2 R}{T^2}\right) = mg,$$

where g is the acceleration as measured at the earth's surface, and N is a measure of the apparent weight of the body, which is thus less than the gravitational force exerted on the body by the earth. If the speed of revolution of the earth increases, the body becomes weightless when the normal force exerted on it by the surface becomes zero. Thus weightlessness occurs when $g_0 = 4\pi^2 R/T^2$ or

$$T = 2\pi\sqrt{\frac{R}{g_0}} = 2\pi\sqrt{\frac{4 \times 10^3 \text{ mi} \times 5280 \text{ ft}\cdot\text{mi}^{-1}}{32.4 \text{ ft}\cdot\text{s}^{-2}}} = \frac{2\pi}{3600 \text{ s}\cdot\text{hr}^{-1}} \times \sqrt{\frac{4 \times 5280 \times 10^3}{32.4}} \text{ s} = 1.41 \text{ hr.}$$

PROBLEM 6.10

Find the period of a communications satellite in a circular orbit 22,300 mi above the earth's surface, given that the radius of the earth is 4000 mi, that the period of the moon is 27.3 days, and that the orbit of the moon is almost circular with a radius of 239,000 mi.

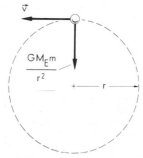

Solution. In any circular orbit of radius r an earth satellite of mass m will have a velocity v, and therefore a period of $T = 2\pi r/v$.

The centripetal force necessary to keep the satellite moving in a circle is supplied by the gravitational force exerted by the earth.

$$\therefore \quad G\frac{M_E m}{r^2} = \frac{mv^2}{r} = \frac{4\pi^2 mr}{T^2}.$$

The same arguments apply to the moon of mass M_M which moves in a circle of radius R with period T_M.

$$\therefore \quad G\frac{M_E M_M}{R^2} = \frac{4\pi^2 M_M R}{T_M^2}; \qquad \therefore \quad \frac{R^2}{r^2} = \frac{T_M^2 r}{T^2 R}.$$

$$\therefore \quad T = T_M\sqrt{\frac{r^3}{R^3}} = 27.3 \text{ days}\sqrt{\frac{(2.63 \times 10^4)^3 \text{ mi}^3}{(2.39 \times 10^5)^3 \text{ mi}^3}} = 1.00 \text{ day.}$$

Such a satellite therefore rotates about the center of the earth with the same period as the earth rotates about its axis. In other words, if it is rotating in the equatorial plane, it is always vertically above the same point on the earth's surface. Three such satellites strategically placed in a triangle about the earth will provide continuous communication between any two points on the earth's surface.

7

Work and Energy

PROBLEM 7.1

A delicate machine weighing 350 lb is lowered gently at constant speed down planks 8 ft long from the tailboard of a truck 4 ft above the ground. The relevant coefficient of sliding friction is 0.5. Must the machine be pulled down or held back? If the required force is applied parallel to the planks, what is its magnitude?

The machine is reloaded in the same manner, a force of 330 lb being applied. With what velocity does it reach the tailboard? What kinetic energy and what potential energy has it then acquired and how much work has been performed in overcoming friction? What relationship exists between these quantities?

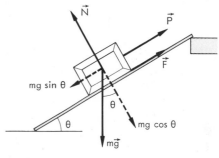

Solution. The forces acting on the machine are four in number. (a) The weight, $m\mathbf{g}$, acting vertically downward. (b) The normal force exerted by the plane, $\mathbf{N}$. (c) The frictional force, $\mathbf{F}$, acting up the plane opposing the motion down it. If μ is the coefficient of sliding friction, this force has magnitude μN. (d) The force $\mathbf{P}$ necessary to keep the machine moving with constant speed. In the diagram this is drawn acting up the plane. If the machine has to be pulled down, $\mathbf{P}$ will be negative.

Resolve the force $m\mathbf{g}$ into its components along the plane and at right angles to the plane. The forces are in equilibrium since there is no acceleration taking place. Hence

$$N = mg \cos \theta \quad \text{and} \quad mg \sin \theta = P + \mu N = P + \mu \, mg \cos \theta.$$

Therefore $P = mg(\sin \theta - \mu \cos \theta)$. But $\sin \theta = \frac{4}{8} = \frac{1}{2}$.

$$\therefore \quad \theta = 30°. \quad \therefore \quad P = 350 \text{ lb} \left(\frac{1}{2} - 0.5 \frac{\sqrt{3}}{2} \right) = 350 \times 0.067 \text{ lb} = 23.45 \text{ lb}.$$

The machine must be held back with a force of this magnitude.

During the loading process, the forces acting are those shown in the second diagram. Compared with the previous case, (a) and (b) are the same as before, (c) is of the same magnitude but, since it still acts against the motion, its direction is now reversed; (d) is replaced by the force $\mathbf{P}'$ supplied by the loaders.

There is no tendency to move at right angles to the plane. Thus $N = mg \cos \theta$. The net force up the plane is

$$P' - mg \sin \theta - \mu N = P' - mg (\sin \theta + \mu \cos \theta)$$

$$= 330 \text{ lb} - 350 \left(\frac{1}{2} + 0.5 \frac{\sqrt{3}}{2} \right) \text{lb} = (330 - 326.55) \text{ lb} = 3.45 \text{ lb}.$$

This force is acting on a mass of $\frac{350}{32}$ slugs, and will produce an acceleration $a = 3.45/(\frac{350}{32})$ ft·s^{-2}. The velocity after the machine has traveled 8 ft from rest is thus given from

$$v^2 = 2 \times \frac{32 \times 3.45 \text{ ft·s}^{-2}}{350} \times 8 \text{ ft} \qquad \text{or} \qquad v = 2.25 \text{ ft·s}^{-1}.$$

The kinetic energy at that time is

$$\frac{1}{2}mv^2 = \frac{1}{2} \times \frac{350}{32} \text{ slugs} \times 2 \times \frac{32 \times 3.45}{350} \times 8 \text{ ft}^2 \cdot \text{s}^{-2} = 27.6 \text{ ft·lb.}$$

Or, alternatively, the kinetic energy is the net force up the plane times 8 ft = 3.45 lb × 8 ft = 27.6 ft·lb.

The potential energy is $\mathbf{W} \cdot \mathbf{h} = Wh = 350$ lb × 4 ft = 1400 ft·lb.

The work done in overcoming friction is $\mathbf{F} \cdot \mathbf{s} = \mu N \times 8$ ft = 8 ft × $\mu mg \cos \theta$ = 1212.4 ft·lb.

The work done by the applied force P' is $\mathbf{P'} \cdot \mathbf{s} = 330$ lb × 8 ft = 2640 ft·lb.

But 27.6 + 1400 + 1212.4 = 2640. Thus the work done by the applied force equals the kinetic energy plus the potential energy gained by the machine added to the work done to overcome friction. This is merely a statement of the conservation of energy applied to this problem.

PROBLEM 7.2

A bricklayer is supplied with bricks by his mate who is 10 ft below him, the mate tossing the bricks vertically upward. If the bricks have a speed of 6 ft·s^{-1} when they reach the bricklayer, what percentage of the energy used up by the mate serves no useful purpose?

Solution. The equation of motion applicable to the movement of each brick is $v^2 = v_0^2 - 2g(x - x_0)$, in the usual notation. Thus

$$v_0^2 = v^2 + 2g(x - x_0) = 36 \text{ ft}^2 \cdot \text{s}^{-2} + 2 \times 32 \text{ ft·s}^{-2} \times 10 \text{ ft} = 676 \text{ ft}^2 \cdot \text{s}^{-2}. \quad \therefore \quad v_0 = 26 \text{ ft·s}^{-1}.$$

The kinetic energy given to each brick, and supplied by the bricklayer's mate, is

$$E_1 = \tfrac{1}{2} m v_0^2 = \text{m} \times 338 \text{ ft}^2 \cdot \text{s}^{-2}.$$

If the bricklayer's mate supplied only just enough energy to the bricks for them to reach the required level and no more, the initial velocity being u, they would have zero velocity at the level of the bricklayer. Hence

$$u^2 = 0 + 2g(x - x_0) = 2 \times 32 \text{ ft·s}^{-2} \times 10 \text{ ft}. \quad \therefore \quad u = 8\sqrt{10} \text{ ft·s}^{-1}.$$

The kinetic energy supplied by the mate in this case is

$$E_2 = \tfrac{1}{2} m u^2 = \text{m} \times 320 \text{ ft}^2 \cdot \text{s}^{-2}.$$

$$\therefore \quad \frac{E_2}{E_1} = \frac{320}{338} \qquad \text{or} \qquad \frac{E_1 - E_2}{E_1} = \frac{338 - 320}{338} \qquad \text{or} \qquad \frac{E_1 - E_2}{E_1} \times 100 = \frac{18}{338} \times 100.$$

Therefore the percentage of the energy uselessly expended is 1800/338 = 5.3%.

PROBLEM 7.3

In the casualty department of a hospital, it is necessary to raise or lower the examination table without disturbing the patient. This is accomplished by mounting the table on a screw jack which has a pitch of $\frac{1}{2}$ in. The raising of the table is accomplished by applying a force of 12.5 lb tangentially at the end of a lever 12 in. long and rotating the lever in a circle. Find the efficiency of this machine if patient and table together have a weight of 480 lb.

Solution. When the lever is rotated through one complete circle, the table is raised by one pitch of the screw. The work done on the machine by the operator is the force applied times the distance traveled in the direction of the force. Thus

$$W_1 = 12\tfrac{1}{2} \text{ lb} \times 2\pi \times 1 \text{ ft} = 25\pi \text{ ft·lb.}$$

The table and patient acquire additional potential energy, since their height above the ground is increased. The additional energy is their combined weight times the extra height. Thus

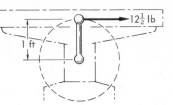

$$W_2 = 480 \text{ lb} \times \tfrac{1}{24} \text{ ft} = 20 \text{ ft·lb}.$$

The efficiency of the machine is the energy gained by the table divided by the energy supplied. Thus the efficiency is

$$E = \frac{W_2}{W_1} = \frac{20 \text{ ft·lb}}{25\pi \text{ ft·lb}} = 0.255 \quad \text{or} \quad E = 25.5\%.$$

PROBLEM 7.4

A bicycle and its rider together weigh 200 lb. If the cyclist free-wheels down a slope of 1 in 100, he has a constant speed of 10 mph, and if he free-wheels down a slope of 1 in 40, he has a constant speed of 20 mph. Suppose that he free-wheels on the level while holding on to the back of a moving truck. Find the power expended by the truck in maintaining his speed at 15 mph. Assume that air resistance varies as the square of his speed, while frictional forces remain constant at all times.

Solution. Let the frictional force be **F** and the force of air resistance **F′** with magnitude kv^2, where k is a constant and v is the speed of the bicycle.

On a slope, the forces acting on the bicycle and rider are the weight **W** acting downward, which can be resolved into components parallel to and perpendicular to the slope, the normal force exerted by the slope **N**, and the forces of friction and air resistance acting up the slope opposing the motion. The forces perpendicular to the slope are equal and opposite and are of no further interest. Since the bicycle is moving with constant speed, the forces parallel to the slope must also cancel out. Hence

$$W \sin \theta = F + kv^2.$$

For the two cases given, values can be inserted. Thus

$$200 \text{ lb} \times \frac{1}{100} = F + k \times 10^2 \text{ mi}^2 \cdot \text{hr}^{-2} \quad \text{and} \quad 200 \text{ lb} \times \frac{1}{40} = F + k \times 20^2 \text{ mi}^2 \cdot \text{hr}^{-2}.$$

$$\therefore \quad 2 \text{ lb} = F + 100k \text{ mi}^2 \cdot \text{hr}^{-2} \quad \text{and} \quad 5 \text{ lb} = F + 400k \text{ mi}^2 \cdot \text{hr}^{-2}.$$

$$\therefore \quad 300k \text{ mi}^2 \cdot \text{hr}^{-2} = 3 \text{ lb} \quad \text{or} \quad k = \frac{1}{100} \text{ lb·(mph)}^{-2} \quad \text{and} \quad F = 1 \text{ lb}.$$

For the case of the bicycle traveling on a level surface, a force **P** must be supplied to overcome the forces of friction and air resistance and keep the bicycle moving with constant speed. Since there is no acceleration,

$$P = F + kv^2 = 1 \text{ lb} + \frac{1}{100} \text{ lb·(mph)}^{-2} \times 225 \text{ (mph)}^2 = 3.25 \text{ lb}.$$

The rate of working is **P·v** and $v = 15 \text{ mph} = 22 \text{ ft·s}^{-1}$.

$$\therefore \quad P \times v = 3.25 \text{ lb} \times 22 \text{ ft·s}^{-1}.$$

But 1 hp = 550 ft·lb·s⁻¹. Therefore:

$$\text{The rate of working} = \frac{3.25 \times 22}{550} \text{ hp} = 0.13 \text{ hp}.$$

PROBLEM 7.5

A small body of mass 1 slug is rotated in a vertical circle at the end of a string 2 ft long. If the tension in the string just vanishes at the top of the circle, what is the velocity of the body and the tension in the string (a) when the string is horizontal, and (b) when the body is at its lowest point?

Solution. At each of the positions of the body in its rotation only two forces act on it, the weight $m\mathbf{g}$ acting downward and the tension of the string **T** acting toward the center of the circle.

At the top of the swing, the two forces act in the same direction and together provide the centripetal force necessary to keep the body in its circular path. Thus

$$mg + T = \frac{mv^2}{r}.$$

When T is just zero at the top,

$$v^2 = rg = 2 \text{ ft} \times 32 \text{ ft} \cdot \text{s}^{-2} = 64 \text{ ft}^2 \cdot \text{s}^{-2}. \qquad \therefore \qquad v = 8 \text{ ft} \cdot \text{s}^{-1}.$$

(a) When the string is horizontal, the body has lost potential energy and gained a corresponding quantity of kinetic energy. If we refer to the diagram,

$$\tfrac{1}{2}mv_1^2 = \tfrac{1}{2}mv^2 + mg \times r \qquad \text{or} \qquad v_1^2 = v^2 + 2gr = 3gr.$$
$$\therefore \qquad v_1 = 8\sqrt{3} \text{ ft} \cdot \text{s}^{-1} = 13.86 \text{ ft} \cdot \text{s}^{-1}.$$

Further, $\mathbf{T}_1$ is the only force acting radially. Hence

$$T_1 = \frac{mv_1^2}{r} = 3mg = 3 \times 1 \text{ slug} \times 32 \text{ ft} \cdot \text{s}^{-2} = 96 \text{ lb}.$$

(b) When the body is at its lowest point, similar arguments about gain of kinetic energy and loss of potential energy apply. Thus $\tfrac{1}{2}mv_2^2 = \tfrac{1}{2}mv^2 + mg \times 2r.$

$$\therefore \qquad v_2^2 = v^2 + 4gr = 5gr. \qquad \therefore \qquad v_2 = 8\sqrt{5} \text{ ft} \cdot \text{s}^{-1} = 17.9 \text{ ft} \cdot \text{s}^{-1}.$$

Although $\mathbf{T}_2$ still acts radially it must not only provide the necessary centripetal force but also balance the weight of the body. Hence

$$T_1 = \frac{mv_2^2}{r} + mg = 5mg + mg = 6mg = 6 \times 1 \text{ slug} \times 32 \text{ ft} \cdot \text{s}^{-2} = 192 \text{ lb}.$$

PROBLEM 7.6

An athlete in his run-up for a pole vault can achieve a speed of 30 ft·s⁻¹. What is the maximum possible record for the pole vault likely to be?

Solution. At the end of the run with a velocity of 30 ft·s⁻¹, the athlete possesses kinetic energy of amount

$$E_k = \tfrac{1}{2} \times m \times 30^2 \text{ ft}^2 \cdot \text{s}^{-2},$$

where m is his mass. By causing rotation about the end of his pole he transforms this kinetic energy into potential energy. The mass of the pole is negligible in comparison with that of the man and need not be considered. Further, the pole must not be made of a material which can boost the athlete's energy by its elastic springiness.

The most favorable case occurs when the athlete plans his jump in such a way that, as he clears the bar, he has negligible kinetic energy left. Thus if h is the height by which the athlete's center of gravity alters in the jump,

$$\tfrac{1}{2}m \times 30^2 \text{ ft}^2 \cdot \text{s}^{-2} = mgh. \qquad \therefore \qquad h = \frac{30^2 \text{ ft}^2 \cdot \text{s}^{-2}}{2g} = 14 \text{ ft} \tfrac{3}{4} \text{ in}.$$

But if the athlete is very tall, his center of gravity may be as much as 3 ft 9 in. from the ground during his run-up. Hence the final height of his center of gravity above the ground is maximally 17 ft 9¾ in. His center of gravity is located inside his body and the bar must be lower than his center of gravity by roughly half the thickness of his body. If we assume a reasonably thin athlete, a minimum of 4½ in. must be subtracted from the height previously mentioned to allow for clearance. The maximum possible record for the pole vault would appear to be 17 ft 5¼ in. The present world record is 17 ft 4 in. (It should be noted that fiber-glass poles do not meet the conditions about elasticity stated above.)

PROBLEM 7.7

Spring-Heel Jack was a legendary English criminal who was never captured because of his ability to jump over high walls and other obstacles which his pursuers were unable to scale. It is believed that he had a powerful spring attached to each shoe for this purpose. Assuming that he weighed 150 lb and that his springs were compressed by 1 in. when he stood on them, by how much did he need to keep his springs compressed on one of his operations in order to be ready to clear a 10-ft wall in the event of an emergency?

Solution. When Jack stood up on his springs, each bore one-half of his weight. The elastic force produced by the compression of each spring must have been equal and opposite to the 75 lb acting down on it. Thus $75 \text{ lb} = k \times \frac{1}{12} \text{ ft}$, where k is the force constant of each spring.

$$\therefore \quad k = 12 \times 75 \text{ lb·ft}^{-1}.$$

If Jack wished to clear a 10-ft wall while remaining erect, the potential energy stored in the springs must have been sufficient to raise his 150-lb weight through a vertical distance of 10 ft. But if x was the compression of each spring, then $2 \times \frac{1}{2}kx^2 = 150 \text{ lb} \times 10 \text{ ft}$.

$$\therefore \quad x^2 = \frac{150 \times 10 \text{ ft·lb}}{12 \times 75 \text{ lb·ft}^{-1}} = \frac{20}{12} \text{ ft}^2. \quad \therefore \quad x = \sqrt{1.67} \text{ ft} = 1.29 \text{ ft}.$$

PROBLEM 7.8

An engine used to pump water out of a mine shaft raises the water 150 ft and discharges it on the surface with a speed of 20 mph. It removes 2 slugs per second from the mine. One-fifth of the work it does is used in overcoming frictional forces. What is the horsepower of the engine?

Solution. During the process of removal from the mine, the water gains both potential and kinetic energy. The potential energy acquired per second is the weight of water ejected per second times the height raised. Thus

$$E_p = 2 \text{ slugs·s}^{-1} \times 32 \text{ ft·s}^{-2} \times 150 \text{ ft} = 9600 \text{ ft·lb·s}^{-1}.$$

The water also acquires kinetic energy, the final speed of ejection being 20 mph $= \frac{88}{3} \text{ ft·s}^{-1}$. The kinetic energy acquired per second is thus

$$E_k = \frac{1}{2} \times 2 \text{ slugs·s}^{-1} \times \left(\frac{88}{3}\right)^2 \text{ ft}^2 \cdot \text{s}^{-2} = 860\frac{4}{9} \text{ ft·lb·s}^{-1}.$$

The total energy acquired by the water is thus

$$E = E_p + E_k = 10{,}460\frac{4}{9} \text{ ft·lb·s}^{-1}.$$

The work done by the engine, including the quantity used in overcoming friction, is

$$W = \tfrac{5}{4}E = \tfrac{5}{4} \times 10{,}460\frac{4}{9} \text{ ft·lb·s}^{-1}$$

and its rate of working is

$$P = \frac{\tfrac{5}{4} \times 10{,}460\frac{4}{9} \text{ ft·lb·s}^{-1}}{550 \text{ ft·lb·s}^{-1} \cdot (\text{hp})^{-1}} = 23.8 \text{ hp}.$$

PROBLEM 7.9

At a colliery, the coal is transported from the shaft to a loading bay in hoppers attached to a cable at intervals of 50 ft. Each hopper holds 1000 lb of coal and rises 100 ft in its journey before tipping its load into the top of the bay which is 1000 ft from the mine shaft. If the speed of the hoppers is 6 mph and one-tenth of the work done is used in overcoming friction, what is the horsepower of the driving motor?

Solution. The hoppers go up full and return empty. Any force due to the rising hoppers which tends to prevent the motion is therefore balanced by an equal and opposite force due to the returning hoppers tending to accelerate the motion; and thus the potential energy supplied to the rising hoppers is returned to the system by the descending ones. Only the coal, which leaves the system at its highest point, has to be supplied by the motor with potential energy which is never recovered.

The cable moves at 6 mph $= 8.8$ ft·s^{-1}. At any instant there are 20 full hoppers on the cable and in 1 s each moves 8.8 ft along the cable, rising 0.88 ft in the process. The increase in potential energy is

$$E_p = 20 \times 1000 \text{ lb} \times 0.88 \text{ ft·s}^{-1} = 1.76 \times 10^4 \text{ ft·lb·s}^{-1}.$$

This represents only nine-tenths of the energy supplied, the other one-tenth being used in overcoming frictional forces. Thus the total energy supplied is

$$E = \frac{10}{9} E_p = 1.956 \times 10^4 \text{ ft·lb·s}^{-1}.$$

The rate of working of the motor is thus

$$P = \frac{E}{550 \text{ ft·lb·s}^{-1}\cdot(\text{hp})^{-1}} = \frac{1.956}{550} \times 10^4 \text{ hp} = 35.6 \text{ hp}.$$

PROBLEM 7.10

Repeat Problem 6.2, using the principle of conservation of energy.

Solution. At the start of the motion, the projectile possesses kinetic energy of amount $\frac{1}{2}mv_0^2$. At its greatest height, h, it possesses kinetic energy due to the component of its velocity in the x-direction only, $\frac{1}{2}mv_0^2 \cos^2 \theta_0$, and also potential energy due to its increased height, mgh. By the principle of conservation of energy,

$$\frac{1}{2}mv_0^2 = \frac{1}{2}mv_0^2 \cos^2 \theta_0 + mgh.$$

$$\therefore \quad h = \frac{v_0^2(1 - \cos^2\theta_0)}{2g} = \frac{v_0^2 \sin^2 \theta_0}{2g}.$$

At half the greatest height, the potential energy possessed by the projectile is

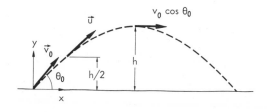

$$mg\frac{h}{2} = mg\frac{v_0^2 \sin^2 \theta_0}{4g} = \frac{1}{4} mv_0^2 \sin^2 \theta_0.$$

At that time it has a velocity u and thus possesses kinetic energy of amount $\frac{1}{2}mu^2$. By the principle of conservation of energy, $\frac{1}{2}mv_0^2 = \frac{1}{2}mu^2 + \frac{1}{4}mv_0^2 \sin^2 \theta_0$.

$$\therefore \quad u^2 = v_0^2 - \frac{1}{2}v_0^2 \sin^2 \theta_0. \quad \text{But} \quad v_0 \cos \theta_0 = \sqrt{\tfrac{6}{7}}u.$$

$$\therefore \quad v_0^2 \cos^2\theta_0 = v_0^2 (1 - \sin^2\theta_0) = \tfrac{6}{7} (v_0^2 - \tfrac{1}{2}v_0^2 \sin^2\theta_0). \quad \therefore \quad \tfrac{8}{14} \sin^2\theta_0 = \tfrac{2}{14}.$$

$$\therefore \quad \sin^2\theta_0 = \tfrac{1}{4}. \quad \therefore \quad \sin \theta_0 = \tfrac{1}{2} \quad \text{or} \quad \theta_0 = 30°.$$

8

Impulse and Momentum

PROBLEM 8.1

A sports car weighing 1200 lb and traveling at 60 mph fails to stop at an intersection and crashes into a 4000-lb delivery truck traveling at 45 mph in a direction at right angles to it. The wreckage becomes locked and travels 54.7 ft before coming to rest. Find the magnitude and direction of the constant force that has produced this deceleration.

Solution. Let the sports car be traveling in the positive x-direction and the truck in the positive y-direction. After the collision at the origin, the combined mass travels in a direction inclined at $\theta°$ to the positive x-axis with a velocity $\mathbf{V}$. Momentum must be conserved in both the x- and y-directions. Therefore, referring to the diagram,

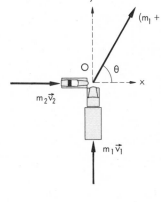

$$m_1 v_1 = (m_1 + m_2)V \sin \theta$$

and

$$m_2 v_2 = (m_1 + m_2)V \cos \theta.$$

$$\therefore \quad \tan \theta = \frac{m_1 v_1}{m_2 v_2} = \frac{m_1 g v_1}{m_2 g v_2} = \frac{4000 \text{ lb} \times 45 \text{ mph}}{1200 \text{ lb} \times 60 \text{ mph}} = 2.5.$$

$$\therefore \quad \theta = 68.2°.$$

Also

$$V^2 (\sin^2 \theta + \cos^2 \theta) = V^2 = \frac{m_1^2 v_1^2 + m_2^2 v_2^2}{(m_1 + m_2)^2} = \frac{m_1^2 g^2 v_1^2 + m_2^2 g^2 v_2^2}{(m_1 g + m_2 g)^2}$$

$$= \frac{(4000 \text{ lb})^2 \times (45 \text{ mph})^2 + (1200 \text{ lb})^2 \times (60 \text{ mph})^2}{(4000 \text{ lb} + 1200 \text{ lb})^2} = 1389.9 \text{ (mph)}^2.$$

$$\therefore \quad V = 37.3 \text{ mph} = 54.7 \text{ ft·s}^{-1},$$

which is the velocity of the combined mass immediately after impact.

The wreckage comes to rest in 54.7 ft. Applying the equation $v^2 = v_0^2 + 2as$, one obtains

$$0 = (54.7 \text{ ft·s}^{-1})^2 + 2a \times 54.7 \text{ ft}. \quad \therefore \quad a = -27.35 \text{ ft·s}^{-2}.$$

The deceleration due to friction is thus 27.35 ft·s^{-2}, and since the mass affected is $(1200 + 4000)/32$ slugs, the magnitude of the frictional force is

$$F = \frac{5200}{32} \text{ slugs} \times 27.35 \text{ ft·s}^{-2} = 4443 \text{ lb}.$$

This decelerating force must act in a direction opposite to that in which the wreckage is traveling in order to bring it to rest. Thus it is a force of 4443 lb acting at an angle of 68.2° to the negative x-axis.

41

PROBLEM 8.2

When a block of wood of mass 1 kg is held in a vise, a bullet of mass 10 g fired into it penetrates to a depth of 10 cm. If the block is now suspended so that it can move freely and a second bullet is fired into it, to what depth will the bullet penetrate? (The retarding force in both cases is assumed constant.)

Solution. In the first case, when the block of mass M is rigidly held, all the kinetic energy of the bullet of mass m is lost in penetrating the wood. If the wood exerts a constant retarding force, $\mathbf{F}$, on the bullet and the depth of penetration is $\mathbf{d}$, the work done in stopping the bullet is the work done when a force F moves through a distance $\mathbf{d}$. Further, this work must be equal to the initial kinetic energy of the bullet, since this work appears as heat and a negligible amount of energy is lost. Thus $\mathbf{F} \cdot \mathbf{d} = Fd = \frac{1}{2}mv^2$.

In the second case the block is free to move and an inelastic collision takes place. The combined block and bullet move off in the direction of travel of the bullet with velocity $\mathbf{V}$, where $mv = (M + m)\mathbf{V}$.

Further, the work done by the retarding force, appearing as heat, can now be equal only to the loss of kinetic energy. The bullet penetrates a lesser distance $\mathbf{d}'$ and

$$\mathbf{F} \cdot \mathbf{d}' = Fd' = \frac{1}{2}mv^2 - \frac{1}{2}(M + m)V^2 = \frac{1}{2}mv^2 - \frac{1}{2}\frac{m^2}{M + m}v^2.$$

Dividing one equation by the other, one obtains

$$\frac{d'}{d} = \frac{m - [m^2/(M + m)]}{m} = \frac{M}{M + m}.$$

$$\therefore \quad \frac{d'}{0.1 \text{ m}} = \frac{1 \text{ kg}}{1.01 \text{ kg}}. \qquad \therefore \quad d' = \frac{1}{10.1}\text{ m} = 0.099 \text{ m} = 9.9 \text{ cm}.$$

PROBLEM 8.3

A moving particle makes a perfectly elastic collision with a second particle, initially at rest, along their line of centers. Find the ratio of the masses which makes the kinetic energy transferred to the second particle a maximum.

If the ratio of the masses is not that calculated above, show that the amount of energy transferred can be increased by inserting a third particle between the first two. For optimal transfer, the mass of the third particle is the geometric mean of the other two.

Solution. Let the energy of the incoming particle be E, and refer to the diagram for the system of notation. Since the collision is perfectly elastic, both energy and momentum are conserved. Therefore

$$E = E_A + E_B \quad \text{and} \quad m_A u = m_A v_A + m_B v_B.$$

But

$$E = \frac{1}{2}m_A u^2 = \frac{m_A^2 u^2}{2m_A} \quad \text{or} \quad m_A u = \sqrt{2m_A E},$$

and similarly for the other kinetic energies. The second equation is therefore

$$\sqrt{2m_A E} = \sqrt{2m_A E_A} + \sqrt{2m_B E_B} \quad \text{or} \quad \sqrt{E} = \sqrt{E_A} + \sqrt{xE_B}, \quad \text{where } x = m_B/m_A.$$

$$\therefore \quad E_A + E_B = E = E_A + xE_B + 2\sqrt{xE_A E_B} \quad \text{or} \quad (1 - x)EB = 2\sqrt{xE_A E_B}.$$

$$\therefore \quad (1 - x)^2 E_B = 4xE_A = 4x(E - E_B).$$

$$\therefore \quad \frac{E_B}{E - E_B} = \frac{4x}{(1 - x)^2} \quad \text{or} \quad \frac{E_B}{E} = \frac{4x}{(1 + x)^2}.$$

$$\therefore \quad \frac{d}{dx}\left(\frac{E_B}{E}\right) = \frac{4}{(1 + x)^2} - \frac{8x}{(1 + x)^3},$$

and for maximum energy transfer, EB should be as large a proportion of E as possible and $(d/dx)(E_B/E)$ should be zero. Thus, for maximum energy transfer,

$$\frac{4}{(1+x)^2} - \frac{8x}{(1+x)^3} = 0 \quad \text{or} \quad 4(1+x) = 8x. \quad \therefore \quad x = 1.$$

Thus the two masses should be equal, when all the energy is transferred to the second particle.

If x has a fixed value not equal to 1, insert a further mass m_C between m_A and m_B. Then in the first collision,

$$\frac{E_C}{E} = \frac{4y}{(1+y)^2},$$

where $y = m_C/m_A$. Now m_C collides with m_B and

$$\frac{E_B}{E_C} = \frac{4z}{(1+z)^2},$$

where $z = m_B/m_C$. But $yz = x$, and therefore

$$\frac{E_B}{E_C} = \frac{4(x/y)}{[1+(x/y)]^2}.$$

$$\therefore \quad \frac{E_B}{E} = \frac{E_B}{E_C} \cdot \frac{E_C}{E} = \frac{16x}{(1+y)^2[1+(x/y)]^2}.$$

$$\frac{d}{dy}\left(\frac{E_B}{E}\right) = -\frac{32x}{(1+y)^3[1+(x/y)]^2} + \frac{32x^2/y^2}{(1+y)^2[1+(x/y)]^3}.$$

For maximum energy transfer to the final mass, this quantity must be zero, and so

$$32x\left(1 + \frac{x}{y}\right) = \frac{32x^2}{y^2}(1+y).$$

$$\therefore \quad y^2 + xy = x + xy \quad \text{or} \quad y^2 = x.$$

$$\therefore \quad \frac{m_C^2}{m_A^2} = \frac{m_B}{m_A} \quad \text{or} \quad m_C = \sqrt{m_A m_B}.$$

For maximum energy transfer the intermediate particle must have a mass which is the geometrical mean of the other two. Further, since the square of any number is always positive,

$$(1 - \sqrt{x})^2 > 0 \quad \text{or} \quad 1 + x > 2\sqrt{x}.$$

$$\therefore \quad 2(1+x) > 1 + x + 2\sqrt{x} = (1+\sqrt{x})^2,$$

or since the quantity on the right of the equation is positive, $4(1+x)^2 > (1+\sqrt{x})^4$.

$$\therefore \quad \frac{4}{(1+\sqrt{x})^4} > \frac{1}{(1+x)^2} \quad \text{or} \quad \frac{16x}{(1+\sqrt{x})^4} > \frac{4x}{(1+x)^2},$$

since x is a positive quantity. But the first term in the final inequality is the maximum transfer of energy when three particles are involved, using the necessary relation $y^2 = x$. The second term is the energy transfer when only two particles are involved. Therefore not only is maximum energy transferred in the three-particle case when $m_C = \sqrt{m_A m_B}$, but the energy acquired by the particle of mass m_B is greater than it is when only two particles are involved.

PROBLEM 8.4

A bullet weighing 4 g is fired at a speed of 600 m·s⁻¹ into a ballistic pendulum of weight 1 kg and thickness 25 cm. The bullet passes through the pendulum and emerges with a speed of 100 m·s⁻¹. Calculate the constant retarding force acting on the bullet in its passage through the block, and the height to which the pendulum rises.

Solution. The three stages of the motion of the system are as shown in the diagram. In the first stage the bullet of mass m approaches with velocity $\mathbf{V}$ the ballistic pendulum of mass M. In the second the bullet, having passed through the pendulum, is moving off with velocity $\mathbf{v}_1$, leaving the pendulum just starting to move with velocity $\mathbf{v}_2$. Since momentum must be conserved, $m\mathbf{V} = m\mathbf{v}_1 + M\mathbf{v}_2$.

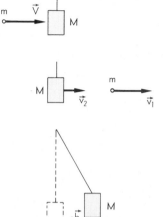

$$\therefore \quad v_2 = \frac{mg(V - v_1)}{Mg} = \frac{4 \times 10^{-3}\,\text{kg}\,(600 - 100)\,\text{m}\cdot\text{s}^{-1}}{1\,\text{kg}} = 2\,\text{m}\cdot\text{s}^{-1}.$$

In the third stage the pendulum, which has acquired kinetic energy $\frac{1}{2}Mv_2^2$, swings through a certain angle such that the bob loses all its kinetic energy but gains an equivalent quantity of potential energy in rising a height $\mathbf{h}$, in accordance with the principle of conservation of energy. But $\mathbf{W}\cdot\mathbf{h} = Mgh = \frac{1}{2}Mv_2^2$. Therefore $h = \sqrt{v_2^2/2g} = 0.45\,\text{m} = 45\,\text{cm}$. The loss of kinetic energy as the bullet passes through the pendulum is

$$\tfrac{1}{2}mV^2 - \tfrac{1}{2}mv_1^2 - \tfrac{1}{2}Mv_2^2 = \frac{4 \times 10^{-3}\,\text{kg}}{2}\,(600^2 - 100^2)\,\text{m}^2\cdot\text{s}^{-2}$$

$$- \frac{1\,\text{kg}}{2} \times 4\,\text{m}^2\cdot\text{s}^{-2} = 698\,\text{J}.$$

By the principle of conservation of energy, this quantity of energy must represent the work done against the retarding force, $\mathbf{F}$, as the bullet pushes its way through the pendulum. Thus

$$\mathbf{F}\cdot\mathbf{s} = F \times 0.25\,\text{m} = 698\,\text{J} \quad \text{or} \quad F = 4\,\text{m}^{-1} \times 698\,\text{J} = 2792\,\text{N}.$$

PROBLEM 8.5

Two space men, each of mass 70 kg, inadvertently cause a leak in a space station on which they are working, and the escaping air sends them drifting from the structure along the same straight line, one with velocity $7\,\text{cm}\cdot\text{s}^{-1}$ and the other with velocity $10\,\text{cm}\cdot\text{s}^{-1}$ relative to the station. The slower man is carrying a hammer of mass 2 kg which he throws to his companion who then hurls it out into space as fast as he can, giving it a speed of $15\,\text{m}\cdot\text{s}^{-1}$ away from the station. What is the maximum velocity with which the first man can throw the hammer if both men are to return to the space station, and what is the speed with which the first man then retraces his path?

Solution. All velocities away from the station are taken as positive; those toward the station are negative.

Three separate events are involved here. In the first event, the slower man and the hammer are initially both traveling at $7\,\text{cm}\cdot\text{s}^{-1}$ relative to the space station. By use of muscle power, the man gives a further velocity, u, to the hammer. He suffers a recoil in consequence, and moves with a total velocity v thereafter. Therefore, since momentum must be conserved,

$$(70 + 2)\,\text{kg} \times 0.07\,\text{m}\cdot\text{s}^{-1} = 2\,\text{kg} \times (u + 0.07\,\text{m}\cdot\text{s}^{-1}) + 70\,\text{kg} \times v.$$

The second event is the catching of the hammer by the faster man. The hammer approaches him with velocity $(u + 0.07\,\text{m}\cdot\text{s}^{-1})$, and he is traveling at $10\,\text{cm}\cdot\text{s}^{-1}$. An inelastic collision takes place, the two continuing with the common velocity U. Applying the principle of conservation of momentum, one obtains

$$2\,\text{kg}\,(u + 0.07\,\text{m}\cdot\text{s}^{-1}) + 70\,\text{kg} \times 0.10\,\text{m}\cdot\text{s}^{-1} = (70 + 2)\,\text{kg} \times U.$$

The final event is the hurling into space of the hammer. The hammer is given a velocity of $15\,\text{m}\cdot\text{s}^{-1}$ and the man's velocity, due to the recoil, changes also. If his companion threw the hammer to him with the maximum possible velocity consistent with both being able to return to the station, his final velocity must be infinitesimally less than zero. That is, he must have a minute velocity back toward the space station. The limiting case is thus for his final velocity to be exactly zero. Applying the principle of conservation of momentum to this case, one has

$$(70 + 2)\,\text{kg} \times U = 2\,\text{kg} \times 15\,\text{m}\cdot\text{s}^{-1} + 0.$$

Combining the last two equations, one obtains

$$2 \text{ kg} \times u + (0.14 + 7.0) \text{ kg} \cdot \text{m} \cdot \text{s}^{-1} = 30 \text{ kg} \cdot \text{m} \cdot \text{s}^{-1}. \qquad \therefore \qquad u = -\frac{22.86 \text{ kg} \cdot \text{m} \cdot \text{s}^{-1}}{2 \text{ kg}} = -11.43 \text{ m} \cdot \text{s}^{-1},$$

and bringing in the first equation, one obtains $72 \text{ kg} \times 0.07 \text{ m} \cdot \text{s}^{-1} = 23.0 \text{ kg} \cdot \text{m} \cdot \text{s}^{-1} + 70 \text{ kg} \times v.$

$$\therefore \qquad v = -\frac{17.96 \text{ kg} \cdot \text{m} \cdot \text{s}^{-1}}{70 \text{ kg}} = -0.257 \text{ m} \cdot \text{s}^{-1} = -25.7 \text{ cm} \cdot \text{s}^{-1}.$$

The slower man therefore returns to the station with a speed of 25.7 cm·s⁻¹ if he throws the hammer to his companion with a speed of 11.43 m·s⁻¹. This is the maximum speed he can impart to it; for otherwise the faster man in catching the hammer acquires a speed so great that he cannot give to the hammer, when in his turn he throws it, a velocity sufficient to produce on himself a recoil which reverses his direction of motion.

PROBLEM 8.6

A confectioner steadily pours pieces of candy from a jar into the scale pan of a balance which was originally reading zero. They drop from a height of 4 ft at the rate of 6 per second. Find the scale reading at the end of 10 s if each piece of candy weighs 1 oz and all collisions are perfectly inelastic.

Solution. Pieces of candy, each of mass m_0, are dropping from a height of 4 ft, losing potential energy in the process and acquiring an equal amount of kinetic energy. If v is the speed with which each piece strikes the scale pan, then $\frac{1}{2}m_0v^2 = m_0gh = m_0 \times 32 \text{ ft} \cdot \text{s}^{-2} \times 4 \text{ ft}$.

$$\therefore \qquad v^2 = 64 \times 4 \text{ ft}^2 \cdot \text{s}^{-2} \qquad \text{or} \qquad v = 16 \text{ ft} \cdot \text{s}^{-1}.$$

In any time interval t, mass m strikes the scale pan and loses its momentum completely, since the collision is inelastic and the scale pan is prevented from moving by the restraining mechanism. The scale pan must therefore exert on the pieces of candy striking it a force $\mathbf{F}$ such that the change in momentum equals the impulse causing it. That is, $m\mathbf{v} = \mathbf{F} \times t$.

$$\therefore \qquad \mathbf{F} = (m/t)\mathbf{v}.$$

But m/t is the mass of candies striking the scale per second; thus

$$F = 6 \times \frac{1}{16 \times 32} \text{ slug} \cdot \text{s}^{-1} \times 16 \text{ ft} \cdot \text{s}^{-1} = \frac{6}{32} \text{ lb} = 3 \text{ oz}.$$

An equal and opposite force must act on the balance. Thus after 10 seconds the forces acting on the balance are the continuous force of 3 oz due to the constant impact plus the weight of the candies already in the pan. Therefore the scale will read $3 \text{ oz} + 60 \times 1 \text{ oz} = 63 \text{ oz} = 3 \text{ lb } 15 \text{ oz}$.

PROBLEM 8.7

A space probe explodes in flight into three equal portions. One portion continues along the original line of flight. The other two go off in directions each inclined at 60° to the original path. The energy released in the explosion is twice as great as the kinetic energy possessed by the probe at the time of the explosion. Determine the kinetic energy of each fragment immediately after the explosion.

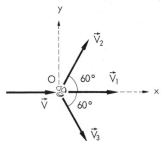

Solution. Take the direction in which the probe is moving immediately prior to the explosion as the positive x-direction and the point at which the explosion takes place as the origin of coordinates. Let M be the mass of the probe and let the quantities applicable to the probe and its fragments be given subscripts as in the diagram.

Momentum must be conserved in the x-direction, the y-direction, and the z-direction independently. It follows that $\mathbf{V}_1$, $\mathbf{V}_2$, $\mathbf{V}_3$, and $\mathbf{V}$ must be coplanar and that

$$MV = \tfrac{1}{3}MV_1 + \tfrac{1}{3}MV_2 \cos 60° + \tfrac{1}{3}MV_3 \cos 60° \quad \text{and} \quad \tfrac{1}{3}MV_2 \sin 60° = \tfrac{1}{3}MV_3 \sin 60°.$$

From the second of these equations $V_3 = V_2$, and thus the first equation becomes $MV = \tfrac{1}{3}MV_1 + \tfrac{1}{3}MV_2$. But

$$E = \frac{1}{2} MV^2 = \frac{M^2 V^2}{2M} \quad \text{or} \quad MV = \sqrt{2ME}.$$

Similarly,

$$\frac{1}{3} MV_1 = \sqrt{\frac{2}{3} ME_1} \quad \text{and} \quad \frac{1}{3} MV_2 = \sqrt{\frac{2}{3} ME_2}.$$

The first equation thus becomes

$$\sqrt{2ME} = \sqrt{\frac{2}{3}ME_1} + \sqrt{\frac{2}{3}ME_2} \quad \text{or} \quad \sqrt{3E} = \sqrt{E_1} + \sqrt{E_2}.$$

$$\therefore \quad 3E = E_1 + E_2 + 2\sqrt{E_1 E_2}.$$

The original kinetic energy of the probe plus the energy released by the explosion must equal the sum of the kinetic energies of the fragments, since no energy can be lost in the process. Hence

$$E + 2E = 3E = E_1 + E_2 + E_3 = E_1 + 2E_2.$$

$$\therefore \quad E_1 + 2E_2 = E_1 + E_2 + 2\sqrt{E_1 E_2} \quad \text{or} \quad E_2 = 2\sqrt{E_1 E_2}.$$

$$\therefore \quad E_2^2 = 4E_1 E_2 \quad \text{or} \quad E_2 = 4E_1.$$

Thus

$$3E = E_1 + 2E_2 = E_1 + 8E_1 \quad \text{or} \quad E_1 = \tfrac{1}{3}E.$$

$$\therefore \quad E_2 = \tfrac{4}{3}E.$$

Thus the fragment that continues in the line of flight has one-third of the original kinetic energy. The other fragments each have four-thirds of the original kinetic energy. The sum of these kinetic energies is three times the original kinetic energy, as required by the conservation principle.

PROBLEM 8.8

A pile of mass M is driven into a bog against a constant resistive force F by a hammer of mass m which is allowed to fall freely at each stroke through a height h. The hammer does not rebound after striking the pile. Find the distance the pile is driven in at each blow.

Show that the total energy expended in raising the hammer during the operation of driving the pile fully in to a depth d is independent of the value of h, and can be decreased by making the hammer more massive.

Solution. The hammer falls through a height $\mathbf{h}$, losing potential energy and gaining kinetic energy. By the principle of conservation of energy, $\mathbf{W} \cdot \mathbf{h} = mgh = \tfrac{1}{2}mv^2$, so that the hammer strikes the pile with velocity $\mathbf{v}$, where $v = \sqrt{2gh}$. An inelastic collision takes place and momentum is conserved, so that $m\mathbf{v} = (m + M)\mathbf{V}$. Therefore the kinetic energy of mass and pile together after the impact is

$$\frac{1}{2}(m + M)V^2 = \frac{1}{2}\frac{m^2}{(m + M)}v^2.$$

When the pile is being driven in, the kinetic energy is lost. If the pile drives in a distance $\mathbf{x}$ at each stroke against the resistive force $\mathbf{F}$, by the principle of conservation of energy,

$$\frac{1}{2}\frac{m^2}{(m + M)}v^2 = \mathbf{F} \cdot \mathbf{x} = Fx \quad \text{or} \quad x = \frac{m^2 v^2}{2F(m + M)} = \frac{ghm^2}{F(m + M)}.$$

If it requires n strokes to drive the pile fully home a distance d,

$$d = nx = \frac{nghm^2}{F(m + M)}.$$

But the energy E supplied to the system is that energy required to raise the hammer n times through a height h. Thus

$$E = nmgh = \frac{Fd(m + M)}{m} = Fd + Fd\frac{M}{m}.$$

Thus the energy does not depend on h and will be decreased if m is made larger.

PROBLEM 8.9

Coal drops at the rate of 25 slugs per second from a hopper onto a horizontal moving belt which transports it to the screening and washing plant. If the belt travels at the rate of 10 ft per second, what is the horsepower of the motor driving the belt? Assume that 5% of the energy available is used in overcoming friction in the pulleys.

Solution. When it strikes the belt, the coal has no horizontal velocity. After it has come in contact with the belt, it moves with a speed of $10 \text{ ft} \cdot \text{s}^{-1}$. It has therefore acquired momentum and the belt must have supplied the impulse to produce the change in momentum. Thus, when we consider any mass of coal m, $m\mathbf{v} = \mathbf{F} \times t$ or $\mathbf{F} = (m/t)\mathbf{v}$.

A constant force $\mathbf{F}$ is thus applied by the belt to the dropping coal of magnitude

$$F = 25 \text{ slugs} \cdot \text{s}^{-1} \times 10 \text{ ft} \cdot \text{s}^{-1} = 250 \text{ lb}.$$

An equal and opposite force must be applied to the belt by Newton's third law. The driving motor must supply a sufficient force to the belt to overcome $\mathbf{F}$, and the rate of working of this force is

$$\mathbf{F} \cdot \mathbf{v} = Fv = 250 \text{ lb} \times 10 \text{ ft} \cdot \text{s}^{-1} = 2500 \text{ ft} \cdot \text{lb} \cdot \text{s}^{-1}.$$

Taking friction into account, the rate of working of the motor is thus

$$P = \frac{100}{95} Fv = \frac{100}{95} \times 2500 \text{ ft} \cdot \text{lb} \cdot \text{s}^{-1} = \frac{100 \times 2500 \text{ ft} \cdot \text{lb} \cdot \text{s}^{-1}}{95 \times 550 \text{ ft} \cdot \text{lb} \cdot \text{s}^{-1} \cdot (\text{hp})^{-1}} = 4.8 \text{ hp}.$$

PROBLEM 8.10

A rocket when unloaded has a mass of 2000 kg, carries a fuel load of 12,000 kg, and has a constant exhaust velocity of 5000 km·hr^{-1}. What are the maximum rate of fuel consumption, the shortest time taken to reach the final velocity, and the value of the final velocity? The greatest permissible acceleration is $7g$. The rocket starts from rest at the earth's surface, and air resistance and variations in g are to be neglected.

Solution. The increment of velocity dv of a vertically accelerating rocket during any time interval dt is given by*

$$dv = -v_r \frac{dm}{m} - g \, dt,$$

where v_r is the velocity of the rocket relative to that of the material ejected—i.e., the reverse of the exhaust velocity—and the mass of the rocket has changed from m to $m + dm$ during the time dt.

Therefore the acceleration at any time is

$$a = \frac{dv}{dt} = -\frac{v_r}{m}\frac{dm}{dt} - g.$$

The velocity v_r is constant and dm/dt must be constant also, so that a varies only with m. The smallest

---

*Cf., for example, *University Physics* (3rd edition), by Sears and Zemansky (Addison-Wesley), Section 8-7.

value of m gives the greatest value of a; but a cannot exceed $7g$. Therefore

$$7g = -\frac{5 \times 10^6 \text{ m} \cdot \text{hr}^{-1}}{60 \text{ min} \cdot \text{hr}^{-1} \times 60 \text{ s} \cdot \text{min}^{-1} \times 2 \times 10^3 \text{ kg}} \frac{dm}{dt} - g.$$

$$\therefore \quad \frac{dm}{dt} = -\frac{8g \times 72 \times 10^5 \text{ kg}}{5 \times 10^6 \text{ m} \cdot \text{s}^{-1}} = -\frac{8 \times 9.8 \text{ m} \cdot \text{s}^{-2} \times 72 \times 10^5 \text{ kg}}{5 \times 10^6 \text{ m} \cdot \text{s}^{-1}} = -112.9 \text{ kg} \cdot \text{s}^{-1},$$

where $-dm/dt$ is the maximum rate of fuel consumption. The time taken to reach the final velocity is thus the total fuel load divided by the rate of consumption. Thus

$$T = \frac{12 \times 10^3 \text{ kg}}{112.9 \text{ kg} \cdot \text{s}^{-1}} = 106.3 \text{ s} = 1.77 \text{ min}.$$

Integrating the original equation, one has $v = -v_r \ln m - gt + C$.
But if m_0 is the total load at time $t = 0$, when $v = 0$, then $0 = -v_r \ln m_0 + C$.

$$\therefore \quad v = v_r \ln \frac{m_0}{m} - gt.$$

The final velocity is thus

$$v = \frac{5 \times 10^6 \text{ m} \cdot \text{hr}^{-1}}{60 \times 60 \text{ s} \cdot \text{hr}^{-1}} \ln \frac{14,000 \text{ kg}}{2000 \text{ kg}} - 9.8 \text{ m} \cdot \text{s}^{-2} \times 106.3 \text{ s} = (2703 - 1042) \text{ m} \cdot \text{s}^{-1} = 1661 \text{ m} \cdot \text{s}^{-1}$$

$$= 5980 \text{ km} \cdot \text{hr}^{-1}.$$

PROBLEM 8.11

A deuterium atom moving with kinetic energy of 0.81×10^{-13} J collides with a similar atom at rest. A nuclear reaction takes place and a neutron is observed to be emitted at right angles to the original direction of motion. Determine its kinetic energy, given that the other product of the reaction is an atom of the light isotope of helium and that the rest masses of a neutron, a deuterium atom, and a light helium atom are 1.6747, 3.3441, and 5.0076, respectively, in units of 10^{-27} kg.

Solution. The total rest mass at the beginning of the reaction was 6.6882×10^{-27} kg. At the end of the reaction it was 6.6823×10^{-27} kg. The difference is 59×10^{-31} kg. This corresponds to an energy

$$E = mc^2 = 59 \times 10^{-31} \text{ kg} \times 9 \times 10^{16} \text{ m}^2 \cdot \text{s}^{-2} = 5.31 \times 10^{-13} \text{ J}.$$

This appears in the form of kinetic energy of the emitted particles. The total kinetic energy available, since energy must be conserved, is thus

$$E_D + E = (0.81 + 5.31) \times 10^{-13} \text{ J} = 6.12 \times 10^{-13} \text{ J} = E_n + E_H.$$

But momentum in the original direction and at right angles to the original direction must also be conserved. From the diagram we see that

$$m_D v = m_H v_2 \cos \theta \quad \text{and} \quad m_n v_1 = m_H v_2 \sin \theta.$$

But $\frac{1}{2} m_D v^2 = E_D$ or $m_D v = \sqrt{2 m_D E_D}$, and similarly for the energy of the neutron, E_n, and of the helium atom E_H. Thus the three conservation equations become

$$E_D + E = 6.12 \times 10^{-13} = E_n + E_H,$$

$$\sqrt{2 m_D E_D} = \sqrt{2 m_H E_H} \cos \theta, \quad \text{and} \quad \sqrt{2 m_n E_n} = \sqrt{2 m_H E_H} \sin \theta.$$

From the last two equations, one can see that

$$2 m_D E_D + 2 m_n E_n = 2 m_H E_H (\cos^2 \theta + \sin^2 \theta) = 2 m_H E_H.$$

$$\therefore \quad m_H E_H - m_n E_n = m_D E_D \quad \text{and} \quad E_H + E_n = E_D + E.$$

$$\therefore \quad (m_H + m_n) E_n = (m_H - m_D) E_D + m_H E.$$

$$\therefore \quad E_n = \frac{m_H - m_D}{m_H + m_n} E_D + \frac{m_H}{m_H + m_n} E = \left(\frac{1.6635}{6.6823} \times 0.81 \times 10^{-13} + \frac{5.0076}{6.6823} \times 5.31 \times 10^{-13} \right) \text{ J}$$

$$= 4.18 \times 10^{-13} \text{ J}.$$

9

Rotation

PROBLEM 9.1

The motor driving a grindstone is switched off when the latter has a rotational speed of 240 rev·min⁻¹. After 10 s the speed is 180 rev·min⁻¹. If the angular retardation remains constant, how many additional revolutions does it make before coming to rest?

Solution. The initial speed ω_0 is 240 rev·min⁻¹ $= 8\pi$ rad·s⁻¹, and the later speed ω is 6π rad·s⁻¹. Thus $\omega = \omega_0 + \alpha t$ or

$$\alpha = \frac{\omega - \omega_0}{t} = -\frac{(8\pi - 6\pi)\,\text{rad·s}^{-1}}{10\,\text{s}} = -\frac{\pi}{5}\,\text{rad·s}^{-2}.$$

Considering the subsequent slowing-down period, the final speed is zero. Hence $0^2 = \omega^2 + 2\alpha\theta$ or

$$\theta = -\frac{\omega^2}{2\alpha} = \frac{36\pi^2\,\text{rad}^2\cdot\text{s}^{-2}}{(2\pi/5)\,\text{rad·s}^{-2}} = 90\pi\,\text{rad} = 45\,\text{rev}.$$

PROBLEM 9.2

Show that the moment of inertia of a body about any axis is equal to the moment of inertia about a parallel axis through the center of mass plus the product of the mass of the body and the square of the distance between the axes. This is called the *parallel-axes theorem*.

Prove also that the moment of inertia of a thin plate about an axis at right angles to its plane is equal to the sum of the moments of inertia about two mutually perpendicular axes concurrent with the first and lying in the plane of the thin plate. This is called the *perpendicular-axes theorem*.

Solution. Let I be the moment of inertia of the body about an arbitrary axis and I_G the moment of inertia about the parallel axis through the center of mass G, the two axes being distance h apart. Orient the diagram so that the distance h lies in the x-direction, and G is at the origin of the coordinate system. Then

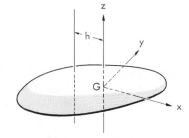

$$I = \Sigma\,m[(x + h)^2 + y^2 + z^2]$$
$$= \Sigma\,m(x^2 + y^2 + z^2) + \Sigma\,mh^2 + 2\Sigma\,mxh$$
$$= I_G + Mh^2 + 2h\Sigma\,mx.$$

But the origin of coordinates is the center of mass. Thus, from the definition of the center of mass, $\Sigma\,mx = 0$.

Hence $I = I_G + Mh^2$.

Take, in the case of the thin plate, the axes in the plane of the plate as the x- and y-axes, and the axis at right angles to the plane as the z-axis. Then

$$I_z = \Sigma\, mr^2 = \Sigma\, m(x^2 + y^2) = \Sigma\, mx^2 + \Sigma\, my^2 = I_x + I_y.$$

These two theorems are of great importance in calculating moments of inertia, as will be seen in the next problem.

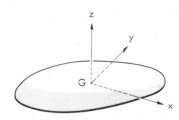

PROBLEM 9.3

Find the moment of inertia of a hollow cube made up of six uniform square plates of mass M and side $2a$ about an axis along one edge of the cube.

Solution. The moment of inertia required can be calculated if we first find values for the moments of inertia of a square plate about axes through the center of gravity (a) lying in the plane of the plate, and (b) perpendicular to the plane of the plate.

The first diagram shows case (a). Consider an element dx as shown, distance x from the axis labeled 1. If the plate has a mass per unit area of ρ, then the moment of inertia of the chosen element about the axis is $\rho\, 2a\, dx \times x^2$.

The moment of inertia of the whole plate is thus

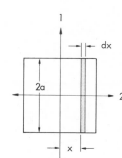

$$I_1 = \int_{-a}^{a} 2\rho\, ax^2\, dx = \tfrac{2}{3}\rho a[x^3]_{-a}^{a} = \tfrac{4}{3}\rho a^4 = \tfrac{1}{3}Ma^2$$

where $M = 4a^2\rho$ is the mass of the plate. By symmetry, the moment of inertia about the axis labeled 2 is the same. Thus $I_2 = \tfrac{1}{3}Ma^2$.

By the perpendicular-axes theorem (cf. Problem 9.2), I_3, the moment of inertia about the axis through the center of gravity and perpendicular to the plate is $I_3 = I_1 + I_2 = \tfrac{2}{3}Ma^2$.

To obtain the moment of inertia of the whole cube about one corner, it is necessary to apply the parallel-axes theorem (cf. Problem 9.2). Thus the moment of inertia of each of sides I and II about the axis shown in the second diagram is

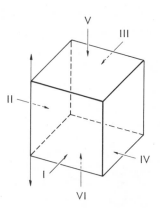

$$I_1 + Ma^2 = \tfrac{4}{3}Ma^2.$$

The moment of inertia of each of sides III and IV (see the third diagram) is

$$I_1 + M(4a^2 + a^2) = \tfrac{16}{3}Ma^2.$$

The moment of inertia of each of sides V and VI is

$$I_3 + M(a^2 + a^2) = \tfrac{8}{3}Ma^2.$$

The total moment of inertia of the cube about one side is thus

$$2(\tfrac{4}{3} + \tfrac{16}{3} + \tfrac{8}{3})Ma^2 = 18\tfrac{2}{3}Ma^2.$$

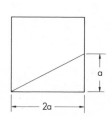

PROBLEM 9.4

Secret agent 008 enters the arch-villain's den and stands on the end of a concealed uniform trapdoor of weight 50 lb freely pivoted at a distance x from the other end. Given that 008's weight is 150 lb, what fraction of the total length must x be in order that he and the end of the trapdoor shall start dropping into the depths with acceleration g when the trapdoor is released?

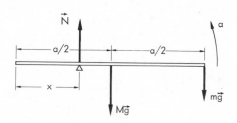

Solution. The forces acting on the trapdoor of length a are its weight $M\mathbf{g}$ acting downward at the center, since it is uniform, 008's weight $m\mathbf{g}$ acting downward at the end, and the normal force **N** exerted by the pivot upward. When we take moments about the pivot, counter-clockwise moments being taken as positive, the couple causing rotational acceleration is

$$-Mg\left(\frac{a}{2} - x\right) - mg(a - x), \quad \text{and thus} \quad -Mg\left(\frac{a}{2} - x\right) - mg(a - x) = I\alpha,$$

where α is the angular acceleration produced and I is the moment of inertia of the system about the pivot. The moment of inertia of the trapdoor about a horizontal line parallel to the pivot and passing through the center of gravity is $\frac{1}{12}Ma^2$, and thus about the pivot is $\frac{1}{12}Ma^2 + M[(a/2) - x]^2$ by the parallel-axes theorem (cf. Problem 9.2). The moment of inertia of 008 about the pivot is $m(a - x)^2$. Hence

$$-Mg\left(\frac{a}{2} - x\right) - mg(a - x) = \alpha\left[\frac{1}{12}Ma^2 + M\left(\frac{a}{2} - x\right)^2 + m(a - x)^2\right].$$

If 008 and the end of the trapdoor are to have a linear acceleration g downward, then $-g = (a - x)\alpha$.

$$\therefore \quad M\left(\frac{a}{2} - x\right)(a - x) + m(a - x)^2 = \frac{1}{12}Ma^2 + M\left(\frac{a}{2} - x\right)^2 + m(a - x)^2.$$

$$\therefore \quad \frac{a}{2}\left(\frac{a}{2} - x\right) = \frac{1}{12}a^2. \quad \therefore \quad 3a^2 - 6ax = a^2. \quad \therefore \quad x = \frac{1}{3}a.$$

The pivot must be located one-third of the length of the trapdoor from the end.

PROBLEM 9.5

A flywheel of mass 12 kg and radius of gyration 20 cm is mounted on a light horizontal axle of radius 5 cm which rotates on frictionless bearings. A string wound round the axle has attached to its free end a hanging mass of 4 kg, and the system is allowed to start from rest. If the string leaves the axle after the mass has descended 3 m, what torque must be applied to the flywheel to bring it to rest in 5 revs?

Solution. Consider the hanging mass. It has two forces acting on it, its weight mg downward and the tension in the string **T** upward. Since the mass descends with acceleration **a**,

$$mg - T = ma.$$

But, if the flywheel rotates with angular acceleration α, then

$$a = r\alpha, \quad \text{and thus} \quad mg - T = mr\alpha.$$

The tension **T** acts at distance r from the axis of the flywheel of mass M and radius of gyration k. Therefore the torque is $\Gamma = Tr = I\alpha = Mk^2\alpha$. But $mgr - Tr = mr^2\alpha$.

$$\therefore \quad mgr = \alpha(mr^2 + Mk^2).$$

$$\therefore \quad \alpha = \frac{mgr}{mr^2 + Mk^2} = \frac{4 \text{ kg} \times 9.8 \text{ m}\cdot\text{s}^{-2} \times 0.05 \text{ m}}{4 \text{ kg} \times (0.05)^2 \text{ m}^2 + 12 \text{ kg} \times (0.2)^2 \text{ m}^2} = \frac{1.96}{0.49}\text{s}^{-2} = 4 \text{ rad}\cdot\text{s}^{-2}.$$

The flywheel starts from rest and accelerates as long as the string is exerting a couple on it. In that time the mass descends 3 m. But in 1 rev the string unwraps $2\pi r$ and the mass descends by this distance. Thus the angular distance the flywheel turns during the period of acceleration is

$$\frac{3}{2\pi \times 0.05} \text{ rev} = \frac{3}{0.05} \text{ rad} = 60 \text{ rad}.$$

The angular speed when the string leaves the axle, using the equation $\omega^2 = \omega_0^2 + 2\alpha\theta$, is thus given by

$$\omega^2 = 2 \times 4 \text{ rad}\cdot\text{s}^{-2} \times 60 \text{ rad} \quad \text{or} \quad \omega = 4\sqrt{30} \text{ rad}\cdot\text{s}^{-1} = 21.9 \text{ rad}\cdot\text{s}^{-1}.$$

If a torque Γ' is now applied to the wheel, it produces a deceleration α', and $0^2 = \omega^2 + 2\alpha' \times 10\pi$ rad.

$$\therefore \quad \alpha' = \frac{\omega^2}{20\pi \text{ rad}} = -\frac{480 \text{ rad}^2 \cdot \text{s}^{-2}}{20\pi \text{ rad}} = -\frac{24}{\pi} \text{ rad} \cdot \text{s}^{-2}.$$

But

$$\Gamma' = I\alpha' = Mk^2\alpha' = -12 \text{ kg} \times 0.04 \text{ m}^2 \times \frac{24}{\pi} \text{ rad} \cdot \text{s}^{-2} = -3.67 \text{ N} \cdot \text{m}.$$

Thus a torque of 3.67 N·m applied against the direction of rotation is necessary.

Note that the result is more easily obtained from a consideration of energy. The mass m descends a height h. In so doing it loses potential energy, which reappears in the form of kinetic energy of the mass and of the flywheel. Thus

$$mgh = \tfrac{1}{2}mv^2 + \tfrac{1}{2}I\omega^2 = \tfrac{1}{2}mr^2\omega^2 + \tfrac{1}{2}Mk^2\omega^2. \quad \therefore \quad \omega^2 = \frac{2mgh}{mr^2 + Mk^2} = 480 \text{ rad}^2 \cdot \text{s}^{-2}.$$

In the final stage, the work done by the retarding torque in the 5 rev $= 10\pi$ radians must equal the kinetic energy possessed by the flywheel before the couple is applied. Thus

$$-10\pi\Gamma = \tfrac{1}{2}I\omega^2 = \tfrac{1}{2}Mk^2\omega^2. \quad \therefore \quad \Gamma = -\frac{Mk^2\omega^2}{20\pi} = -3.67 \text{ N} \cdot \text{m}.$$

PROBLEM 9.6

Delivery trucks which operate by making use of the energy stored in a rotating flywheel have been in use for some time in Germany. The trucks are "charged up" before leaving by using an electric motor to get the flywheel up to its top speed of 6000 rev·min^{-1}. If one such flywheel is a solid homogeneous cylinder of weight 1120 lb and diameter 6 ft, how long can the truck operate before returning to its base for "recharging," if its average power requirement is 10 hp?

Solution. The kinetic energy possessed by a flywheel rotating at 6000 rev·min^{-1} = 200π rad·s^{-1} is

$$\tfrac{1}{2}I\omega^2 = \tfrac{1}{2} \times \tfrac{1}{2}Mr^2\omega^2 = \frac{1}{4} \times \frac{1120}{32} \text{ slugs} \times 9 \text{ ft}^2 \times 4\pi^2 \times 10^4 \text{ s}^{-2} = \frac{63\pi^2}{2} \times 10^5 \text{ ft} \cdot \text{lb}.$$

But the truck works at a rate of 10 hp = 10×550 ft·lb·s^{-1}. Thus, assuming friction to be negligible, the truck can work for

$$\frac{63\pi^2 \times 10^5 \text{ ft} \cdot \text{lb}}{2 \times 5500 \text{ ft} \cdot \text{lb} \cdot \text{s}^{-1}} = \frac{63\pi^2 \times 10^5}{2 \times 5500 \times 60} \text{ min} = 94.2 \text{ min}.$$

The flywheel must therefore be "recharged" before this time has elapsed.

PROBLEM 9.7

The flywheel of a cutting machine weighs 2000 lb and has a radius of gyration of 3 ft. At the beginning of the cutting stroke it has a rotational speed of 120 rev·min^{-1}, and at the end a speed of 90 rev·min^{-1}. If it cuts in a 6-in. stroke, what is the average cutting force exerted?

Solution. The energy lost during the stroke is the difference between the rotational kinetic energies of the flywheel at the beginning and at the end of the operation. If $I = Mk^2$ is the moment of inertia of the flywheel and ω_0 and ω the initial and final rotational speeds, then the energy lost is $\tfrac{1}{2}I(\omega_0^2 - \omega^2) = \tfrac{1}{2}Mk^2(\omega_0^2 - \omega^2)$. This energy is lost in producing the cutting stroke. If **F** is the average cutting force exerted over the distance **d**, then $\mathbf{F} \cdot \mathbf{d} = Fd = \tfrac{1}{2}Mk^2(\omega_0^2 - \omega^2)$ or

$$F = \frac{\tfrac{1}{2}Mk^2(\omega_0^2 - \omega^2)}{d} = \frac{\tfrac{1}{2} \times \frac{2000}{32} \text{ slugs} \times 9 \text{ ft}^2[(4\pi)^2 - (3\pi)^2] \text{ s}^{-2}}{\tfrac{1}{2} \text{ ft}} = 38,860 \text{ lb}.$$

PROBLEM 9.8

A uniform rod of mass M and length $2a$ stands vertically on a rough horizontal floor and is allowed to fall. Assuming that slipping has not occurred, show that, when the rod makes an angle θ with the vertical,

$$\omega^2 = (3g/2a)(1 - \cos \theta).$$

Also find the normal force exerted by the floor on the rod in this position, and the coefficient of static friction involved if slipping occurs when $\theta = 30°$.

Solution. The forces acting on the rod are the weight $m\mathbf{g}$ acting downward and the normal force $\mathbf{N}$ and the frictional force $\mathbf{F}$ of magnitude μN exerted by the floor at the end O in contact with the floor.

When one takes moments about O, the only force producing rotation about O is the weight of the rod. Hence

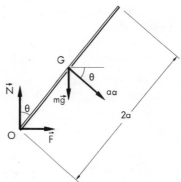

$$mga \sin \theta = I_0 \alpha = \tfrac{4}{3} ma^2 \alpha.$$

$$\therefore \quad \alpha = \frac{d\omega}{dt} = \frac{d\omega}{d\theta} \times \frac{d\theta}{dt} = \omega \frac{d\omega}{d\theta} = \frac{3}{4} \frac{g}{a} \sin \theta.$$

$$\therefore \quad \int_0^\omega \omega \, d\omega = \int_0^\theta \frac{3}{4} \frac{g}{a} \sin \theta \, d\theta.$$

$$\therefore \quad \left[\frac{1}{2} \omega^2 \right]_0^\omega = \left[-\frac{3}{4} \frac{g}{a} \cos \theta \right]_0^\theta \quad \text{or} \quad \omega^2 = \frac{3g}{2a}(1 - \cos \theta).$$

The center of gravity G has an angular acceleration α about O, and thus a linear acceleration $a\alpha$ at right angles to the direction of the rod. This linear acceleration can be split into two components, $a\alpha \cos \theta$ horizontally and $a\alpha \sin \theta$ vertically downward. The horizontal acceleration of the center of gravity is due to the force μN and the vertical acceleration is due to the net effect of the forces mg and N. Thus

$$mg - N = ma\alpha \sin \theta = \tfrac{3}{4} mg \sin^2 \theta$$

and

$$\mu N = ma\alpha \cos \theta = \tfrac{3}{4} mg \sin \theta \cos \theta.$$

$$\therefore \quad N = mg - \frac{3}{4} mg \sin^2 \theta = \frac{mg}{4}(4 - 3 \sin^2 \theta).$$

Also

$$\mu = \frac{\tfrac{3}{4} mg \sin \theta \cos \theta}{N} = \frac{3 \sin \theta \cos \theta}{4 - 3 \sin^2 \theta}.$$

But when $\theta = 30°$, slipping just commences. At this angle μ has its limiting, maximum value of μ_s, the coefficient of static friction, in which

$$\mu_s = \frac{3 \times \tfrac{1}{2} \times (\sqrt{3}/2)}{4 - \tfrac{3}{4}} = \frac{3\sqrt{3}}{13} = 0.400.$$

PROBLEM 9.9

A cable drum of inner and outer radii r and R is lying on rough ground, the cable being wound round the inner cylinder and being pulled off from the bottom at an angle θ to the horizontal. An inquiring student strolling by notes that when the cable is pulled by a workman, with θ a small angle, the drum rolls without slipping toward the workman. Whereas, if θ is large, the drum rolls without slipping in the opposite direction. He works out a value for the critical angle θ_0 which separates the two types of motion. What is the value of θ_0?

Solution. The diagram shows the drum with the forces acting on it. The force applied by the workman acts tangentially to the inner cylinder at such a position that the angle between this tangent and the horizontal is θ. It follows that the angle between the corresponding radius and the vertical is θ also, and that this radius is at right angles to the tangential force **F**.

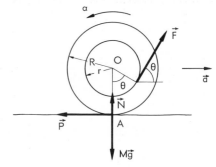

The other forces acting are the weight $M\mathbf{g}$ of the cable drum, the normal forces exerted by the ground on the drum at the two points of contact, which combine into a resultant **N** passing through the center of gravity, and the frictional forces at the same points of contact which combine to form a single resultant force **P** of magnitude μN. In the limiting case μ will be the coefficient of static friction.

There is no movement in the vertical direction. Hence $N = Mg - F \sin \theta$.

The forces in the horizontal direction produce an acceleration a. Thus

$$F \cos \theta - \mu N = F \cos \theta - \mu Mg + \mu F \sin \theta = Ma.$$

Further, the moments of the forces about the center of mass O produce a rotational acceleration about that point. The only forces whose lines of action do not pass through the center of gravity are F and μN. Hence

$$Fr - \mu NR = I\alpha \quad \text{or} \quad Fr - \mu RMg + \mu RF \sin \theta = I\alpha,$$

where I is the moment of inertia of the drum about its center of mass.

At the points at which the drum touches the ground no slipping occurs. Therefore instantaneously these points are at rest. But all points of the drum have an acceleration a forward and in addition the points of contact, due to the rotation about the center of mass, have a further linear acceleration $R\alpha$ forward. Thus $a + R\alpha = 0$ or $\alpha = -a/R$.

Rewriting the two fundamental equations given above, and multiplying by constants where necessary, we obtain

$$FR^2 \cos \theta - \mu R^2 Mg + \mu FR^2 \sin \theta = MaR^2, \qquad FrR - \mu R^2 Mg + \mu FR^2 \sin \theta = IR\alpha = -Ia.$$

Thus, subtracting, we have

$$FR(R \cos \theta - r) = a(MR^2 + I) \quad \text{or} \quad R \cos \theta - r = \frac{a}{FR}(MR^2 + I).$$

Hence a is positive or negative as $R \cos \theta >$ or $< r$. Therefore the drum rolls to the workman if $R \cos \theta > r$ and away from him if $R \cos \theta < r$. The critical angle θ_0 occurs for

$$R \cos \theta_0 = r \quad \text{or} \quad \cos \theta_0 = \frac{r}{R}.$$

This result could be obtained more easily by considering rotation about A the line of the drum instantaneously at rest. The only force that does not pass through A is F, the applied force. If the line of action of F cuts the ground to the left of A, F has a negative moment about A and the drum rolls to the right. If the line of action of F cuts the ground to the right of A, F has a positive moment about A and the motion is to the left. If the line of action of F passes through A, the drum is stationary and θ has the critical value θ_0.

The second diagram, at the right, shows this situation. Since the line of action of **F** is tangential to the inner cylinder, OB and AB are at right angles and $\angle AOB$ is θ_0.

$$\therefore \quad \cos \theta_0 = \frac{r}{R}.$$

PROBLEM 9.10

Two men, each of whom weighs 150 lb, stand opposite each other on the rim of a small uniform circular platform which weighs 900 lb. Each man simultaneously walks clockwise and at a fixed speed once around the rim. The platform is free to rotate about a vertical axis through its center. Find the angle in space through which each man has turned.

Solution. Each man walks once around the rim in a time t. In doing so each traverses a distance in space which subtends an angle θ at the center of the platform. The angular velocity of each man in space is thus θ/t. Therefore the angular momentum of the two men during the tour of the platform is

$$2I_m \frac{\theta}{t} = \frac{2 \times 150 \text{ slugs}}{32} \times r^2 \frac{\theta}{t},$$

where I_m is the moment of inertia of either man about the center of the platform, which is of radius r. But, by the principle of conservation of angular momentum, the platform must acquire equal and opposite angular momentum. Let the angle through which the platform turns in this time t be ϕ. Thus

$$I_p \frac{\phi}{t} = \frac{1}{2} \frac{900 \text{ slugs}}{32} \times r^2 \frac{\phi}{t} = 2 \times \frac{150 \text{ slugs}}{32} r^2 \frac{\theta}{t},$$

where I_p is the moment of inertia of the platform about an axis through its center.

$$\therefore \quad 450\phi = 300\theta. \quad \therefore \quad \phi = \tfrac{2}{3}\theta.$$

The radius vector on which each man was originally standing turns through an angle ϕ while the man moves through an angle θ, and after the time t each man is on the same radius vector as he started. Thus $\theta + \phi = 2\pi$.

$$\therefore \quad \tfrac{5}{3}\theta = 2\pi \quad \text{or} \quad \theta = 216° \quad \text{and} \quad \phi = 144°.$$

PROBLEM 9.11

A man of mass 80 kg is standing on the rim of a stationary uniform circular platform, of mass 140 kg and diameter 8 m, which is free to rotate about its center. The man throws to a companion on the ground in a direction tangential to the rim a package of mass 1 kg at a speed of 20 m·s⁻¹ relative to the ground. What angular velocity of the man and platform is produced in consequence?

The man then walks so as to bring him to a position halfway between the rim and the center of the platform. What is the new angular velocity of the system?

Solution. The package is thrown tangentially at a speed of 20 m·s⁻¹ relative to the ground and consequently has an initial angular momentum about the center of the platform of amount

$$1 \text{ kg} \times 20 \text{ m·s}^{-1} \times 4 \text{ m} = 80 \text{ kg·m}^2\text{·s}^{-1}.$$

By the principle of conservation of angular momentum, the platform and man must acquire equal and opposite angular momentum, since the whole system was initially at rest. The man has a moment of inertia of (80×4^2) kg·m², and the platform a moment of inertia of $(\tfrac{1}{2} \times 140 \times 4^2)$ kg·m² about the center. Hence

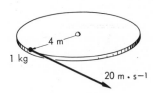

$$(80 \times 4^2 + \tfrac{1}{2} \times 140 \times 4^2) \text{ kg·m}^2 \times \omega = 80 \text{ kg·m}^2\text{·s}^{-1},$$

where ω is the angular velocity of platform and man produced by the throwing of the package. Hence

$$\omega = \frac{80 \text{ s}^{-1}}{80 \times 16 + 70 \times 16} = \frac{1}{30} \text{ rad·s}^{-1}.$$

If the man walks toward the center, his moment of inertia about the center decreases. At the halfway position, his moment of inertia is (80×2^2) kg·m². But the angular momentum must stay the same, and so the angular velocity must increase to ω', where

$$(80 \times 4^2 + \tfrac{1}{2} \times 140 \times 4^2)\ \text{kg·m}^2 \times \omega = (80 \times 2^2 + \tfrac{1}{2} \times 140 \times 4^2)\ \text{kg·m}^2 \times \omega'.$$

$$\therefore \qquad \omega' = \frac{150}{90}\omega = \frac{1}{18}\ \text{rad·s}^{-1}.$$

PROBLEM 9.12

Two circular cylinders have the same mass and dimensions, but one is solid while the other is a thin hollow shell. If they are released together to roll without slipping down a plane inclined at 30° to the horizontal, how far apart will they be after 10 s?

Solution. In either case the forces acting on the cylinder are as shown in the diagram. The weight $m\mathbf{g}$ acting downward is split up into its components parallel to and perpendicular to the plane. The other two forces acting on the cylinder are the normal force $\mathbf{N}$ exerted by the plane and the frictional force attempting to prevent motion, $\mathbf{F}$, which has magnitude μN.

Since the cylinder does not lift from the plane,

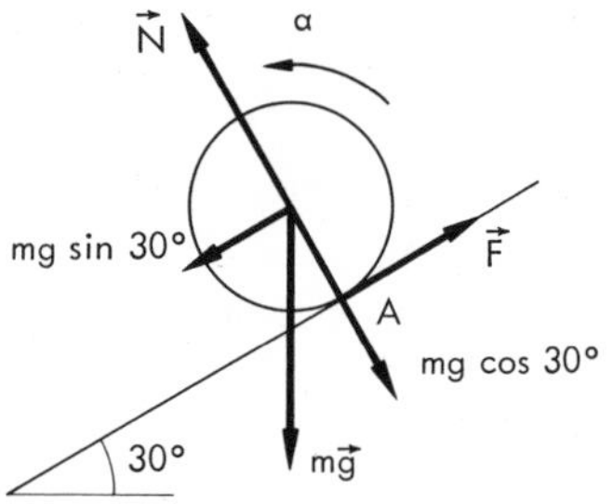

$$N = mg \cos 30.$$

Further,

$$mg \sin 30 - \mu N = mg(\sin 30 - \mu \cos 30) = ma,$$

where m is the mass of the cylinder and a the acceleration produced. Rotation about the center of the cylinder also takes place, and

$$\mu N r = \mu r\, mg \cos 30 = I\alpha,$$

where r is the radius, I the moment of inertia and α the rotational acceleration of the cylinder. Since no slipping takes place, the point A is instantaneously at rest. Hence $a = r\alpha$, and

$$mg(\sin 30 - \mu \cos 30) = ma, \qquad \mu r\, mg \cos 30 = \frac{Ia}{r}.$$

$$\therefore \qquad mg\, r^2 \sin \theta - Ia = mar^2 \qquad \text{or} \qquad a = \frac{mgr^2 \sin \theta}{I + mr^2}.$$

For the solid cylinder,

$$a_1 = \frac{mgr^2 \sin \theta}{\tfrac{1}{2}mr^2 + mr^2} = \tfrac{2}{3}g \sin \theta,$$

and for the hollow cylinder,

$$a_2 = \frac{mgr^2 \sin \theta}{mr^2 + mr^2} = \tfrac{1}{2}g \sin \theta.$$

The distances traveled in 10 s from rest are

$$S_1 = 0 + \tfrac{1}{2}a_1 t^2 = \tfrac{1}{2} \times \tfrac{2}{3} \times 32\ \text{ft·s}^{-2} \times \tfrac{1}{2} \times 100\ \text{s}^2 = \frac{1600}{3}\ \text{ft}$$

and

$$S_2 = \tfrac{1}{2}a_2 t^2 = \tfrac{1}{2} \times \tfrac{1}{2} \times 32\ \text{ft·s}^{-2} \times \tfrac{1}{2} \times 100\ \text{s}^2 = 400\ \text{ft}.$$

$$\therefore \qquad S_1 - S_2 = (533.3 - 400)\ \text{ft} = 133.3\ \text{ft}.$$

PROBLEM 9.13

The flywheel in the delivery truck of Problem 9.6 is mounted with its axis vertical, and thus acts as a stabilizing gyroscope for the truck. Calculate the torque that would have to be applied to it when it is rotating at full speed to make it precess in a vertical plane at the rate of 1 rad per min.

Solution. The vector torque must be in a direction at right angles to the angular momentum vector which lies along the rotation axis of the flywheel. The torque must therefore be a horizontal vector. Its magnitude is obtained from the relation $\Gamma = I\omega\Omega$, the symbols having their usual significance. Taking the data from Problem 9.6, we have

$$\Gamma = \frac{1}{2}Mr^2\omega\Omega = \frac{1}{2} \times \frac{1120}{32} \text{ slugs} \times 9 \text{ ft}^2 \times 200\pi \text{ s}^{-1} \times \frac{1}{60} \text{ s}^{-1} = 525\pi \text{ ft·lb} = 1649.3 \text{ ft·lb}.$$

PROBLEM 9.14

Would the missile of Problem 5.7 actually hit the spaceship? (Assume that the Martians have not been able to fit their missile with a homing device.)

Solution. To an observer outside the planet, Mars and the missile on the surface are rotating about the axis of the planet with angular velocity ω_0. When the missile is fired radially from the surface, its distance from the center of Mars increases and thus its moment of inertia about the rotation axis increases also. But its angular momentum about the axis must remain constant, since no force with a moment about that axis is acting on it. Of necessity therefore the angular velocity of the missile about the rotation axis must decrease.

The radius vector passing through the launching pad and the spaceship continues to rotate with angular velocity ω_0. The missile has an angular velocity ω which drops more and more from the value ω_0 as the missile rises.   At the height of the spaceship, the moment of inertia of the rocket about the axis of rotation is $m \times (25.4 \times 10^6 \text{ m})^2$, whereas, at the launching pad, its moment of inertia is only $m \times (3.4 \times 10^6 \text{ m})^2$. Thus, finally,

$$\frac{\omega}{\omega_0} = \frac{(3.4 \times 10^6 \text{ m})^2}{(25.4 \times 10^6 \text{ m})^2} = 0.018.$$

The missile thus moves further and further from the vertical as it rises and will miss the spaceship (unless the missile is fitted with a homing device).

To an observer on the planet, the departure of the missile from the vertical is, of course, also observed and is explained in terms of the Coriolis force associated with a rotating frame of reference.

10

Elasticity

PROBLEM 10.1

A steel shaft 12 ft long and 8 in. in diameter is part of a hydraulic press used to raise up cars in a garage. When it is supporting a car weighing 3200 lb, what is the decrease in length of the shaft? Young's modulus for steel is 29×10^6 lb·in^{-2}.

Solution. The formula for Young's modulus is

$$Y = \frac{F_n/A}{\Delta l/l_0},$$

where the symbols have their usual significance. Thus the decrease in length is

$$\Delta l = \frac{F_n l_0}{YA} = \frac{3200 \text{ lb} \times 144 \text{ in.}}{29 \times 10^6 \text{ lb·in}^2 \times 16\pi \text{ in}^2} = 3.16 \times 10^{-4} \text{ in.}$$

PROBLEM 10.2

A technician hangs a uniform bar of mass 12 kg horizontally from the roof of a laboratory by means of three steel wires each 1 mm in diameter. Two of the wires are 200 cm long and one, by an oversight, 200.05 cm long. The long wire is fastened to the middle of the bar, the others to the two ends. By how much is each wire stretched, and how much of the weight does each wire carry? Young's modulus for steel $= 2.0 \times 10^{12}$ dynes·cm^{-2}.

Solution. If the bar is hanging horizontally, two of the wires will be extended Δl and one $\Delta l - 0.05$ cm. Now the formula for Young's modulus is

$$Y = \frac{F_n/A}{\Delta l/l_0},$$

where the symbols have their usual significance. Thus

$$F_n = \frac{AY \Delta l}{l_0}.$$

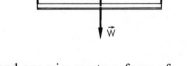

Hence two wires exert upward forces on the bar of magnitude F_n, and one wire exerts a force of magnitude

$$F_n' = \frac{AY(\Delta l - 0.05 \text{ cm})}{l_0 + 0.05 \text{ cm}}.$$

But the bar is in equilibrium. Hence, ignoring 0.05 in comparison with l_0 in the denominator of the expression for F'_n, we obtain $W = 2F_n + F'_n = (AY/l_0)(2\Delta l + \Delta l - 0.05 \text{ cm})$. Therefore

$$\Delta l = \frac{1}{3}\left(\frac{l_0 W}{AY} + 0.05 \text{ cm}\right) = \frac{1}{3}\left(\frac{200 \text{ cm} \times 12 \times 981 \times 10^3 \text{ dynes}}{(\pi/4) \times 10^{-2} \text{ cm}^2 \times 2 \times 10^{12} \text{ dynes} \cdot \text{cm}^{-2}} + 0.05 \text{ cm}\right)$$

$$= \frac{1}{3}(0.15 + 0.05) \text{ cm} = 0.0667 \text{ cm} = 0.667 \text{ mm}.$$

Thus two of the wires are stretched by 0.667 mm and the other by 0.167 mm. Also

$$\frac{F_n}{F'_n} = \frac{\Delta l}{\Delta l - 0.05 \text{ cm}} = \frac{0.667 \text{ mm}}{0.167 \text{ mm}} = 4; \qquad 12 \text{ kg} = W = 2F_n + F'_n = 9F'_n.$$

$$\therefore \qquad F'_n = 1\tfrac{1}{3} \text{ kg} \qquad \text{and} \qquad F_n = 5\tfrac{1}{3} \text{ kg}.$$

PROBLEM 10.3

A ship is being towed by a tug by means of a steel wire. If the drag on the ship is equivalent to 2×10^6 lb, and if the breaking strain of the wire is 0.025, what is the smallest permissible diameter of wire that may be used?

Solution. If the ship is being towed, it eventually settles down at a steady speed so that the force being exerted by the tow wire is equal and opposite to the drag on the ship. Now the formula for Young's modulus is

$$Y = \frac{F_n/A}{\Delta l/l_0},$$

where the symbols have their usual significance. Thus $A = F_n l_0 / Y \Delta l$, where F_n, the normal force on the wire, is equal to the force exerted by the wire on the ship, which balances the drag force. Further, the strain $\Delta l/l_0$ must be less than 0.025, the strain at which the wire breaks. Hence

$$A \geq \frac{2 \times 10^6 \text{ lb}}{29 \times 10^6 \text{ lb} \cdot \text{in}^{-2} \times 0.025} \qquad \text{or} \qquad \frac{\pi D^2}{4} \geq \frac{80}{29} \text{ in}^2.$$

$$\therefore \qquad D \geq \sqrt{320/29\pi} \text{ in.} = 1.87 \text{ in.},$$

which is the smallest possible diameter for the tow wire.

PROBLEM 10.4

A cubic foot of sea water at the surface weighs 64.00 lb. What volume of water weighs 100 lb at the sea bed, where the water pressure is 4000 lb $\cdot$ ft^{-2}? The compressibility of sea water is 36×10^{-7} in$^2 \cdot$lb^{-1}.

Solution. At the surface 100 lb of water occupies $\frac{100}{64}$ ft^3. Where the water pressure is 4000 lb $\cdot$ ft^{-2} $= \frac{4000}{144}$ lb $\cdot$ in^{-2}, the volume will have decreased by ΔV, and the compressibility of sea water is given by the formula $k = (1/p)(\Delta V/V)$.

$$\therefore \qquad \frac{\Delta V}{V} = kp = \frac{4000}{144} \text{ lb} \cdot \text{in}^{-2} \times 36 \times 10^{-7} \text{ in}^2 \cdot \text{lb}^{-1} = 10^{-4}.$$

$$\therefore \qquad \frac{V - \Delta V}{V} = 1 - 10^{-4} \qquad \text{or} \qquad V - \Delta V = \frac{100}{64}(1 - 10^{-4}) \text{ ft}^3.$$

Thus the volume occupied at the lower level is 1.5623 ft^3.

11

Harmonic Motion

PROBLEM 11.1

A particle which is performing simple harmonic motion passes through two points 20 cm apart with the same velocity, taking 1 s to get from one point to the other. It takes a further 2 s to pass through the second point in the opposite direction. What are the period and amplitude of the motion?

Solution. From the equations of simple harmonic motion, the velocity at any displacement x has a value $v = \omega\sqrt{A^2 - x^2}$, where ω is the angular frequency of the motion and A its amplitude. Thus v can be the same at two points only if the displacements of these points are $\pm x$. If the origin of the time scale is taken at the mean position of the motion, as shown in the rotor diagram, and if the second point is reached t_0 thereafter, the displacement at the first point is

$$-x = A \sin \omega(t_0 - 1\ \text{s}),$$

at the second point,

$$+x = A \sin \omega t_0,$$

and at the second point on the return journey,

$$+x = A \sin \omega(t_0 + 2\ \text{s}).$$

Hence $\sin \omega t_0 = x/A = -\sin \omega(t_0 - 1\ \text{s})$.

$$\therefore \quad t_0 = -(t_0 - 1\ \text{s}) \quad \text{or} \quad t_0 = \tfrac{1}{2}\ \text{s}.$$

Also $\sin \omega(t_0 + 2\ \text{s}) = x/A = \sin \omega t_0$. Hence $\omega(t_0 + 2\ \text{s}) = \pi - \omega t_0$ or $\pi/\omega = 2t_0 + 2\ \text{s} = 3\ \text{s}$.

$$\therefore \quad \omega = \frac{\pi}{3}\ \text{rad}\cdot\text{s}^{-1}.$$

Also

$$\sin \omega(t_0 - 1\ \text{s}) = \sin\left(\frac{\pi}{3}\ \text{rad}\cdot\text{s}^{-1} \times -\frac{1}{2}\ \text{s}\right) = -\sin\frac{\pi}{6} = -\frac{1}{2}.$$

But $\sin \omega(t_0 - 1\ \text{s}) = -x/A = -(0.1/A)$ m.

$$\therefore \quad \frac{1}{2} = \frac{0.1}{A}\ \text{m} \quad \text{or} \quad A = 0.2\ \text{m}.$$

PROBLEM 11.2

A horizontal shelf moves vertically with simple harmonic motion, the period of which is 1 s and the amplitude of which is 30 cm. A light particle is laid on the shelf when it is at its lowest position. Determine the point at which the particle leaves the shelf and the height to which it rises from that position, g being taken as π^2 m·s^{-2}.

Solution. The period of a simple harmonic motion is given by the expression $T = 2\pi/\omega$. Therefore the angular frequency in this case is $\omega = 2\pi/T = 2\pi/1 \text{ s} = 2\pi \text{ rad} \cdot \text{s}^{-1}$.

The only forces acting on the particle are its weight mg downward and the normal force $\mathbf{N}$ exerted by the shelf upward. At any time, $N - mg = ma$, where a is the upward acceleration of shelf and particle. If $a = -g$, N becomes zero and, if a becomes more negative, the shelf is retarded at a greater rate than the particle; therefore the particle moves away from the shelf. Since $a = -\omega^2 x$, the displacement x at which the particle leaves the shelf is given by

$$-g = -\omega^2 x \quad \text{or} \quad x = \frac{g}{\omega^2} = \frac{\pi^2 \text{ m} \cdot \text{s}^{-2}}{4\pi^2 \text{ rad}^2 \cdot \text{s}^{-2}} = \frac{1}{4} \text{ m}.$$

The particle thus leaves the shelf when it is $\frac{1}{4}$ m above the mean position. At that point the common velocity of shelf and particle is $v = \pm\omega\sqrt{A^2 - x^2}$, where A is the amplitude of the motion. Since the shelf is rising, v is positive and

$$v = 2\pi \text{ rad} \cdot \text{s}^{-1} \times \sqrt{(0.3 \text{ m})^2 - (0.25 \text{ m})^2} = 2\pi\sqrt{0.0275} \text{ m} \cdot \text{s}^{-1}.$$

The kinetic energy of the particle after it leaves the shelf is turned into potential energy as it rises to its maximum height h.

$$\therefore \quad \frac{1}{2}mv^2 = mgh \quad \text{or} \quad h = \frac{v^2}{2g} = \frac{4\pi^2 \times 0.0275 \text{ m}^2 \cdot \text{s}^{-2}}{2 \times \pi^2 \text{ m} \cdot \text{s}^{-2}} = 0.055 \text{ m} = 5.5 \text{ cm}.$$

PROBLEM 11.3

At a carnival, the people who go on a certain ride sit in chairs around the rim of a horizontal circular platform which is oscillating rapidly with angular simple harmonic motion about a vertical axis through its center. The period of the motion is 2 s and the amplitude 0.2 rad.

One of the chairs becomes unbolted and just starts to slip when the angular displacement is a maximum. Calculate the coefficient of friction between chair and platform. (The rim is 12 ft from the center.)

Solution. The angular acceleration α is related to the displacement θ by the relation $\alpha = -\omega^2\theta$, where ω is the angular frequency. But the periodic time T is given by $T = 2\pi/\omega$. Thus the maximum value of α is

$$\alpha_0 = -\frac{4\pi^2}{T^2}\theta_0 = -0.2\pi^2 \text{ rad} \cdot \text{s}^{-2},$$

and the maximum linear acceleration at the rim is

$$a_0 = R\alpha_0 = -2.4\pi^2 \text{ ft} \cdot \text{s}^{-2}.$$

Since the chair has become unbolted, the force producing this acceleration must be provided by friction. If the chair just starts to slip, the magnitude of the frictional force $\mathbf{F}$ is $F = \mu_s N$, where μ_s is the coefficient of static friction between chair and platform and $\mathbf{N}$ is the normal force exerted by the platform on the chair. Since there is no vertical movement, the weight mg and N must balance. Hence $F = \mu_s N = \mu_s mg$. But

$$F = \mu_s mg = m|a_0| = 2.4 \, m\pi^2 \text{ ft} \cdot \text{s}^{-2}.$$

$$\therefore \quad \mu_s = \frac{2.4\pi^2 \text{ ft} \cdot \text{s}^{-2}}{g} = \frac{2.4\pi^2 \text{ ft} \cdot \text{s}^{-2}}{32 \text{ ft} \cdot \text{s}^{-2}} = 0.74.$$

PROBLEM 11.4

If a tunnel were drilled through the earth along one of its diameters and if a stone were dropped into it from one end, how long would it be before the stone returned? Compare the answer with the period of an earth satellite in an orbit of minimum radius and comment on the two values. Assume the earth to be of uniform density, and make use of the information that a body inside the earth at a distance r from the center has a gravitational force acting on it due only to the portion of the earth of radius r.

Solution. At any distance r from the center the stone is acted on by a force in the direction of increasing r of magnitude

$$F = -\frac{GM'm}{r^2} = -\frac{Gm}{r^2} \times \frac{4}{3}\pi\rho r^3 = -\frac{4}{3}\pi\rho Gmr,$$

where m is the mass of the stone, ρ the density of the earth, and M' the mass of that portion of the earth of radius r. Therefore

$$F = ma = -\frac{4}{3}\pi\rho Gmr \quad \text{or} \quad a = -\frac{4}{3}\pi\rho Gr.$$

The stone thus executes simple harmonic motion of period $T = 2\pi/\sqrt{\frac{4}{3}\pi\rho G}$. But at the surface of the earth

$$mg = \frac{GMm}{R^2} = \frac{4}{3}\pi\rho GmR,$$

where R is the radius of the earth. Thus

$$T = 2\pi\sqrt{\frac{R}{g}} = 2\pi\sqrt{\frac{6370 \times 10^3 \text{ m}}{9.8 \text{ m}\cdot\text{s}^{-2}}} = 5061.6 \text{ s} = 84.4 \text{ min.}$$

The time period of an earth satellite in a circular orbit* is $T' = 2\pi d^{3/2}/R\sqrt{g}$, where d is the distance of the satellite from the center of the earth. If the height of the satellite above the earth's surface is negligible in comparison with the radius of the earth, then to a first approximation $d = R$, and $T' = 2\pi\sqrt{R/g}$, the same period as that of the stone undergoing simple harmonic motion along the tunnel. This is not surprising, since any simple harmonic motion may be considered the projection on a diameter of the motion of a point in a circle with constant speed. Thus we should expect the period of an earth satellite near the earth's surface to be the same as the period of a particle undergoing simple harmonic motion along a diameter of the circle.

PROBLEM 11.5

Martians in a flying saucer are attempting to locate the exact position of the gold reserves at Fort Knox by measuring the variation of g in the area, since a large mass of gold will exert an appreciable additional gravitational attraction on a body in the vicinity. They hover above selected spots and observe the movement of a mass suspended from a light spring. If the system has a natural period of 2 s, and the smallest movement of the mass which can be detected is 10^{-6} m, what is the minimum change in g which they can observe?

Solution. At a point at which the acceleration due to gravity is g, the mass when in equilibrium has two forces acting on it: the weight mg down and the restoring force kx up, and these must be equal. Thus $g = (k/m)x$.

At another point, where local conditions vary, the stretching of the spring will be $x + dx$ if the value of the acceleration due to gravity is $g + dg$.

$$\therefore \quad g + dg = \frac{k}{m}(x + dx) \quad \text{or} \quad dg = \frac{k}{m}dx.$$

But, if the system is allowed to oscillate, its period is given by

$$T = \frac{2\pi}{\omega} = 2\pi\sqrt{\frac{m}{k}}. \quad \therefore \quad dg = \frac{4\pi^2}{T^2}dx.$$

If the smallest value of dx observable is 10^{-6} m, the smallest value dg detectable is thus

$$dg = \frac{4\pi^2}{4 \text{ s}^2} \times 10^{-6} \text{ m} = 9.87 \times 10^{-6} \text{ m}\cdot\text{s}^{-2}.$$

---

*Cf., for example, *University Physics* (3rd edition), 1964, by Sears and Zemansky (Addison-Wesley), Eq. (6–17).

PROBLEM 11.6

The period of a compound pendulum is 2 s on the earth's surface. What is its period if it is aboard a rocket accelerating upward with an acceleration of 4.3 m·s^{-2}?

Solution. When on the surface the compound pendulum has a period $T = 2\pi\sqrt{I_0/Mgh}$, where the symbols have their usual significance.

Under acceleration **a** upward, the forces acting on the body when it is displaced through an angle θ are those shown in the diagram, the weight Mg downward and the vertical force **F** and horizontal force **R** exerted by the pivot on the pendulum.

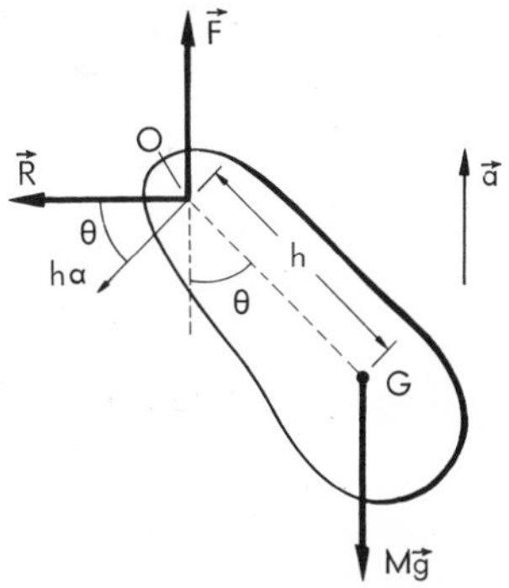

Consider the linear accelerations, horizontal and vertical, acting on the body at its center of mass and the rotational acceleration about the center of mass. Applying Newton's law and the corresponding torque law, we find that

$$R = Ma_H, \quad F - Mg = Ma_V, \quad \text{and} \quad Rh\cos\theta - Fh\sin\theta = I_G\alpha.$$

The point O thus has an acceleration a_H horizontally, an acceleration a_V vertically, and a further linear acceleration $h\alpha$ due to the rotation about G at right angles to OG. But the point O does not move sideways, only upward with an acceleration a. Thus

$$a_H + h\alpha\cos\theta = 0 \quad \text{and} \quad a_V - h\alpha\sin\theta = a.$$

$$\therefore \quad R = -Mh\alpha\cos\theta, \quad F = M(g + a + h\alpha\sin\theta),$$

and

$$I_G\alpha = Rh\cos\theta - Fh\sin\theta = -Mh^2\alpha\cos^2\theta - Mh^2\alpha\sin^2\theta - M(g+a)h\sin\theta.$$

$$\therefore \quad (I_G + Mh^2)\alpha = I_0\alpha = -M(g+a)h\sin\theta.$$

But the angle θ is small, and $\sin\theta$ can be replaced by θ.

$$\therefore \quad \alpha = -\frac{M(g+a)h}{I_0}\theta.$$

It follows from the theory of simple harmonic motion that the period of the oscillation is

$$T' = 2\pi\sqrt{\frac{I_0}{M(g+a)h}}; \quad \frac{T'}{T} = \sqrt{\frac{g}{g+a}} = \sqrt{\frac{9.8\ \text{m·s}^{-2}}{(9.8+4.3)\ \text{m·s}^{-2}}} = \frac{1}{1.2} \quad \therefore \quad T' = \frac{2\ \text{s}}{1.2} = 1.67\ \text{s}.$$

Note that the result can be obtained more quickly if the idea of an accelerated frame of reference is applied. An observer in the rocket considers the point of support of the pendulum at rest relative to himself. To explain the observed equilibrium he finds it necessary to postulate a force Ma acting downward on the body in addition to the weight Mg. Hence the pendulum acts as if the weight were $M(\mathbf{g} + \mathbf{a})$ instead of $M\mathbf{g}$, when the formula follows immediately.

PROBLEM 11.7

A uniform circular disk of radius 25 cm is pivoted at a point 20 cm from its center and allowed to oscillate in a vertical plane under the action of gravity. What is the period of its small oscillations? Take g as π^2 m·s^{-2}.

Solution. The moment of inertia of a uniform circular disk of radius R and mass M about an axis through its center perpendicular to its plane is $\frac{1}{2}MR^2$. By the parallel-axes theorem proved in Problem 9.2, the moment of inertia about a parallel axis a distance h from the first is $I = \frac{1}{2}MR^2 + Mh^2$.

The disk is acting as a physical pendulum, and hence its period for small oscillations is given by

$$T = 2\pi\sqrt{\frac{I}{Mgh}} = 2\pi\sqrt{\frac{\frac{1}{2}MR^2 + Mh^2}{Mgh}} = 2\pi\sqrt{\frac{\frac{1}{2}\times 0.25^2\ \text{m}^2 + 0.2^2\ \text{m}^2}{\pi^2\ \text{m·s}^{-2}\times 0.2\ \text{m}}} = 2\sqrt{0.35625}\ \text{s} = 1.193\ \text{s}.$$

PROBLEM 11.8

A pendulum which has a period of 1 s in London where $g = 32.200$ ft·s^{-2} is taken to Paris, where it is found to lose 20 s per day. What is the value of g in Paris?

Solution. Since the period of the pendulum is 1 s in London, the number of oscillations it performs per day is $60 \times 60 \times 24 = 86,400$. In Paris it loses 20 s per day, i.e., it makes only 86,380 complete oscillations.

In all pendulum formulas the period is $T = k/\sqrt{g}$, where k is a constant depending on the shape and possibly the mass of the pendulum. Thus, in London, $T = k/\sqrt{g}$, and in Paris $T' = k/\sqrt{g'}$. But while $T = 1$ s, $T' = 86,400/86,380$ s. Thus

$$\frac{T}{T'} = \frac{86,380}{86,400} = \sqrt{\frac{g'}{g}} \quad \text{or} \quad g' = \left(\frac{8638}{8640}\right)^2 g = \left(1 - \frac{2}{8640}\right)^2 g = \left(1 - \frac{4}{8640}\right) \times 32.200 \text{ ft·s}^{-2}$$

$$= 32.185 \text{ ft·s}^{-2}.$$

PROBLEM 11.9

Show that the center of oscillation of a physical pendulum is also the center of percussion.

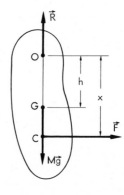

Solution. In the diagram, O is the point of suspension, G is the center of gravity and C the center of percussion. The distances involved are shown clearly. C has the property that, if a horizontal force $\mathbf{F}$ is applied to it, no extra force is applied at O. Thus, if M is the mass of the pendulum and I_G and I_O are the moment of inertia about G and O, respectively,

$$R = Mg, \qquad F = Ma, \qquad F(x - h) = I_G \alpha.$$

But if there is no force other than $\mathbf{R}$ applied to the body at O by the pivot, O cannot move under the application of the force $\mathbf{F}$. Thus the linear acceleration a due to the force $\mathbf{F}$ must be balanced by the acceleration $h\alpha$ due to the angular acceleration about G. Therefore $a = h\alpha$.

$$\therefore \quad x - h = \frac{I_G}{M}\frac{\alpha}{a} = \frac{I_G}{Mh} \quad \text{or} \quad x = \frac{I_G}{Mh} + h = \frac{I_G + Mh^2}{Mh} = \frac{I_O}{Mh} = L,$$

where L is the length of the equivalent simple pendulum. The center of percussion is thus also the center of oscillation.

12

Hydrostatics

PROBLEM 12.1

In order to determine their density, drops of blood are placed in a mixture of xylene of density 0.867 $g \cdot cm^{-3}$ and bromobenzene of density 1.497 $g \cdot cm^{-3}$, the mixture being altered until the drops do not rise or sink. The mixture then contains 72% of xylene and 28% of bromobenzene by volume. What is the density of the blood?

Solution. Every 72 cm³ of xylene have a mass of $72 \times 0.867 = 62.424$ g, and every 28 cm³ of bromobenzene have a mass of $28 \times 1.497 = 41.916$ g. Thus 100 cm³ of the mixture have a mass of $(62.424 + 41.916)$ g $= 104.340$ g. Thus the density of the mixture is 1.0434 $g \cdot cm^{-3}$.

But blood neither rises nor sinks in this mixture, showing that the blood has no net force acting on it. Thus the weight of any drop of blood is exactly equal to the upthrust acting on it. But the upthrust is the weight of an equal volume of mixture. Hence the blood and the mixture have the same densities; thus the density of blood is 1.0434 $g \cdot cm^{-3}$.

PROBLEM 12.2

The pressure in a static water pipe in the basement of an apartment house is 42 $lb \cdot in^{-2}$, but four floors up it is only 20 $lb \cdot in^{-2}$. What is the height between the basement and the fourth floor?

Solution. Since the water system is static, the difference in pressure between the floors is purely hydrostatic. This difference is $(42 - 20)$ $lb \cdot in^{-2} = 22 \times 144$ $lb \cdot ft^{-2}$, and from the laws of hydrostatic pressure

$$22 \times 144 \text{ lb} \cdot ft^{-2} = \rho g h = 1.94 \text{ slugs} \cdot ft^{-3} \times 32 \text{ ft} \cdot s^{-2} \times h,$$

where h is the height required.

$$\therefore \quad h = \frac{22 \times 144 \text{ lb} \cdot ft^{-2}}{1.94 \times 32 \text{ lb} \cdot ft^{-3}} = \frac{99}{1.94} \text{ ft} = 51.03 \text{ ft.}$$

PROBLEM 12.3

A barge of mass 15,000 kg, made from metal of density 7500 $kg \cdot m^{-3}$, is being loaded in a closed dock of surface area 6633 m² with ore of density 3 $g \cdot cm^{-3}$. When 80,000 kg of ore are aboard, the barge sinks. How does the water level in the dock alter? The area of the barge is assumed negligible in comparison with the area of the dock.

Solution. Before the sinking the total mass of barge plus load was 95,000 kg. Since the barge floated, the upthrust of the water must have equaled the weight of 95,000 kg. The mass of displaced water was thus 95,000 kg and the volume 95 m³.

The volume of the material of the barge is 15,000 kg/7500 kg·m⁻³ = 2 m³, and the volume of the ore of density 3 g·cm⁻³ = 3 × 10³ kg·m⁻³ is $\frac{80}{3}$ = 26⅔ m³. The total volume occupied by the metal of the barge and the ore in the water after sinking is thus 28⅔ m³. This is the amount of displaced water after the barge sinks.

The displaced water has therefore decreased by 66⅓ m³. The water level in the dock thus falls by an amount h, equal to the decrease in volume divided by the surface area of the dock, the surface area of the barge being negligible. Therefore

$$h = \frac{66\frac{1}{3}}{663.3} = \frac{1}{10}\,\text{m} = 10\,\text{cm}.$$

PROBLEM 12.4

A ball of volume 500 cm³ is hung from the end of a wire of cross-sectional area 2 × 10⁻³ cm². Young's modulus for the material of the wire is 7 × 10¹¹ dynes·cm⁻². When the ball is immersed in water the length of the wire decreases by 0.05 cm. What is the length of the wire?

Solution. When the ball is immersed in water, it suffers an upthrust equal to the weight of a similar volume of water. Thus immersion causes a compressive force on the wire of magnitude

$$F = 500\,\text{cm}^3 \times \rho g = 500\,\text{cm}^3 \times 1\,\text{g·cm}^{-3} \times 981\,\text{cm·s}^{-2} = 49 \times 10^4\,\text{dynes}.$$

But Young's modulus for the wire is given by the formula $Y = (F/A)/(\Delta l/l_0)$, where the symbols have their usual significance. Hence

$$l_0 = \frac{AY\Delta l}{F} = \frac{2 \times 10^{-3}\,\text{cm}^2 \times 7 \times 10^{11}\,\text{dynes·cm}^{-2} \times 5 \times 10^{-2}\,\text{cm}}{49 \times 10^4\,\text{dynes}} = 142.9\,\text{cm}.$$

PROBLEM 12.5

When a metal cylinder of height 14 cm which is floating upright in mercury is set into vertical oscillation, the period of the motion is found to be 0.56 s. What is the density of the metal? The density of mercury is 13,600 kg·m⁻³ and g is π² m·s⁻².

Solution. Let the cylinder have a cross-sectional area A, length l, and density ρ, and let it float in the mercury of density ρ' immersed to a height y. In this position, shown by the solid line in the diagram, the weight and upthrust balance. Hence $\rho lAg = \rho'yAg$.

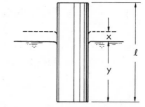

If the cylinder is pushed in a further distance x the upthrust is greater than the weight, and there is a restoring force attempting to return the cylinder to its original position. If a is the downward acceleration,

$$\rho lAg - \rho'(y+x)Ag = -\rho'xAg = \rho lAa. \qquad \therefore \qquad a = -\frac{\rho'g}{\rho l}x.$$

Comparing this with the expression $a = -\omega^2 x$, it is clear that the cylinder when released undergoes simple harmonic motion of period $T = 2\pi/\omega = 2\pi\sqrt{\rho l/\rho'g}$. Hence

$$\frac{\rho l}{\rho'g} = \frac{T^2}{4\pi^2} \quad \text{or} \quad \rho = \frac{\rho'gT^2}{4\pi^2 l} = \frac{13,600\,\text{kg·m}^{-3} \times \pi^2\,\text{m·s}^{-2} \times (0.56)^2\,\text{s}^2}{4\pi^2 \times 0.14\,\text{m}} = 7616\,\text{kg·m}^{-3}.$$

Any motion of the mercury is ignored in the above analysis.

PROBLEM 12.6

Army engineers have thrown a pontoon bridge 10 ft in width over a river 50 yd wide. When twelve identical trucks cross the river simultaneously the bridge sinks 1 ft. What is the weight of one truck? The density of water is 1.94 slugs·ft⁻³.

Solution. When the trucks are on the bridge, the extra volume of the bridge immersed is 1 ft deep, 10 ft wide, and 50 yd = 150 ft long, i.e., 1500 ft³. The upthrust on this extra volume immersed in water is the weight of an equal volume of water. Thus

$$U = 1500 \text{ ft}^3 \times 1.94 \text{ slugs} \cdot \text{ft}^{-3} \times 32 \text{ ft} \cdot \text{s}^{-2} = 9.312 \times 10^4 \text{ lb}.$$

But this upthrust just balances the weight of the twelve trucks. Hence one truck has a weight

$$W = \frac{U}{12} = \frac{9.312 \times 10^4 \text{ lb}}{12} = 7760 \text{ lb}.$$

PROBLEM 12.7

A rectangular post 4 in. thick is floating in a pond with three-quarters of its volume immersed. An oil tanker skids off the road and ends up overturned at the edge of the pond with oil of 1.26 slugs·ft⁻³ density leaking from it into the water. When the upper face of the post is just level with the surface of the liquid, what is the depth of the oil layer? What happens if more oil keeps pouring into the pond?

Solution. Before the oil is spilled, the post is floating in the water symmetrically. Let its cross-sectional area be A and its density ρ. Then, if three-quarters of the volume is immersed, only 1 in. is above the surface and 3 in. below the surface. The weight downward and the upthrust upward balance. Hence if ρ_0 is the density of water,

$$\rho Ag \times 4 \text{ in.} = \rho_0 Ag \times 3 \text{ in.}$$

$$\therefore \qquad \rho = \frac{3}{4}\rho_0.$$

When the oil of density ρ' pours on, it stays above the water. The water extends up to a height y and the oil fills the other (4 in. $- y$). Since equilibrium is still achieved, the weight downward must equal the sum of the two upthrusts due to the water and the oil. Hence $\rho Ag \times 4 \text{ in.} = \rho_0 Agy + \rho' Ag(4 \text{ in.} - y)$.

$$\therefore \qquad \rho \times 4 \text{ in.} = \rho_0 \times 3 \text{ in.} = \rho_0 y + \rho'(4 \text{ in.} - y).$$

$$\therefore \qquad y = \frac{\rho_0 \times 3 \text{ in.} - \rho' \times 4 \text{ in.}}{\rho_0 - \rho'} = \frac{1.94 \text{ slugs} \cdot \text{ft}^{-3} \times 3 \text{ in.} - 1.26 \text{ slugs} \cdot \text{ft}^{-3} \times 4 \text{ in.}}{(1.94 - 1.26) \text{ slugs} \cdot \text{ft}^{-3}}$$

$$= \frac{0.78}{0.68} \text{ in.} = 1.15 \text{ in.}$$

Thus the depth of the oil layer is 2.85 in.

If oil keeps pouring onto the pond, the post must stay as it is with respect to the water–oil interface. While the oil poured on initially, the post rose from the water to compensate for the extra upthrust from the oil by diminishing the upthrust from the water. Once the post is totally immersed, it is at the correct position with respect to the water–oil interface for the sum of the two upthrusts to equal the weight. Adding further oil cannot alter this.

PROBLEM 12.8

A triangular plate is immersed in water with one vertex at the surface and the others at depths of 6 in. and 12 in. What is the thrust on the plate? Its area is 63 in².

Solution. At depth z the pressure is $g\rho z$, the symbols having their usual significance. The total thrust on the small element, parallel to the surface, shown in the sketch is

$$dF = g\rho zy \, dz.$$

The total thrust on the plate is

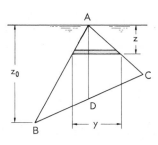

$$F = \int_0^{z_0} g\rho yz \, dz = g\rho \frac{\int_0^{z_0} yz \, dz}{\int_0^{z_0} y \, dz} \times \int_0^{z_0} y \, dz.$$

The area of the plate is $\int_0^{z_0} y\, dz$ and $\int_0^{z_0} yz\, dz / \int_0^{z_0} y\, dz$ gives the distance below the surface of the center of mass of the plate. The total thrust on the plate is thus seen to be the pressure at the center of mass of the plate multiplied by the area of the plate. This is a general result for all plates, as can be seen from the general nature of the derivation.

In the particular case of the triangular plate, the area of 63 in² $= \frac{63}{144}$ ft² is given. The center of mass of a triangular plate is two-thirds of the way from a vertex to the middle of the opposite side. Since B and C are 6 in. and 12 in. from the surface, D, which is the midpoint of BC, must be [(6 + 12)/2] in. = 9 in. from the surface. But the center of mass is two-thirds of AD from A and must be 6 in. $= \frac{1}{2}$ ft from the surface. In this case, therefore,

$$F = g\rho \times \tfrac{1}{2}\,\text{ft} \times \tfrac{63}{144}\,\text{ft}^2 = 32\ \text{ft} \cdot \text{s}^{-2} \times 1.94\ \text{slugs} \cdot \text{ft}^{-3} \times \tfrac{1}{2}\,\text{ft} \times \tfrac{63}{144}\,\text{ft}^2 = 15.58\ \text{lb}.$$

13

Surface Tension

PROBLEM 13.1

A thin square metal sheet of side 6 cm is suspended vertically from a balance so that the lower edge of the sheet dips into water in such a way that it is parallel to the surface. If the sheet is clean, the angle of contact between water and metal is $0°$, and the sheet appears to weigh 4700 dynes. If the sheet is greasy, the contact angle is $180°$ and the weight appears to be 3000 dynes. What is the surface tension of water?

Solution. In either case there are three forces acting on the sheet: the tension in the suspension which gives the apparent weight, the actual weight of the sheet, and the total surface-tension force. In the first case the angle of contact is zero and the surface tension force acts downward. Thus $F_1 = W + 2T$, the factor 2 being necessary since there are two sides to the sheet. In the second case the angle of contact is $180°$ and thus the surface-tension force is acting upward. Hence $F_2 = W - 2T$.

In both cases $T = \gamma l$, where γ is the surface tension of water and l is the length of the sheet. Therefore $4T = 4\gamma l = F_1 - F_2$

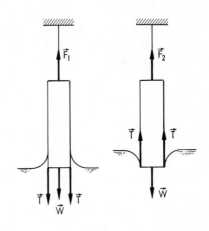

or $\quad \gamma = \dfrac{F_1 - F_2}{4l} = \dfrac{(4700 - 3000)\,\text{dynes}}{4 \times 6\,\text{cm}} = 70.8\,\text{dynes}\cdot\text{cm}^{-1}.$

PROBLEM 13.2

A soap bubble formed from 5 mg of soap solution will just float in air of density 1.290 g·liter when filled with hydrogen of density 0.090 g·liter. The surface tension of soap solution is 25 dynes·cm^{-1}. What is the excess pressure in the bubble?

Solution. When the bubble is floating in air, the weight of soap solution plus the weight of the hydrogen must just be balanced by the upthrust due to the displaced air. Hence, if the bubble has a volume of y,

$$5 \times 10^{-3}\,\text{g} + 0.09 \times 10^{-3}\,\text{g}\cdot\text{cm}^{-3} \times y = 1.29 \times 10^{-3}\,\text{g}\cdot\text{cm}^{-3} \times y. \quad \therefore \quad y = \frac{5\,\text{cm}^3}{1.2} = \frac{25}{6}\,\text{cm}^3.$$

But the bubble is spherical and of radius r. Thus

$$\frac{4}{3}\pi r^3 = \frac{25}{6}\,\text{cm}^3. \quad \therefore \quad r^3 = \frac{25 \times 3\,\text{cm}^3}{24\pi} \quad \text{or} \quad r = 1\,\text{cm}.$$

The excess pressure in the bubble is

$$P = \frac{4\gamma}{r} = \frac{4 \times 25\,\text{dynes}\cdot\text{cm}^{-1}}{1\,\text{cm}} = 100\,\text{dynes}\cdot\text{cm}^{-2}.$$

PROBLEM 13.3

A capillary tube of internal radius 0.25 mm is dipped into water of surface tension 72 dynes·cm⁻¹. How high does the water rise in the tube? The capillary tube is gradually lowered into the water until only 1 cm is left above the surface. Explain what happens to the water in the tube.

Solution. The expression for the rise of liquid in a capillary tube is $y = 2\gamma \cos\theta/\rho g r$, where the symbols have their usual significance. Since the liquid in this case is water, the angle of contact is 0°, and the density is 1 g·cm⁻³. Hence

$$y = \frac{2 \times 72 \text{ dynes·cm}^{-1}}{1 \text{ g·cm}^{-3} \times 980 \text{ cm·s}^{-2} \times 0.025 \text{ cm}} = 5.88 \text{ cm}.$$

As long as more than 5.88 cm of tube show above the liquid surface, there is no problem. The liquid rises to that height. But, as the tube is lowered, a stage will be reached when less than 5.88 cm are above the surface.

What can *not* happen is that liquid pour out over the top. If it did, the liquid pouring over the edge could be used to drive a water wheel to provide energy; and the process would continue as liquid would always rise up the tube to take the place of that pouring from the end. In other words, a perpetual motion machine would be established, which is in direct contradiction to the principle of conservation of energy.

What does happen is that the angle of contact at the top of the tube increases. Only the vertical component of the surface tension is used to balance the weight of the water column held up. As the height of the projecting tube gets smaller and smaller, the angle of contact gets larger and larger until, with $y = 0$, $\theta = 90°$, and the surface at the top of the tube is flat.

In particular, when $y = 1$ cm,

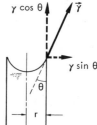

$$1 \text{ cm} = \frac{2\gamma \cos\theta}{\rho g r} = 5.88 \cos\theta \text{ cm}.$$

$$\therefore \quad \cos\theta = \frac{1}{5.88} = 0.17 \quad \therefore \quad \theta = 80.2°.$$

14

Hydrodynamics and Viscosity

PROBLEM 14.1

At two points on a horizontal tube of varying circular cross section carrying water, the radii are 1 cm and 0.4 cm and the pressure difference between these points is 4.9 cm of water. How much liquid flows through the tube per second?

Solution. Since the tube is horizontal there is no pressure difference along the tube due to hydrostatic effects. Thus Bernoulli's equation is $p_1 + \frac{1}{2}\rho v_1^2 = p_2 + \frac{1}{2}\rho v_2^2$, where the symbols have their usual significance. But the equation of continuity shows that the constant quantity of water flowing through the tube per second at the two points is $A_1 v_1 = A_2 v_2$, where A_1 and A_2 are the respective areas. Thus

$$v_2^2 - v_1^2 = 2(p_1 - p_2)/\rho = 2g\rho \times 4.9 \text{ cm}/\rho = 98^2 \text{ cm}^2 \cdot \text{s}^{-2},$$

and

$$\frac{v_1}{v_2} = \frac{A_2}{A_1} = \frac{\pi \times 0.4^2 \text{ cm}^2}{\pi \times 1^2 \text{ cm}^2} = 0.16.$$

$$\therefore \quad v_2^2(1 - 0.16^2) = 98^2 \text{ cm}^2 \cdot \text{s}^{-2} \quad \text{or} \quad v_2 = \sqrt{\frac{98^2 \text{ cm}^2 \cdot \text{s}^{-2}}{0.9744}}.$$

The quantity of water flowing through the tube per second is thus

$$A_1 v_1 = A_2 v_2 = \pi \times 0.16 \text{ cm}^2 \times \sqrt{\frac{98^2 \text{ cm}^2 \cdot \text{s}^{-2}}{0.9744}} = 50 \text{ cm}^3 \cdot \text{s}^{-1}.$$

PROBLEM 14.2

The seal over a circular hole of diameter 1 cm in the side of an aquarium tank ruptures. The water level is 1 m above the hole and the tank is standing on a smooth plastic surface. What force must an attendant apply to the tank to prevent it from being set into motion?

Solution. The pressures above the tank and outside the hole are both atmospheric pressure. Applying Bernoulli's theorem to this case, we thus have

$$p_a + 0 + \rho g h = p_a + \frac{1}{2}\rho v^2 + 0.$$

Here v is the velocity of efflux from the hole, the reference level for height being taken as the horizontal level through the hole. Since the cross section of the tank is very much larger than the area of the hole, the liquid in the tank is assumed to have zero velocity. Thus $v = \sqrt{2gh}$.

Let A be the area of the hole. The mass of fluid ejected in time dt is $\rho A v \, dt$, and thus the momentum acquired in time dt is $\rho A v^2 \, dt$. The escaping fluid therefore has a rate of change of momentum of $\rho A v^2$ and thus by Newton's second law the force causing this is $\rho A v^2$. By Newton's third law, an equal and opposite force acts on the tank. Hence, to prevent the tank from moving backward, the attendant must apply to the tank a force of magnitude

$$F = \rho A v^2 = \rho \frac{\pi d^2}{4} \times 2gh = 10^3 \text{ kg} \cdot \text{m}^{-3} \times \frac{\pi}{4} \times 10^{-4} \text{ m}^2 \times 2 \times 9.8 \text{ m} \cdot \text{s}^{-2} \times 1 \text{ m} = 1.54 \text{ N}.$$

PROBLEM 14.3

Water flows into a water tank of large cross-sectional area at a rate of $10^{-4} \text{m}^3 \cdot \text{s}^{-1}$, but flows out from a hole of area 1 cm², which has been punched through the base. How high does the water rise in the tank?

Solution. When the water reaches its maximum height in the tank the pressure head is great enough to produce an outflow exactly equal to the inflow. Equilibrium is then reached and the water level in the tank stays constant.

Since the cross-sectional area of the tank is large in comparison with the area of the hole, the water in the tank may be considered to have zero velocity. Further, the air above the tank and outside the hole are each at atmospheric pressure. Applying Bernoulli's theorem, we have

$$p_a + \rho g h + 0 = p_a + 0 + \tfrac{1}{2}\rho v^2,$$

where v is the velocity of efflux from the hole. Hence $v = \sqrt{2\,gh}$.

But at equilibrium v is the rate of influx divided by the area of the hole. That is,

$$v = \frac{10^{-4} \text{ m}^3 \cdot \text{s}^{-1}}{10^{-4} \text{ m}^2} = 1 \text{ m} \cdot \text{s}^{-1}.$$

Therefore the maximum height of water in the tank is

$$h = \frac{v^2}{2g} = \frac{1^2 \text{ m}^2 \cdot \text{s}^{-2}}{2 \times 9.8 \text{ m} \cdot \text{s}^{-2}} = 5.1 \text{ cm}.$$

PROBLEM 14.4

A water tank standing on the floor has two small holes vertically above one another punched in one side. The holes are 3.6 cm and 10 cm above the floor. How high does water stand in the tank when the jets from the holes hit the floor at the same point?

Solution. The arguments of Problem 14.3 apply equally to this case, though here the velocities of efflux are horizontal from both holes. For the upper hole,

$$v_1 = \sqrt{2g(h - h_1)},$$

and for the lower one,

$$v_2 = \sqrt{2g(h - h_2)}.$$

Water from the upper hole has a horizontal velocity v_1 and no initial vertical velocity. In time t_1, applying the formula $(y - y_0) = ut_1 + \tfrac{1}{2}gt_1^2$ to the vertical motion, one obtains $h_1 = 0 + \tfrac{1}{2}gt_1^2$ or $t_1 = \sqrt{2h_1/g}$.

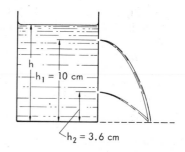

In that time the horizontal distance gone is $v_1 t_1$, which is the distance from the tank at which the jet strikes the floor.

Similarly the distance at which the jet from the lower hole strikes the floor is $v_2 t_2$, where $t_2 = \sqrt{2h_2/g}$. But these distances are equal, and thus $v_1 t_1 = v_2 t_2$ or

$$2g(h - h_1) \times \frac{2h_1}{g} = 2g(h - h_2) \times \frac{2h_2}{g}.$$

$$\therefore \quad h = \frac{h_1^2 - h_2^2}{h_1 - h_2} = h_1 + h_2. \qquad \therefore \quad h = 13.6 \text{ cm}.$$

PROBLEM 14.5

An old-fashioned water clock consists of a circular cylinder 10 cm in diameter and 25 cm high with a vertical capillary tube 40 cm in length and 0.5 mm in diameter attached to the bottom. The viscosity of water is 0.01 poise. What is the distance between hour divisions at the top of the vessel and at the bottom of the vessel?

Solution. When we apply Poiseuille's formula to this case, the symbols having their usual significance, we obtain

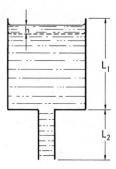

$$\frac{Q}{t} = \frac{\pi}{8} \frac{R^4}{\eta} \frac{p_1 - p_2}{L_2} = \frac{\pi}{8} \frac{R^4}{\eta} \frac{\rho g(L_1 + L_2)}{L_2},$$

where ρ is the density of water.

The quantity of water, Q, flowing from the capillary in time t causes a drop in the level of the cylinder, h. The area of the cylinder is A, and thus $Q/t = Ah/t$.

$$\therefore \quad \frac{h}{t} = \frac{\pi}{8A} \frac{R^4}{\eta} \frac{\rho g(L_1 + L_2)}{L_2}.$$

When the cylinder is full, $L_1 = 25$ cm, and

$$\frac{h}{t} = \frac{\pi \times (0.25 \times 10^{-3}\,\text{m})^4 \times 10^3\,\text{kg·m}^{-3} \times 9.8\,\text{m·s}^{-2} \times 0.65\,\text{m}}{8 \times \pi/4 \times 10^{-2}\,\text{m}^2 \times 10^{-3}\,\text{N·s·m}^{-2} \times 0.40\,\text{m}}$$

$$= 3.11 \times 10^{-6}\,\text{m·s}^{-1} = 1.12\,\text{cm·hr}^{-1}.$$

When the cylinder is empty, $L_1 = 0$ cm, and

$$\frac{h'}{t} = \frac{h}{t} \times \frac{0.40}{0.65} = 0.69\,\text{cm·hr}^{-1}.$$

Thus hour divisions are separated by 1.12 cm at the top and 0.69 cm at the bottom.

Note that L_1 varies slightly during the hour and, to be quite exact, an integration ought to be performed. The error involved is, however, slight, since the variation in L_1 is very small in comparison with $L_1 + L_2$.

PROBLEM 14.6

One of the Middle East oil pipelines is 30 cm in diameter and has six pumping stations equally placed along its 7.2×10^5 m length, the first station being at the beginning of the pipeline. Oil at atmospheric pressure passes into each station and is ejected into the next section at the maximum allowable pressure, the oil being finally delivered at the end of the pipeline at atmospheric pressure. The density and viscosity of crude oil are 850 kg·m^{-3} and 1 poise, respectively, and 10^6 kg of oil are delivered per day. What is the maximum allowable pressure in the pipeline?

Solution. The rate of flow of oil is 10^6 kg per day:

$$\frac{Q}{t} = \frac{10^6\,\text{kg·day}^{-1}}{850\,\text{kg·m}^{-3} \times 24\,\text{hr·day}^{-1} \times 60\,\text{min·hr}^{-1} \times 60\,\text{s·min}^{-1}} = 1.36 \times 10^{-2}\,\text{m}^3\text{·s}^{-1}.$$

Poiseuille's formula, in the usual notation, is

$$\frac{Q}{t} = \frac{\pi}{8} \frac{R^4}{\eta} \frac{p_1 - p_2}{L}. \qquad \therefore \quad p_1 - p_2 = \frac{8Q\eta L}{\pi t R^4}.$$

Between each pumping station the length is $(7.2/6) \times 10^5$ m. Further, η is 1 poise $= 10^{-1}$ N·s·m^{-2}. Thus the pressure difference across a pumping station is

$$p_1 - p_2 = \frac{8 \times 1.36 \times 10^{-2}\,\text{m}^3\text{·s}^{-1} \times 10^{-1}\,\text{N·s·m}^{-2} \times 1.2 \times 10^5\,\text{m}}{\pi \times (0.15)^4\,\text{m}^4} = 8.2 \times 10^5\,\text{N·m}^{-2} = 8.1\,\text{atm}.$$

Since the pipeline finally delivers the oil at atmospheric pressure, the maximum allowable pressure is 9.1 atm.

PROBLEM 14.7

Spherical particles of pollen are shaken up in water and allowed to stand. The depth of water is 2 cm. What is the diameter of the largest particles remaining in suspension 1 hr later? Density of pollen $= 1.8 \text{ g·cm}^{-3}$.

Solution. The terminal velocity of the particles after they are allowed to settle will very quickly be reached. After 1 hr the only particles left in suspension are those which take longer than 1 hr to fall 2 cm. The larger, heavier particles have already settled. The particles which have just not settled are those which take exactly 1 hr to fall 2 cm. That is,

$$v_T = \frac{2 \text{ cm}}{60 \times 60 \text{ s}} = \frac{1}{1800} \text{ cm·s}^{-1}.$$

But the expression for the terminal velocity is $v_T = \frac{2}{9}(r^2 g/\eta)(\rho - \rho')$, where the symbols have their usual significance.

The radius of the largest particles still just in suspension is thus given by

$$r^2 = \frac{9}{2} \frac{\eta v_T}{g(\rho - \rho')} = \frac{9}{2} \frac{1 \times 10^{-2} \text{ poise} \times \frac{1}{1800} \text{ cm·s}^{-1}}{980 \text{ cm·s}^{-2}(1.8 - 1) \text{ g·cm}^{-3}} = \frac{10^{-4}}{64 \times 49} \text{ cm}^2$$

or

$$d = 2r = \frac{2 \times 10^{-2}}{8 \times 7} \text{ cm} = 3.57 \times 10^{-4} \text{ cm}.$$

PROBLEM 14.8

An aircraft wing requires a lift of 25.4 lb·ft^{-2}. If the speed of flow of the air along the bottom surface of the wing is to be 500 ft·s^{-1}, what must be the speed of flow over the top surface to give the required lift? The density of air is $2.54 \times 10^{-3} \text{ slug·ft}^{-3}$.

Solution. From Bernoulli's theorem, $p_1 + \frac{1}{2}\rho v_1^2 = p_2 + \frac{1}{2}\rho v_2^2$, where the subscript 1 refers to the lower surface and the subscript 2 to the upper surface of the wing. Thus the dynamic lift per unit area is $p_1 - p_2 = \frac{1}{2}\rho(v_2^2 - v_1^2)$.

$$\therefore \quad v_2^2 = \frac{2(p_1 - p_2)}{\rho} + v_1^2 = \frac{2 \times 25.4 \text{ lb·ft}^{-2}}{2.54 \times 10^{-3} \text{ slug·ft}^3} + 25 \times 10^4 \text{ ft}^2\text{·s}^{-2}$$

$$= (2 \times 10^4 + 25 \times 10^4) \text{ ft}^2\text{·s}^{-2} = 27 \times 10^4 \text{ ft}^2\text{·s}^{-2}.$$

$$\therefore \quad v_2 = 519.6 \text{ ft·s}^{-1},$$

which is the speed of flow of the air over the top surface.

15

Temperature. Expansion

PROBLEM 15.1

The pressure of the nitrogen in a constant-volume gas thermometer is 78.0 cm at 0°C and 107.1 cm at 100°C, respectively. What is the temperature of a liquid in which the bulb of the thermometer is immersed when the pressure is seen to be 87.7 cm?

Solution. The thermometric property of the thermometer, in this case the pressure, is taken as being directly proportional to the Kelvin temperature. Thus

$$\frac{T_2}{T_1} = \frac{p_2}{p_1} \quad \text{or} \quad \frac{T_2 - T_1}{T_1} = \frac{p_2 - p_1}{p_1}.$$

Taking the first and second cases mentioned, we have

$$\frac{100°C}{T_1} = \frac{(107.1 - 78.0)\,\text{cm}}{78.0\,\text{cm}} = \frac{29.1}{78.0}.$$

Taking the first and the third cases mentioned, we have

$$\frac{T_3 - T_1}{T_1} = \frac{t}{T_1} = \frac{(87.7 - 78.0)\,\text{cm}}{78.0\,\text{cm}} = \frac{9.7}{78.0}.$$

Dividing the last two equations one by the other yields

$$\frac{t}{100°C} = \frac{9.7}{29.1} = \frac{1}{3}. \quad \therefore \quad t = \frac{100°C}{3} = 33\frac{1}{3}°C.$$

PROBLEM 15.2

At what temperature are the readings on a Fahrenheit and on a Celsius thermometer the same? At what temperature is the Fahrenheit reading three times the Celsius reading?

Solution. If t_F °F is the Fahrenheit temperature and t°C the Celsius temperature, $t_F = \frac{9}{5}t + 32$.

  (a) $t_F = t$. Thus $(\frac{9}{5}t - t_F) = \frac{4}{5}t = -32$. Therefore $t = -\frac{5}{4} \times 32 = -40$. Both scales read the same at -40°C or -40°F.

  (b) $t_F = 3t$. Thus $(t_F - \frac{9}{5}t) = (3 - \frac{9}{5})t = \frac{6}{5}t = 32$. Therefore $t = \frac{160}{6} = 26\frac{2}{3}$. The temperature is $26\frac{2}{3}$°C = 80°F.

PROBLEM 15.3

The brass scale attached to a barometer reads correctly at 20°C. The barometer height is read as 75.34 cm of mercury when the temperature is 25°C. What is the true height at 0°C? The coefficients of volume expansion of mercury and of linear expansion of brass are 18×10^{-5}C deg^{-1} and 1.8×10^{-5}C deg^{-1}, respectively.

Solution. The brass scale at 25°C reads 75.34 cm, but the scale is correct at 20°C. The length of mercury is thus equal to that of a brass scale of length 75.34 cm that has expanded due to being raised in temperature by 5°C. The length of the mercury column is thus

$$l = 75.34 \text{ cm } (1 + 1.8 \times 10^{-5} \text{ deg}^{-1} \times 5 \text{ deg}).$$

This is the length at 25°C. We require to know the height of the mercury if the temperature were dropped 25C deg. This length l_0, since the density increases with decreasing temperature, is

$$l_0 = l(1 - 18 \times 10^{-5} \text{ deg}^{-1} \times 25 \text{ deg}) = 75.34 \text{ cm } (1 + 1.8 \times 10^{-5} \times 5)(1 - 18 \times 10^{-5} \times 25)$$
$$= 75.34(1 - 4.5 \times 10^{-3} + 9 \times 10^{-5}) \text{ cm} = 75.01 \text{ cm}.$$

PROBLEM 15.4

A steel tube, whose coefficient of linear expansion is 18×10^{-6} per °C, contains mercury, whose coefficient of absolute expansion is 180×10^{-6} per °C. The volume of mercury contained in the tube is 10^{-5} m^3 at 0°C, and it is desired that the length of the mercury column should remain constant at all normal temperatures. This is achieved by inserting into the mercury column a rod of silica, whose thermal expansion is negligible. Calculate the volume of the silica rod.

Solution. At 0°C, let the volume of the silica rod be V_0, the volume of mercury be V, and the cross-sectional area and length of the column be A_0 and l_0, respectively. Then

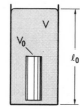

$$l_0 A_0 = V + V_0.$$

At any temperature t, l_0 and V_0 remain constant but A_0 increases to $A_0(1 + 2\alpha t)$, where α is the coefficient of linear expansion of steel. Similarly the volume of mercury increases to $V(1 + \beta t)$, where β is the coefficient of cubical expansion of mercury. Hence

$$l_0 A_0 (1 + 2\alpha t) = (V + V_0)(1 + 2\alpha t) = V(1 + \beta t) + V_0.$$

$$\therefore \quad V_0(1 + 2\alpha t - 1) = V(1 + \beta t - 1 - 2\alpha t) \quad \text{or} \quad V_0 = \frac{V(\beta - 2\alpha)t}{2\alpha t} = \frac{V(\beta - 2\alpha)}{2\alpha}.$$

$$\therefore \quad V_0 = \frac{10^{-5} \text{ m}^3 (180 \times 10^{-6} - 36 \times 10^{-6}) \text{ deg}^{-1}}{36 \times 10^{-6} \text{ deg}^{-1}} = \frac{10^{-5} \times 144}{36} \text{ m}^3 = 4 \times 10^{-5} \text{ m}^3.$$

The silica rod thus occupies four-fifths of the total volume at 0°C.

PROBLEM 15.5

A clock is controlled by a pendulum which correctly beats seconds at 20°C. The pendulum is a light iron rod, of coefficient of linear expansion 16×10^{-6} C deg^{-1}, with a concentrated mass at one end. How much does it lose in a week if the temperature is kept at 30°C?

Solution. If the length of the pendulum is l at 20°C, at 30°C its length will be $l(1 + \alpha \times 10 \text{ deg})$, where α is the coefficient of linear expansion of iron. The pendulum is a simple one, but, if the iron rod were not light, making the pendulum a compound one, the same argument would apply to the length of the equivalent simple pendulum, since all portions of the iron expand by the same amount.

The period of the pendulum is given by $T = 2\pi\sqrt{l/g}$, and the variation in l, and thus the variation in T, is small:

$$\log T = \log \frac{2\pi}{\sqrt{g}} + \frac{1}{2} \log l.$$

$$\therefore \quad \frac{\Delta T}{T} = \frac{1}{2} \frac{\Delta l}{l} = \frac{1}{2} \alpha \times 10 \text{ deg.}$$

$$\therefore \quad \Delta T = 2 \text{ s} \times \tfrac{1}{2} \times 16 \times 10^{-6} \text{ deg}^{-1} \times 10 \text{ deg} = 1.6 \times 10^{-4} \text{ s.}$$

The number of seconds lost in a week is thus

$$1.6 \times 10^{-4} \times 7 \times 24 \times 60 \times \tfrac{6.0}{2} = 48.4 \text{ s.}$$

PROBLEM 15.6

The intelligent physics student whom we have already met in these pages decides to amuse his nephew by building him a submarine. He takes a rectangular block of wood cut with its length parallel to the grain and floats it in alcohol at 10°C. He then raises the temperature of the system gradually. At what temperature will the block just begin to sink? The coefficients of linear expansion of the wood along and across the grain are 4×10^{-6} C deg^{-1} and 18×10^{-6} C deg^{-1}, the coefficient of volume expansion of alcohol is 1.1×10^{-3} C deg^{-1}, and the densities of wood and alcohol at 10°C are 0.75 g·cm^{-3} and 0.80 g·cm^{-3}, respectively.

Solution. When the wood just begins to sink, the weight of alcohol displaced must be equal to the weight of the wood. The weight of the wood does not alter during the temperature rise; the mass of alcohol with this weight occupies a volume V at 10°C when its density is ρ. If the wood at 10°C has a volume V_0 and a density ρ_0, then $\rho_0 V_0 = \rho V$.

At temperature t when the wood starts to sink, the volumes of wood and displaced alcohol are equal, as well as their weights. The volume of alcohol has become $V[1 + 1.1 \times 10^{-3}$ deg$^{-1}(t - 10$ deg$)]$. The length of the wood along the grain has increased from l_0 to $l_0[1 + 4 \times 10^{-6}$ deg$^{-1}(t - 10$ deg$)]$, and the lengths across the grain have increased from l_1 and l_2 to $l_1[1 + 18 \times 10^{-6}$ deg$^{-1}(t - 10$ deg$)]$ and $l_2[1 + 18 \times 10^{-6}$ deg$^{-1}(t - 10$ deg$)]$. Thus the volume of the wood has increased from $V_0 = l_0 l_1 l_2$ to

$$V_1 = l_0 l_1 l_2 [1 + 4 \times 10^{-6} \text{ deg}^{-1}(t - 10 \text{ deg})][1 + 18 \times 10^{-6} \text{ deg}^{-1}(t - 10 \text{ deg})]^2$$

$$= V_0[1 + (4 \times 10^{-6} + 2 \times 18 \times 10^{-6}) \text{ deg}^{-1} \times (t - 10 \text{ deg})].$$

Hence

$$V[1 + 1.1 \times 10^{-3} \text{ deg}^{-1}(t - 10 \text{ deg})] = \frac{\rho_0 V_0}{\rho} \times [1 + 1.1 \times 10^{-3} \text{ deg}^{-1}(t - 10 \text{ deg})]$$

$$= V_0[1 + (4 \times 10^{-6} + 2 \times 18 \times 10^{-6}) \text{ deg}^{-1} \times (t - 10 \text{ deg})].$$

$$\therefore \quad t - 10°\text{C} = \frac{1 - (\rho_0/\rho)}{(\rho_0/\rho) \times 1.1 \times 10^{-3} - 4 \times 10^{-5}} \text{ deg}$$

$$= \frac{1 - (0.75 \text{ g·cm}^{-3}/0.80 \text{ g·cm}^{-3})}{(0.75 \text{ g·cm}^{-3}/0.80 \text{ g·cm}^{-3}) \times 1.1 \times 10^{-3} - 4 \times 10^{-5}} \text{ deg} = 63.1°\text{C.}$$

$$\therefore \quad t = 73.1°\text{C.}$$

PROBLEM 15.7

Two rods of the same diameter, one made of brass and of length 25 cm, the other of steel and of length 50 cm, are placed end to end and pinned to two rigid supports. The temperature of the rods rises 40°C. What is the stress in each rod? Young's moduli for steel and brass are 20×10^{11} dynes·cm^{-2} and 10×10^{11} dynes·cm^{-2}, respectively, and their respective coefficients of expansion are 1.2×10^{-5} C deg^{-1} and 1.8×10^{-5} C deg^{-1}.

Solution. The temperature rises and the rods, if permitted to, would expand. Since they are rigidly held, they cannot do so and therefore suffer a compressive stress. The forces in the two rods must be the same. If they were not, then at the interface between them, the forces would not balance, equilibrium would not exist, and the interface would move until the forces were equal. If then the stresses are equal, $Y_B(\Delta l_B/l_B) = Y_S(\Delta l_S/l_S)$, where the first term on each side is the appropriate Young's modulus and the other term is the corresponding strain. But the total decrease in length $(\Delta l_B + \Delta l_S)$ is the amount the rods have not been allowed to expand when the temperature rose. Hence

$$\Delta l_B + \Delta l_S = l_B \alpha_B \times 40°\text{C} + l_S \alpha_S \times 40°\text{C} \qquad \text{or} \qquad \Delta l_B \left(1 + \frac{Y_B}{Y_S} \frac{l_S}{l_B}\right) = (l_B \alpha_B + l_S \alpha_S) \times 40°\text{C}.$$

$$\therefore \qquad \Delta l_B = \frac{40°\text{C} \times (25\,\text{cm} \times 1.8 \times 10^{-5}\,\text{deg}^{-1} + 50\,\text{cm} \times 1.2 \times 10^{-5}\,\text{deg}^{-1})}{1 + (10 \times 10^{11}/20 \times 10^{11}) \times (50/25)} = 2.1 \times 10^{-2}\,\text{cm}$$

and

$$\Delta l_S = \frac{Y_B}{Y_S} \frac{l_S}{l_B} \Delta l_B = \frac{1}{2} \times \frac{50}{25} \times \Delta l_B = 2.1 \times 10^{-2}\,\text{cm}.$$

The stress in each rod is

$$Y_B \frac{\Delta l_B}{l_B} = Y_S \frac{\Delta l_S}{l_S} = 10 \times 10^{11}\,\text{dynes} \cdot \text{cm}^{-2} \times \frac{2.1 \times 10^{-2}\,\text{cm}}{25\,\text{cm}} = 0.84\,\text{dyne} \cdot \text{cm}^{-2}.$$

16

Heat and Heat Measurement

PROBLEM 16.1

The entire power from a 100-hp automobile engine is used to agitate 50 kg of water thermally insulated from its surroundings. How long will it take for the temperature of the water to rise 10 Celsius degrees?

Solution. Since 1 hp = 746 watts (W), the power available is 7.46×10^4 W. All this power is turned to heat in the agitation of the water. The rate at which heat is supplied to the water is thus $(7.46 \times 10^4/4.186)$ cal·s^{-1}. In time τ the heat supplied is thus 1.782×10^4 cal·s$^{-1} \times \tau$.

The temperature rise takes place according to the following equation, the specific heat capacity of water being assumed constant and of value 1 cal·g^{-1}·C deg^{-1} over the range of temperature considered: $Q = mc(t_2 - t_1)$, the symbols having their usual significance. Thus

$$1.782\tau \times 10^4 \text{ cal·s}^{-1} = 5 \times 10^4 \text{ g} \times 1 \text{ cal·g}^{-1}\text{·C deg}^{-1} \times 10 \text{ C deg} \qquad \text{or} \qquad \tau = \frac{50}{1.782} \text{ s} = 28 \text{ s.}$$

PROBLEM 16.2

Water flows at a rate of 2.5 m^3·s^{-1} over a waterfall of height 15 m. What is the maximum difference in temperature between the water at the top and at the bottom of the waterfall and what usable power is going to waste? The density of water is 10^3 kg·m^{-3} and its specific heat capacity is 10^3 cal·kg^{-1}·C deg^{-1}.

Solution. The water loses potential energy and gains kinetic energy in falling over the waterfall. The maximum possible temperature difference between the water at the top and at the bottom of the falls occurs if all this kinetic energy is converted to heat. The potential energy lost, mgh, is completely converted to heat in this case. The power available is the potential energy lost per second, and is given by the equation

$$P = \frac{m}{\tau} gh = \rho \frac{V}{\tau} gh = 10^3 \text{ kg·m}^{-3} \times 2.5 \text{ m}^3\text{·s}^{-1} \times 9.8 \text{ m·s}^{-2} \times 15 \text{ m} = 3.675 \times 10^5 \text{ W} = 367.5 \text{ kW.}$$

In any time interval a mass ρV loses potential energy ρVgh and rises in temperature by an amount Δt, where $\rho Vgh = \rho Vc\,\Delta t$.

$$\therefore \quad \Delta t = \frac{gh}{c} = \frac{9.8 \text{ m·s}^{-2} \times 15 \text{ m}}{4.186 \times 10^3 \text{ J·kg}^{-1}\text{·C deg}^{-1}} = 0.035\,°\text{C.}$$

PROBLEM 16.3

A skier descends a slope of 30° at a constant speed of 15 m·s^{-1}. His total mass is 80 kg. How much snow melts beneath his skis in 1 min, if the latent heat of fusion of snow is 340 J·g^{-1} and it is assumed that all the friction goes into melting snow?

79

Solution. When the skier is descending the slope, the forces acting on him are his weight mg vertically downward and the two forces exerted on him by the slope, the normal force **N** at right angles to the slope and the frictional force **F** opposing the motion. Since the skier does not rise from the snow and is traveling with constant speed, all forces perpendicular to the slope, and all forces parallel to the slope, must cancel out. Hence $N = mg \cos \theta$ and $F = mg \sin \theta$.

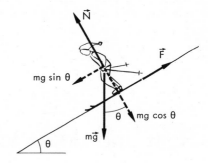

By Newton's third law, an equal and opposite force **F** is exerted by the skier on the snow. This equal and opposite force moves its point of application a distance **v** in 1 s, where **v** is the constant velocity of the skier. Hence the rate of working of the frictional force acting on the snow is

$$P = \mathbf{F \cdot v} = Fv = mg \sin \theta v = 80 \text{ kg} \times 9.8 \text{ m} \cdot \text{s}^{-2} \times \tfrac{1}{2} \times 15 \text{ m} \cdot \text{s}^{-1} = 5880 \text{ W.}$$

If all this power is used in melting snow, the energy available per min is $Q = 5880 \times 60 \text{ J} \cdot \text{min}^{-1}$. But if a mass m of snow is melted per min, the heat required is mL, where L is the latent heat of fusion of snow. Hence

$$m \times 340 \text{ J} \cdot \text{g}^{-1} = 5880 \times 60 \text{ J} \cdot \text{min}^{-1} \quad \text{or} \quad m = \frac{5880 \times 60 \text{ g} \cdot \text{min}^{-1}}{340} = 1038 \text{ g} \cdot \text{min}^{-1}$$

$$= 1.038 \text{ kg} \cdot \text{min}^{-1}.$$

PROBLEM 16.4

The temperatures of three different liquids are maintained at 15°C, 20°C, and 25°C, respectively. When equal masses of the first two liquids are mixed, the final temperature is 18°C, and when equal masses of the last two liquids are mixed, the final temperature is 24°C. What temperature will be achieved by mixing equal masses of the first and the last liquid?

Solution. Let the mass used in all cases be m, and label the specific heat capacities of the liquids c_1, c_2, and c_3, respectively. Then in the first mixing, the heat lost by the second liquid must equal the heat gained by the first. Thus

$$mc_2 \times (20 - 18)°C = mc_1 \times (18 - 15)°C \quad \text{or} \quad 2c_2 = 3c_1.$$

Similarly, for the second mixing,

$$mc_3 \times (25 - 24)°C = mc_2 \times (24 - 20)°C \quad \text{or} \quad c_3 = 4c_2.$$

It follows that $c_3 = 6c_1$.

If the third mixing produces a final temperature t, then one applies the same argument as before, to obtain $mc_3 \times (25°C - t) = mc_1 \times (t - 15°C)$.

$$\therefore \quad 6c_1(25°C - t) = c_1(t - 15°C) \quad \text{or} \quad 150°C - 6t = t - 15°C.$$

$$\therefore \quad t = \frac{165}{7}°C = 23\frac{4}{7}°C.$$

PROBLEM 16.5

Near the absolute zero of temperature, the specific heats of solids obey the Debye equation $c = kT^3$, where T is measured in °K. For a particular solid k has the value $2.85 \times 10^{-2} \text{ cal} \cdot \text{g}^{-1} \cdot \text{K deg}^{-4}$. Calculate the heat that must be supplied to raise 50 g of the solid from 10°K to 20°K and the mean specific heat capacity of the solid in this interval.

Solution. The specific heat capacity varies markedly with temperature. Over the range 10°K to 20°K its mean value will be

$$\bar{c} = \frac{1}{(20-10)°K}\int_{10°K}^{20°K} c\,dT = \frac{1}{10°K}\int_{10°K}^{20°K} kT^3\,dT = \frac{1}{10°K}\left[\frac{1}{4}kT^4\right]_{10°K}^{20°K} = \frac{1}{40°K} \times 2.85$$

$$\times\,10^{-2}\,\text{cal}\cdot\text{g}^{-1}\cdot\text{K deg}^{-4}[20^4 - 10^4]\text{K deg}^4 = 106.9\,\text{cal}\cdot\text{g}^{-1}\cdot\text{K deg}^{-1}.$$

This compares with a magnitude for c of 28.5 cal·g^{-1}·K deg^{-1} at 10°C and 228 cal·g^{-1}·K deg^{-1} at 20°C. The heat that must be supplied to raise the temperature of 50 g through the range of temperature is

$$Q = m\bar{c}(T_2 - T_1) = 50\,\text{g} \times 106.9\,\text{cal}\cdot\text{g}^{-1}\cdot\text{K deg}^{-1} \times 10\,\text{K deg} = 53,450\,\text{cal}.$$

PROBLEM 16.6

An immersion heater in an insulated vessel of negligible heat capacity brings 100 g of water to the boiling point from 16°C in 7 min. The water is replaced by 200 g of alcohol, which is heated from the same initial temperature to the boiling point of 78°C in 6 min 12 s. Then 30 g are vaporized in 5 min 6 s. Determine the specific heat and the heat of vaporization of alcohol, and the power of the heater.

Solution. In 7 min 100 g of water are raised in temperature by $(100 - 16)°C = 84°C$. The heat acquired per second is

$$Q = \frac{mc\,dt}{\tau} = \frac{100\,\text{g} \times 1\,\text{cal}\cdot\text{g}^{-1}\cdot\text{C deg}^{-1} \times 84\,\text{C deg}}{7 \times 60\,\text{s}} = 20\,\text{cal}\cdot\text{s}^{-1}.$$

The power of the heater is thus $P = 20 \times 4.186\,\text{J}\cdot\text{s}^{-1} = 83.7\,\text{W}.$

When alcohol replaces the water, 200 g rise in temperature by $(78 - 16)°C = 62°C$ in 6 min 12 s, which equals 372 s. Thus

$$20\,\text{cal}\cdot\text{s}^{-1} = Q = \frac{200\,\text{g} \times c \times 62\,\text{C deg}}{372\,\text{s}} \qquad \text{or} \qquad c = 0.6\,\text{cal}\cdot\text{g}^{-1}\cdot\text{C deg}^{-1}.$$

Further, 30 g vaporize in 5 min 6 s = 306 s thereafter. When we use the equation $Q = mL/\tau$, then $20\,\text{cal}\cdot\text{s}^{-1} = (30\,\text{g} \times L)/306\,\text{s}.$

$$\therefore \qquad L = 204\,\text{cal}\cdot\text{g}^{-1}.$$

PROBLEM 16.7

A piece of iron of mass 20 g is placed in liquid air until thermal equilibrium is achieved. When it is quickly taken out and placed in water at 0°C, a coating of ice of mass 5.22 g forms on it. The mean specific heat capacity of iron over the range of temperature of the experiment is 0.095 cal·g^{-1}·C deg^{-1} and the heat of fusion of water is 80 cal·g^{-1}. What is the temperature of the liquid air?

Solution. The heat acquired by the iron must be equal to the heat lost by the water in turning to ice if no heat is lost in the process. Hence, if t is the temperature of liquid air,

$$20\,\text{g}(0°C - t) \times 0.095\,\text{cal}\cdot\text{g}^{-1}\cdot\text{C deg}^{-1} = 5.22\,\text{g} \times 80\,\text{cal}\cdot\text{g}^{-1}.$$

$$\therefore \qquad t = \frac{-5.22 \times 80}{0.095 \times 20}°C = -220°C.$$

PROBLEM 16.8

An aluminum calorimeter of mass 50 g contains 95 g of a mixture of water and ice at 0°C. When 100 g of aluminum which has been heated in a steam jacket is dropped into the mixture, the temperature rises to 5°C. Find the mass of ice originally present if the specific heat capacity of aluminum is 0.22 cal·g^{-1}·C deg^{-1}.

Solution. The heat lost by the cooling aluminum must equal the heat gained by the calorimeter and contents. If a mass y of ice were originally present, the total heat gained would have to include the heat acquired by the ice in melting, the heat gained by the 95 g of water in rising in temperature, and the heat gained by the calorimeter in doing likewise. Thus

$$100 \text{ g} \times 0.22 \text{ cal} \cdot \text{g}^{-1} \cdot \text{C deg}^{-1} \times (100 - 5)°\text{C} = y \times 80 \text{ cal} \cdot \text{g}^{-1} + 95 \text{ g} \times 1 \text{ cal} \cdot \text{g}^{-1} \cdot \text{C deg}^{-1}$$

$$\times (5 - 0)°\text{C} + 50 \text{ g} \times 0.22 \text{ cal} \cdot \text{g}^{-1} \cdot \text{C deg}^{-1} \times (5 - 0)°\text{C}.$$

$$\therefore \quad 80 \, y \text{ cal} \cdot \text{g}^{-1} = [0.22(9500 - 250) - 95 \times 5] \text{ cal}. \quad \therefore \quad y = \frac{1560}{80} = 19.50 \text{ g}.$$

17

Transfer of Heat

PROBLEM 17.1

Determine the power required to maintain a temperature difference of 20°C between the faces of a glass window of area 2 m² and thickness 3 mm. Why does a much lower power suffice to keep a room with such a window at a temperature 20°C above the outside? The thermal conductivity of glass is 25×10^{-4} cal·s⁻¹·cm⁻¹·C deg⁻¹.

Solution. The equation appropriate to thermal conductivity is

$$\frac{Q}{\tau} = KA \frac{t_2 - t_1}{L}.$$

In this particular case

$$\frac{Q}{\tau} = 25 \times 10^{-4}\,\text{cal·s}^{-1}\text{·cm}^{-1}\text{·C deg}^{-1} \times 2 \times 10^4\,\text{cm}^2 \times \frac{20\,\text{C deg}}{0.3\,\text{cm}} = 3.33 \times 10^3\,\text{cal·s}^{-1}.$$

Thus 3.33×10^3 cal $= 13.95 \times 10^3$ J are required per second to replace the lost heat. The power required is thus 13.95 kilowatts (kW).

  A much smaller power than this is required in practice because the inner surface of the window and the air in contact with it drops in temperature because of the heat loss through the glass. Heat is conducted from the rest of the room through air, the thermal conductivity of which is very low. The inner surface of the window is thus not maintained at a temperature 20°C above the outside. A similar effect will occur on the outside of the window. The temperature difference across the window may well drop to only a few degrees, in which case only a fraction of the above power needs to be supplied, giving a much more reasonable figure for the heat that needs to be supplied per second.

PROBLEM 17.2

How long will it take to form a thickness of 4 cm of ice on the surface of a lake when the air temperature is −6°C? The thermal conductivity of ice is 4×10^{-3} cal·s⁻¹·cm⁻¹·C deg⁻¹ and its density is 0.92 g cm⁻³.

Solution. Once a layer of ice of thickness y is formed, the heat from the next thickness dy at temperature 0°C is conducted through the layer of ice to the outside air in time $d\tau$ when the water freezes. The heat lost by the freezing water is $\rho A\,dyL$, where ρ is the density of ice, L its latent heat of fusion, and A the area of ice formed. This must equal the heat transmitted through the layer of ice already formed, $KA[(t_2 - t_1)/y]d\tau$, K being the thermal conductivity of ice and t_1 and t_2 the temperature of water and air, respectively. Then

$$\rho A\,dyL = KA \frac{t_2 - t_1}{y}\,d\tau \quad \text{or} \quad d\tau = \frac{\rho L}{K(t_2 - t_1)}\,y\,dy.$$

For the whole process, we obtain the following:

$$\int_0^\tau d\tau = \frac{\rho L}{K(t_2 - t_1)} \int_0^{4\ cm} y\, dy = \frac{\rho L}{K(t_2 - t_1)} \left[\frac{1}{2} y^2\right]_0^{4\ cm}$$

or

$$\tau = \frac{\rho L \times 8\ cm^2}{K(t_2 - t_1)} = \frac{8\ cm^2 \times 0.92\ g\cdot cm^{-3} \times 80\ cal\cdot g^{-1}}{4 \times 10^{-3}\ cal\cdot s^{-1}\cdot cm^{-1}\cdot C\ deg^{-1} \times 6\ C\ deg} = 24.53 \times 10^3\ s$$

$$= 409\ min = 6\ hr\ 49\ min.$$

PROBLEM 17.3

Sheets of brass and steel, each of thickness 1 cm, are placed in contact. The outer surface of the brass is kept at 100°C and the outer surface of the steel is kept at 0°C. What is the temperature of the common interface? The thermal conductivities of brass and steel are in the ratio of 2 : 1.

Solution.   Once equilibrium conditions have been attained, the same quantity of heat must pass through all sections of the system in unit time. In other words, the heat current flowing through the system is constant; otherwise alterations in the temperature at various points would take place. This would be contrary to the condition that equilibrium had been established. Thus, in the usual notation,

$$H = K_1 A \frac{100°C - t}{L} = K_2 A \frac{t - 0°C}{L},$$

where K_1 and K_2 are the thermal conductivities of brass and steel, respectively, and t is the temperature of the common interface. Hence $K_1/K_2 = 2/1 = t/100°C - t$.

$$\therefore \quad 200°C - 2t = t \quad \text{or} \quad t = \frac{200°C}{3} = 66.7°C.$$

PROBLEM 17.4

The passenger compartment of a jet transport is essentially a cylindrical tube of diameter 3 m and length 20 m. It is lined with 3 cm of insulating material of thermal conductivity $10^{-4}\ cal\cdot cm^{-1}\cdot C$ $deg^{-1}\cdot s^{-1}$, and must be maintained at 20°C for passenger comfort, although the average outside temperature is −30°C at its operating height. What rate of heating is required in the compartment, neglecting the end effects?

Solution.   The hull of the aircraft is a good conductor of heat and may be considered to be at the outside temperature. The circular cylinder of insulating material has thus a temperature of 20°C inside and −30°C outside.

Consider a cylinder of the material at distance R from the center of the craft and of thickness dR. By the normal equation of conductivity, the flow of heat across this infinitesimal cylinder per second is

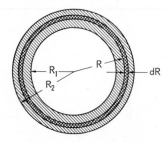

$$H = KA \frac{dt}{dR} = K 2\pi RL \frac{dt}{dR},$$

where L is the length of the cylinder. Thus

$$\frac{dR}{R} = \frac{2\pi KL}{H} dt.$$

The quantity H is a constant since the system is in equilibrium. If the same quantity of heat did not pass over every cross section of the insulating material, heat would build up somewhere and the temperature would rise. This is contrary to the condition that equilibrium shall have been attained.

For the whole cylinder of insulating material,

$$\int_{R_1}^{R_2} \frac{dR}{R} = \frac{2\pi KL}{H} \int_{t_1}^{t_2} dt. \qquad \therefore \qquad \ln \frac{R_2}{R_1} = \frac{2\pi KL}{H}(t_2 - t_1).$$

Hence

$$H = \frac{2\pi KL(t_2 - t_1)}{\ln(R_2/R_1)} = \frac{2\pi \times 10^{-4}\,\text{cal}\cdot\text{cm}^{-1}\cdot\text{C deg}^{-1}\cdot\text{s}^{-1} \times 20 \times 10^2\,\text{cm}\,[20 - (-30)]^\circ\text{C}}{\ln(300/294)}$$

$$= 3100\,\text{cal}\cdot\text{s}^{-1} = 12{,}980\,\text{J}\cdot\text{s}^{-1} = 13.0\,\text{kW}.$$

This is the heat which must be supplied to the compartment to make up for the heat flow through the walls.

PROBLEM 17.5

A hot plate of area 0.2 m² is maintained at a temperature of 59°C by a 100-W heater when the room temperature is 20°C. The appropriate convection coefficient is $0.6 \times 10^{-4}(\Delta t)^{1/4}\,\text{cal}\cdot\text{s}^{-1}\cdot\text{cm}^{-2}\cdot\text{C deg}^{-1}$. What fraction of the heat supplied is lost by natural convection?

Solution. The value of the convection coefficient h in this case is $0.6 \times 10^{-4}(\Delta t)^{1/4}$ and $\Delta t = (59 - 20)°C$. Thus

$$h = 0.6 \times 10^{-4}(39)^{1/4} = 1.5 \times 10^{-4}\,\text{cal}\cdot\text{s}^{-1}\cdot\text{cm}^{-2}\cdot\text{C deg}^{-1}.$$

The heat current due to convection is therefore

$$H = hA\,\Delta t = 1.5 \times 10^{-4}\,\text{cal}\cdot\text{s}^{-1}\cdot\text{cm}^{-2}\cdot\text{C deg}^{-1} \times 2 \times 10^3\,\text{cm}^2 \times 39\,\text{C deg} = 11.7\,\text{cal}\cdot\text{s}^{-1}$$

$$= 49\,\text{J}\cdot\text{s}^{-1} = 49\,\text{W}.$$

The fraction of the supplied heat lost by convection is thus $\frac{49}{100} = 0.49$.

PROBLEM 17.6

The solar constant, or the quantity of radiation received by the earth from the sun, is $0.14\,\text{W}\cdot\text{cm}^{-2}$. Assuming that the sun may be regarded as an ideal radiator, calculate the surface temperature of the sun. The ratio of the radius of the earth's orbit to the radius of the sun is 216.

Solution. The radiation received by the earth from the sun is $0.14\,\text{W}\cdot\text{cm}^{-2}$. The total radiation from the sun per second is thus $Q = 0.14\,\text{W}\cdot\text{cm}^{-2} \times 4\pi R^2$, where R is the radius of the earth's orbit. But by Stefan's law the quantity of radiation from the sun at surface temperature T is

$$Q = \sigma \times 4\pi r^2 \times T^4$$

where r is the radius of the sun. Thus $4\pi r^2 \sigma T^4 = 4\pi R^2 \times 0.14\,\text{W}\cdot\text{cm}^{-2}$ or

$$T^4 = \frac{0.14\,\text{W}\cdot\text{cm}^{-2}}{\sigma} \times \left(\frac{R}{r}\right)^2 = \frac{0.14\,\text{W}\cdot\text{cm}^{-2}}{5.6 \times 10^{-12}\,\text{W}\cdot\text{cm}^{-2}\cdot\text{K deg}^{-4}} \times (216)^2.$$

$$\therefore \qquad T = 5.84 \times 10^{3}\,°\text{K}.$$

PROBLEM 17.7

A wire 0.5 mm in diameter is stretched along the axis of a cylinder 5 cm in diameter and 25 cm in length. The wire is maintained at a temperature of 750°K by passing a current through it, the cylinder is kept at 250°K, and the gas in it has a thermal conductivity of $6 \times 10^{-5}\,\text{cal}\cdot\text{cm}^{-1}\cdot\text{C deg}^{-1}\cdot\text{sec}^{-1}$. Find the rates at which the heat is dissipated both by conduction through the gas and by radiation, if the wire is perfectly black.

Solution. From Problem 17.4 we know that the heat current due to conductivity through a hollow cylinder is given by

$$H = \frac{2\pi KL(t_2 - t_1)}{\ln(R_2/R_1)},$$

the symbols having their usual significance. In this case, therefore,

$$H = \frac{2\pi \times 6 \times 10^{-5}\,\text{cal}\cdot\text{cm}^{-1}\cdot\text{C deg}^{-1}\cdot\text{s}^{-1} \times 25\,\text{cm} \times (750 - 250)\,\text{C deg}}{\ln(2.5\,\text{cm}/0.025\,\text{cm})} = 1.02\,\text{cal}\cdot\text{s}^{-1}.$$

The heat lost by radiation is the net outflow according to Stefan's law. Thus, in the usual notation,

$$H' = \sigma A(T^4 - T_0^4) = \sigma \times 2\pi R_1 L \times (T^4 - T_0^4).$$

$$\therefore \quad H' = \frac{5.67 \times 10^{-12}\,\text{W}\cdot\text{cm}^{-2}\cdot\text{K deg}^{-4} \times 2\pi \times 0.025\,\text{cm} \times 25\,\text{cm}\,(750^4 - 250^4)(\text{K deg})^4}{4.186\,\text{J}\cdot\text{cal}^{-1}}$$

$$= 1.67\,\text{cal}\cdot\text{s}^{-1}.$$

PROBLEM 17.8

A cubical tank of water of volume 1 m³ is kept at a steady temperature of 65°C by a 1-kW heater. The heater is switched off. How long does the tank take to cool to 50°C if the room temperature is 15°C?

Solution. While the heater is operating, the heat supplied by it, 1 kW = 240 cal·s⁻¹, is just sufficient to make up for the heat loss that would take place according to Newton's law of cooling:

$$\frac{dt}{d\tau} = -k(t - t_s).$$

$$\therefore \quad -\frac{Q}{d\tau} = \frac{mc\,dt}{d\tau} = -mck(t - t_s).$$

Thus

$$mck = \frac{Q}{d\tau(t - t_s)} = \frac{240\,\text{cal}\cdot\text{s}^{-1}}{(65 - 15)°\text{C}} = 4.8\,\text{cal}\cdot\text{s}^{-1}\cdot\text{C deg}^{-1}.$$

But the mass of 1 m³ of water is 10^6 g and the specific heat capacity of water is 1 cal·g⁻¹·C deg⁻¹. Hence $k = 4.8 \times 10^{-6}\,\text{s}^{-1}$. When the heater is switched off, the tank cools according to the equation $dt/d\tau = -k(t - t_s)$.

$$\therefore \quad \int_{65°\text{C}}^{50°\text{C}} \frac{dt}{t - t_s} = -k\int_0^\tau d\tau.$$

$$\therefore \quad \tau = \frac{1}{k}\ln\left(\frac{65 - 15}{50 - 15}\right) = \frac{10^6}{4.8}\ln\frac{10}{7}\,\text{s} = \frac{10^6 \times 0.3567}{4.8 \times 60 \times 60}\,\text{hr} = 20.64\,\text{hr}.$$

18

Thermal Properties of Matter

PROBLEM 18.1

A cylinder containing gas at 27°C is divided into two parts of equal volume, each of 100 cm³, and at equal pressure, by a piston of cross-sectional area 15 cm². The gas in one part is raised in temperature to 100°C; the other volume is maintained at the original temperature. The piston and walls are perfect insulators. How far will the piston move during the change in temperature?

Solution. The heating of one side of the cylinder increases the pressure of the gas in that portion. If the piston were fixed, the volumes on the two sides would stay equal and there would be a pressure difference across the piston. Since the piston is movable, it alters its position until there is no pressure difference between its two sides: the hotter gas expands and thus drops in pressure, and the cooler gas is compressed and thus increases in pressure. When equilibrium has been reached, the two pressures are equal at p_0; the cooler gas now occupies a volume smaller by an amount dV and the hotter gas a volume greater by a corresponding amount dV. With the usual notation, the original situation in either half is given by the equation $pV = nRT$. After the heating, when equilibrium is achieved,

$$p_0(V - dV) = nRT \quad \text{and} \quad p_0(V + dV) = nRT'.$$

$$\therefore \quad \frac{V - dV}{V + dV} = \frac{T}{T'} \quad \text{or} \quad \frac{dV}{V} = \frac{T' - T}{T' + T}.$$

$$\therefore \quad dV = \frac{(373 - 300)°C}{(373 + 300)°C} \times 100 \text{ cm}^3 = 10.85 \text{ cm}^3.$$

The piston has an area of 15 cm². Hence it moves a distance of 10.85 cm³/15 cm² = 0.723 cm.

PROBLEM 18.2

Two bulbs of equal volume joined by a narrow tube of negligible volume contain hydrogen at 0°C and 1 atm pressure. What is the pressure of the gas when one of the bulbs is immersed in steam at 100°C and the other in liquid oxygen at −190°C?

The volume of each bulb is 10^{-3} m³ and the density of hydrogen is 0.09 kg·m⁻³ at 0°C and 1 atm. What mass of hydrogen passes along the connecting tube?

Solution. When the two bulbs are at different temperatures, one bulb contains n_1 moles at temperature T_1 occupying volume V, and the other n_2 moles at temperature T_2 also occupying volume V. Once equilibrium has been attained, both must be at the same pressure p. If the bulbs are now returned to the original common temperature T_0, the pressure throughout the system is p_0 and from the symmetry of the arrangement each bulb of volume V must contain $\frac{1}{2}(n_1 + n_2)$ moles.

87

We use the gas equation and obtain

$$pV = n_1 RT_1 = n_2 RT_2 \quad \text{and} \quad p_0 V = \frac{n_1 + n_2}{2} RT_0.$$

$$\therefore \quad \frac{p}{p_0} = \frac{2n_1 T_1}{(n_1 + n_2)T_0} = \frac{2T_1}{[1 + (n_2/n_1)]T_0} = \frac{2T_1}{[1 + (T_1/T_2)]T_0} = \frac{2 \times 83°K}{[1 + (83°K/373°K)] \times 273°K}.$$

$$\therefore \quad p = 0.497\,p_0 = 0.497 \text{ atm.}$$

Further, one bulb contained $\frac{1}{2}(n_1 + n_2)$ moles at temperature T_0 and n_1 at temperature T_1. Thus $\frac{1}{2}(n_1 - n_2)$ moles passed along the connecting tube during the temperature change. But, from the first equation, we have $n_1/n_2 = T_2/T_1 = 373°K/83°K$.

$$\therefore \quad \frac{\frac{1}{2}(n_1 - n_2)}{\frac{1}{2}(n_1 + n_2)} = \frac{373 - 83}{373 + 83} = \frac{290}{456}.$$

Thus $\frac{290}{456}$ of the mass in either bulb at 0°C passed along the tube during the temperature change. But each bulb held 10^{-3} m³ at 0°C. That is,

$$10^{-3} \text{ m}^3 \times 0.09 \text{ kg·m}^{-3} = 9 \times 10^{-5} \text{ kg.}$$

The mass passing along the tube is thus

$$\tfrac{290}{456} \times 9 \times 10^{-5} \text{ kg} = 5.72 \times 10^{-5} \text{ kg} = 0.0572 \text{ g.}$$

PROBLEM 18.3

A barometer tube extends 89.4 cm above a free mercury surface and has air in the region above the mercury column. The height of the column is 74.5 cm at 25°C when the reading on a true barometer is 76 cm. On a day when the temperature is 11°C it reads 75.2 cm. What is the true atmospheric pressure?

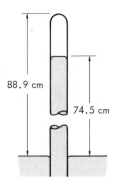

Solution. Since there is a fixed mass of air at all times in the top of the barometer tube, the gas law $(pV/T) = $ const may be applied to it directly.

In the first case when the temperature is 25°C = 298°K, the barometric height is 76 cm of mercury. This is the pressure exerted at the free surface of mercury and thus, by the laws of hydrostatic pressure, at the same horizontal level inside the barometer tube. At points in the tube higher than this, the pressure drops off with height. In particular at the top of the mercury the pressure exerted on the trapped air must be equal to that exerted by $(76 - 74.5) = 1.5$ cm of mercury. The volume of the trapped air is $(89.4 - 74.5)A$ cm³ = $14.9A$ cm³, where A cm² is the cross-sectional area of the tube.

In the second case when the temperature is 284°K, the pressure on the trapped air is $(p_0 - 75.2$ cm of mercury), where p_0 is the atmospheric pressure on that day. The volume of trapped air is $(89.4 - 75.2)A$ cm³ = $14.2A$ cm³. Hence

$$\frac{1.5 \text{ cm} \times 14.9A \text{ cm}^3}{298°C} = \frac{(p_0 - 75.2 \text{ cm})14.2A \text{ cm}^3}{284°C}.$$

$$\therefore \quad p_0 - 75.2 \text{ cm} = 1.5 \text{ cm} \quad \text{or} \quad p_0 = 76.7 \text{ cm of mercury.}$$

PROBLEM 18.4

A circular cylinder of cross-sectional area 100 ft² and height 8 ft is closed at the top and open at the bottom and is used as a diving bell. To what depth must it be lowered into water so that the air inside is compressed to $\frac{5}{6}$ of its original volume, if the atmospheric pressure at that time is 30 in. of mercury?

Air is pumped from the surface to keep the bell full of air. How many moles of air have passed through the pump when it is at the depth calculated above, if the atmospheric temperature is 10°C?

Solution. Applying Boyle's law to the first part of the problem, in the usual notation, we obtain

$$p_0 V_0 = p \times \tfrac{5}{6} V_0.$$

$$\therefore \quad p = \tfrac{6}{5} p_0. \qquad \therefore \quad \Delta p = \tfrac{1}{5} p_0.$$

$$\therefore \quad g\rho h = \tfrac{1}{5} g\rho_m h_0,$$

where ρ_m and ρ are the densities of mercury and water, respectively, and h_0 is the barometric height. Thus

$$h = \frac{1}{5} \times \frac{13.6}{1} \times \frac{30}{12} \text{ ft} = 6.80 \text{ ft}.$$

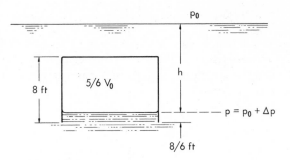

The water level in the bell is at a depth of 6.80 ft below the surface. The depth of the foot of the bell is thus 6.80 ft $+ \tfrac{8}{6}$ ft $= 8.13$ ft. The bell has thus been lowered 8.13 ft into the water.

If air filled the whole jar at this depth, the pressure on it would be that due to atmospheric pressure plus 8.13 ft of water. And 6.80 ft of water produce a pressure of $\tfrac{1}{5}$ atm. Thus 8.13 ft of water produce a pressure of

$$\frac{8.13}{6.80} \times \frac{1}{5} \text{ atm} = 0.239 \text{ atm}.$$

The pressure acting on the air in the bell is thus 1.239 atm. The number of moles in this volume of 800 ft^3 = 800 × 28.32 liters is obtained from the gas equation

$$n = \frac{pV_0}{RT} = \frac{1.239 \text{ atm} \times 800 \times 28.32 \text{ liters}}{0.0821 \text{ liter} \cdot \text{atm} \cdot \text{mole}^{-1} \cdot \text{K deg}^{-1} \times 283°\text{K}} = 1208 \text{ moles}.$$

On the surface of the water the number of moles in the diving bell is

$$n_0 = \frac{p_0 V_0}{RT} = \frac{1 \text{ atm} \times 800 \times 28.32 \text{ liters}}{0.0821 \text{ liter} \cdot \text{atm} \cdot \text{mole}^{-1} \cdot \text{K deg}^{-1} \times 283°\text{K}} = 975 \text{ moles}.$$

The number of moles that have passed through the pump is thus 233.

PROBLEM 18.5

A capillary tube of length 50 cm is closed at both ends. It contains dry air at each end separated by a mercury column 10 cm long. With the tube horizontal, the air columns are both 20 cm long, but with the tube vertical the columns are 15 cm and 25 cm long. What is the pressure in the capillary tube when it is horizontal?

Solution. When the mercury column is vertical, the pressure on the gas in the two parts is as shown in the diagram, where p_1 is the pressure at the foot of the mercury column and p_2 the pressure at the top. But the difference in pressure at two levels in a vertical column of liquid is known from the laws of hydrostatic pressure. Thus $p_2 = p_1 - \rho g h$.

Applying Boyle's law to both gases, with A the cross-sectional area of the tube, one obtains

$$p_1 A l_1 = p_0 A l_0 \qquad \text{and} \qquad p_2 A l_2 = p_0 A l_0,$$

where p_0 and l_0 refer to conditions when the tube is horizontal. Thus

$$p_1 = p_0 \frac{l_0}{l_1} \qquad \text{and} \qquad p_2 = p_0 \frac{l_0}{l_2}.$$

$$\therefore \quad p_1 - p_2 = \rho g h = p_0 l_0 \left(\frac{1}{l_1} - \frac{1}{l_2}\right). \qquad \therefore \quad p_0 = \frac{\rho g h \, l_1 l_2}{l_0(l_2 - l_1)}.$$

$$\therefore \quad \frac{p_0}{\rho g} = \frac{l_1 l_2}{l_0(l_2 - l_1)} h = \frac{15 \text{ cm} \times 25 \text{ cm}}{20 \text{ cm} (25 - 15) \text{ cm}} \times 10 \text{ cm} = 18.75 \text{ cm of mercury}.$$

PROBLEM 18.6

The dew point of a mass of air at 15°C is 10°C. Calculate the relative humidity and the mass of 1 liter of the moist air if the barometric height is 76 cm of mercury. The gram-molecular weight of air is 28.9 g and the saturated aqueous vapor pressures at 10°C and 15°C are 9.2 mm of mercury and 12.8 mm of mercury, respectively.

Solution.   The relative humidity is

$$100 \times \frac{\text{saturated vapor pressure at the dew point}}{\text{saturated vapor pressure at the given temperature}}.$$

Therefore the relative humidity is

$$\text{RH} = \frac{9.2}{12.8} \times 100\% = 71.9\%.$$

Using the gas law, one can calculate the number of moles present independently for (a) the dry air and (b) the water vapor. Measuring the pressure in atmospheres and the volume in liters gives

$$\text{(a)} \quad n = \frac{pV}{RT} = \frac{1 \text{ atm} \times 1 \text{ liter}}{0.082 \text{ liter} \cdot \text{atm} \cdot \text{mole}^{-1} \cdot \text{K deg}^{-1} \times 288\,°\text{K}} = 0.0424 \text{ mole}$$

and

$$\text{(b)} \quad n' = \frac{p'V}{RT} = \frac{(9.2/760) \text{ atm} \times 1 \text{ liter}}{0.082 \text{ liter} \cdot \text{atm} \cdot \text{mole}^{-1} \cdot \text{K deg}^{-1} \times 288\,°\text{K}} = 0.00051 \text{ mole}.$$

The mass of moist air is thus

$$M = 0.0424 \text{ mole} \times 28.9 \text{ g} \cdot \text{mole}^{-1} + 0.0051 \text{ mole} \times 18.0 \text{ g} \cdot \text{mole}^{-1}$$
$$= (1.2254 + 0.0092) \text{ g} = 1.2346 \text{ g}.$$

PROBLEM 18.7

A horizontal capillary tube closed at one end contains a column of air imprisoned by means of a small volume of water. At 7°C and a barometric pressure of 76.0 cm of mercury, the length of the air column is 15.0 cm. What is the length at 17°C if the saturation pressures of water vapor at 7°C and 17°C are 0.75 cm and 1.42 cm of mercury, respectively?

Solution.   Since the tube is horizontal and the pressure at the open end of the water column is always atmospheric, the pressure at the closed end of the water column is also always atmospheric. The pressure in the moist air is made up of the partial pressures of air and of water vapor. But the pressure of the water vapor is always the saturated vapor pressure at that temperature, since the air is always in contact with water. Hence in the two cases the pressures exerted by the air are (76.00 − 0.75) cm of mercury and (76.00 − 1.42) cm of mercury, respectively. Applying the gas law to the air alone, since the air and water vapor exert effects independent of one another,

$$\frac{pV}{T} = \frac{p'V'}{T'} \quad \text{or} \quad \frac{75.25 \text{ cm} \times 15 \text{ cm} \times A}{280\,°\text{K}} = \frac{74.58 \text{ cm} \times yA}{290\,°\text{K}},$$

where A is the cross-sectional area of the tube and y is the length of the column at the temperature of 17°C. Hence

$$y = \frac{290 \times 75.25 \times 15}{280 \times 74.58} \text{ cm} = 15.68 \text{ cm}.$$

19

The Laws of Thermodynamics

PROBLEM 19.1

A solid has a volume of 2.5 liters when the external pressure is 1 atm. The bulk modulus of the material is 2×10^{12} dynes·cm^{-2}. What is the change in volume when the body is subjected to a pressure of 16 atm? What additional energy per unit volume is now stored in the material?

Solution. The expression for the bulk modulus in the usual notation is $B = -\Delta p/(\Delta V/V_0)$. Here $\Delta p = (16 - 1) = 15$ atm $= 15 \times 1.013 \times 10^6$ dynes·cm^{-2}. Hence

$$-\Delta V = \frac{\Delta p V_0}{B} = \frac{15 \times 1.013 \times 10^6 \, \text{dynes·cm}^{-2} \times 2.5 \times 10^3 \, \text{cm}^3}{2 \times 10^{12} \, \text{dynes·cm}^{-2}} = 18.99 \times 10^{-3} \, \text{cm}^3.$$

For any small change of pressure dp, there will be a change of volume dV, and $dp = -B \, dV/V$. The work done on the system in that change and the energy stored in the material is $dW = -p \, dV = (V/B)p \, dp$. In the change mentioned in the question the total work done is

$$W = -\int_{V_1}^{V_2} p \, dV = \int_{p_1}^{p_2} \frac{V}{B} p \, dp.$$

The volume V changes in the process, and account should be taken of this in the integration. In fact the change ΔV is negligible in comparison with V_0, and V may be treated as a constant throughout. Hence

$$W = \frac{V_0}{B} \int_{p_1}^{p_2} p \, dp = \frac{1}{2} \frac{V_0}{B} (p_2^2 - p_1^2).$$

The extra energy stored per unit volume is thus

$$\frac{W}{V_0} = \frac{1}{2B}(p_2^2 - p_1^2) = \frac{1}{2} \times \frac{1}{2 \times 10^{12} \, \text{dynes·cm}^{-2}} (16^2 - 1^2) \, \text{atm}^2 \times 1.013^2 \times 10^{12} \, \text{dynes}^2 \cdot \text{cm}^{-4} \cdot \text{atm}^{-2}$$

$$= 65.4 \, \text{ergs·cm}^{-3}.$$

PROBLEM 19.2

One liter of an ideal gas under a pressure of 1 atm is expanded isothermally until its volume is doubled. It is then compressed to its original volume at constant pressure and further compressed isothermally to its original pressure. Plot the process on a p–V diagram and calculate the total work done on the gas. If 50 J of heat were removed during the constant-pressure process, what would be the total change in internal energy?

Solution. During an isothermal change, T is constant. The work done on the gas in such a change is

$$W = -\int_{V_1}^{V_2} p \, dV = -\int_{V_1}^{V_2} nRT \frac{dV}{V} = nRT \ln\left(\frac{V_2}{V_1}\right) = -p_1 V_1 \ln\left(\frac{V_2}{V_1}\right) = -p_1 V_1 \ln\left(\frac{p_1}{p_2}\right).$$

Thus the work done on the gas in the first change is

$$W_1 = -1.013 \times 10^6 \text{ dynes·cm}^{-2} \times 10^3 \text{ cm}^3 \times \ln 2$$

$$= -7.022 \times 10^8 \text{ ergs} = -70.22 \text{ J}.$$

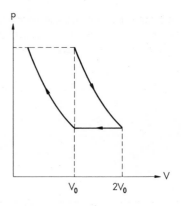

Further, since the volume is doubled, by the application of Boyle's law we find that the pressure is halved.

The work done on the gas in the second change is

$$W_2 = \frac{p}{2}(2V - V) = \frac{1.013 \times 10^6 \text{ dynes·cm}^{-2} \times 10^3 \text{ cm}^3}{2 \times 10^7 \text{ ergs·J}^{-1}} = 50.65 \text{ J}.$$

The work done on the gas in the final change is

$$W_3 = -\frac{1.013 \times 10^6 \text{ dynes·cm}^{-2} \times 10^3 \text{ cm}^3 \times \ln\left(\frac{1}{2}\right)}{2 \times 10^7 \text{ ergs·J}^{-1}} = 35.11 \text{ J}.$$

The total work done on the gas is thus $W_1 + W_2 + W_3 = (85.76 - 70.22) \text{ J} = 15.54 \text{ J}.$

In the first and third processes the temperature does not change. In an ideal gas the internal energy depends only on the temperature, so that no change of internal energy takes place in the first and third processes. Any work done on the gas in these changes is equal to the heat transfer taking place.

The second process is isobaric. The change in internal energy during the process is given by the first law of thermodynamics as $\Delta U = Q - W$, where Q is the heat energy added to the system and W the work done by the system. Hence $\Delta U = -50 \text{ J} - (-50.65 \text{ J}) = +0.65 \text{ J}$. The internal energy thus increases by 0.65 J during the three processes.

PROBLEM 19.3

The density of air at STP is $0.00129 \text{ g·cm}^{-3}$, the specific heat capacity at constant pressure is $0.238 \text{ cal·g}^{-1} \cdot \text{K deg}^{-1}$, and the ratio of the principal specific heats is 1.40. What is the mechanical equivalent of heat?

Solution. The equation of state of an ideal gas may be written in the form $p/\rho = RT/M$, where M is the molecular weight. Thus

$$\frac{R}{M} = \frac{p}{\rho T} = \frac{1.013 \times 10^6 \text{ dynes·cm}^{-2}}{0.00129 \text{ g·cm}^{-3} \times 237° \text{ K}} = \frac{1.013 \times 10^9}{1.29 \times 273} \text{ ergs·g}^{-1} \cdot \text{K deg}^{-1}.$$

Also $C_p - C_v = R$, where C_p and C_v are the appropriate molar heat capacities. Thus $c_p - c_v = R/M$, where c_p and c_v are the corresponding specific heat capacities per unit mass. Further, $c_p/c_v = \gamma$.

$$\therefore \quad \frac{R}{M} = (c_p - c_v) = c_p\left(1 - \frac{1}{\gamma}\right) = 0.238 \text{ cal·g}^{-1} \cdot \text{K deg}^{-1} \times \left(1 - \frac{1}{1.40}\right)$$

$$= \frac{0.238 \times 0.40}{1.40} \text{ cal·g}^{-1} \cdot \text{K deg}^{-1}.$$

The value of R/M is thus given in two systems of units, one mechanical and the other thermal. The mechanical equivalent of heat is thus obtained by dividing one by the other. Hence

$$J = \frac{1.013 \times 10^9}{1.29 \times 273} \text{ ergs·g}^{-1} \cdot \text{K deg}^{-1} \times \frac{1.40}{0.238 \times 0.40 \text{ cal·g}^{-1} \cdot \text{K deg}^{-1}} = 4.23 \times 10^7 \text{ ergs·cal}^{-1}.$$

PROBLEM 19.4

A small boy pumps up his bicycle tires on a day when the temperature is 300°K. Find the maximum temperature of the air in the bicycle pump if the tire pressures are to be 24.5 lb·in^{-2} and the air in the pump is assumed to be compressed adiabatically. For air, $\gamma = 1.40$.

Solution. In the final stages of the pumping, air at 300°K and atmosphere pressure $= 14.7 \text{ lb} \cdot \text{in}^{-2}$ is drawn into the bicycle pump and compressed adiabatically to a pressure of 24.5 lb·in^{-2} and an unknown temperature T_2. But, since the process is adiabatic, $T_1 p_1^{(1-\gamma)/\gamma} = T_2 p_2^{(1-\gamma)/\gamma}$.

$$\therefore \quad \log\left(\frac{T_2}{T_1}\right) = \frac{1-\gamma}{\gamma} \log\left(\frac{p_1}{p_2}\right) = -\frac{0.40}{1.40} \log\left(\frac{14.7}{24.5}\right) = 0.0634.$$

$$\therefore \quad \frac{T_2}{T_1} = 1.157. \qquad \therefore \quad T_2 = 1.157 \times 300°K = 347.1°K = 74.1°C.$$

PROBLEM 19.5

In a Wilson cloud chamber at a temperature of 20°C, particle tracks are made visible by causing condensation on ions by an approximately reversible adiabatic expansion of the volume in the ratio 1.375 to 1. The ratio of the specific heats of the gas is 1.41. Estimate the gas temperature after the expansion.

Solution. Since the expansion is adiabatic, $T_1 V_1^{\gamma-1} = T_2 V_2^{\gamma-1}$.

$$\therefore \quad \log\left(\frac{T_2}{T_1}\right) = (\gamma - 1)\log\left(\frac{V_1}{V_2}\right) = 0.41 \log\left(\frac{1}{1.375}\right) = -0.0567 = \bar{1}.9433.$$

$$\therefore \quad T_2 = 0.878\, T_1 = 0.878 \times 293°K = 257.2°K = -15.8°C.$$

PROBLEM 19.6

A cylinder contains an ideal gas at a pressure of 2 atm, the volume being 5 liters at a temperature of 250°K. The gas is heated at constant volume to a pressure of 4 atm, and then at constant pressure to a temperature of 650°K. Calculate the total heat input during these processes. For the gas C_v is 21.0 J·mole^{-1}·K deg^{-1}.

The gas is then cooled at constant volume to its original pressure and then at constant pressure to its original volume. Find the total heat output during these processes and the total work done by the gas in the whole cyclic process.

Solution. The gas equation allows the calculation of the number of moles originally present. For

$$n = \frac{pV}{RT} = \frac{2 \text{ atm} \times 5 \text{ liters}}{0.0821 \text{ liter} \cdot \text{atm} \cdot \text{mole}^{-1} \cdot \text{K deg}^{-1} \times 250°K} = 0.487 \text{ mole.}$$

Also

$$C_p = C_v + R = (21.0 + 8.317) \text{ J} \cdot \text{mole}^{-1} \cdot \text{K deg}^{-1}$$
$$= 29.317 \text{ J} \cdot \text{mole}^{-1} \cdot \text{K deg}^{-1}.$$

In the first change p/T is constant and thus, since p doubles, T doubles also to 500°K. The heat input is therefore

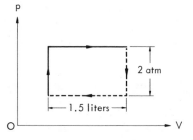

$$H_1 = nC_v(T_2 - T_1)$$
$$= 0.487 \text{ mole} \times 21.0 \text{ J} \cdot \text{mole}^{-1} \cdot \text{K deg}^{-1} \times (500 - 250)°K$$
$$= 2558 \text{ J.}$$

In the second change V/T is constant and, since T increases in the ratio 650/500, then V becomes 6.5 liters. The heat input is therefore

$$H_2 = nC_p(T_3 - T_2) = 0.487 \text{ mole} \times 29.317 \text{ J} \cdot \text{mole}^{-1} \cdot \text{K deg}^{-1} \times (650 - 500)°K = 2143 \text{ J.}$$

The total heat input during these two processes is thus $H = H_1 + H_2 = 4701$ J.

During the first cooling process p is halved, and thus T halves to 325°K. The heat output is

$$H_1' = nC_v(T_3 - T_4) = 0.487 \text{ mole} \times 21.0 \text{ J} \cdot \text{mole}^{-1} \cdot \text{K deg}^{-1} \times (650 - 325)°K = 3325 \text{ J.}$$

In the second cooling process V is reduced in the ratio 5/6.5, and thus T becomes 250°K, the original temperature, as expected. The heat output is therefore

$$H_2' = nC_p(T_4 - T_1) = 0.487 \text{ mole} \times 29.317 \text{ J}\cdot\text{mole}^{-1}\cdot\text{K deg}^{-1} \times (325 - 250)°\text{K} = 1072 \text{ J}.$$

The total heat output during the cooling processes is thus

$$H' = H_1' + H_2' = 4397 \text{ J}.$$

The difference between heat input and heat output is 304 J. This must appear as work done by the gas, since the internal energy of the gas must be the same at the beginning and at the end of a cyclic process. The figure of 304 J should therefore agree with the value of the area inside the cyclic curve, which represents the work done by the gas. This is a rectangle of height 2 atm and length 1.5 liters. The area under the curve is thus

$$W = 2 \times 1.013 \times 10^6 \text{ dynes}\cdot\text{cm}^{-2} \times 1.5 \times 10^3 \text{ cm}^3 = 3.04 \times 10^9 \text{ ergs} = 304 \text{ J},$$

which agrees with the net heat input.

PROBLEM 19.7

A house near a lake is kept warm by a heat engine. In winter, water from beneath the ice covering the lake is pumped through the heat engine. Heat is extracted until the water is on the point of freezing when it is ejected. The outside air is used as a sink. Assume that the air temperature is −15°C and the temperature of the water from the lake is 2°C. Calculate the rate at which water must be pumped to the engine.

The efficiency of the engine is one-fifth that of a Carnot engine and the house requires 10 kW.

Solution. The efficiency of a Carnot engine is $[1 - (T_1/T_2)]$ in the usual notation. Thus for the practical heat engine of the problem,

$$\frac{Q_2 - Q_1}{Q_2} = \frac{1}{5}\left(\frac{T_2 - T_1}{T_2}\right).$$

Heat is taken from the lake water as it cools from 2°C to 0°C before ejection. The mean temperature of the hot-temperature source is thus 274°K. If m is the mass of water flowing through in time t, the heat taken in at the hot reservoir in unit time is $Q_2/t = (m/t)c \times 2°\text{C}$, where c is the specific heat capacity of water.

Heat is rejected to the air as sink at a temperature of −15°C = 258°K, the amount of air available being assumed infinite so that the temperature remains constant. Further, the work done $(Q_2 - Q_1)$ is given as 10 kW = 10^4 J·s^{-1}. Thus, from the first equation, we have

$$\frac{10^4 \text{ J}\cdot\text{s}^{-1}}{(m/t) \times 4.18 \text{ J}\cdot\text{g}^{-1}\cdot\text{C deg}^{-1} \times 2 \text{ C deg}} = \frac{1}{5}\frac{(274 - 258)°\text{K}}{274°\text{K}}.$$

$$\therefore \quad \frac{m}{t} = \frac{5 \times 274 \times 10^4}{2 \times 4.18 \times 16} \text{ g}\cdot\text{s}^{-1} = 102.4 \times 10^3 \text{ g}\cdot\text{s}^{-1}.$$

The rate of water flow necessary is thus 102.4 liters·s^{-1}.

PROBLEM 19.8

A refrigerator which has a coefficient of performance one-third that of a Carnot refrigerator is operated between two reservoirs at temperatures of 200°K and 350°K. It absorbs 500 J from the low-temperature reservoir. How much heat is rejected at the high-temperature reservoir?

Solution. The coefficient of performance of a Carnot refrigerator is

$$E_c = \frac{Q_1}{Q_2 - Q_1} = \frac{T_1}{T_2 - T_1},$$

where Q_1 is the heat absorbed at temperature T_1 and Q_2 is the heat rejected at temperature T_2. The actual refrigerator has thus a coefficient of performance

$$\frac{Q_1}{Q_2 - Q_1} = \frac{1}{3}\frac{T_1}{T_2 - T_1} \qquad \text{or} \qquad \frac{Q_2 - 500 \text{ J}}{500 \text{ J}} = \frac{3(350 - 250)°\text{K}}{250°\text{K}}.$$

$$\therefore \qquad Q_2 = 1100 \text{ J}.$$

PROBLEM 19.9

When 100 g of water at 0°C are mixed with 50 g of water at 50°C, what is the change of entropy on mixing?

Solution. The 100 g of water at 0°C are arbitrarily said to have zero entropy. The 50 g of water at 50°C have a greater entropy than the same quantity of water at 0°C by an amount

$$S_2 - S_1 = \int_{273°\text{K}}^{323°\text{K}} \frac{dQ}{T} = \int_{273°\text{K}}^{323°\text{K}} m_2 c\frac{dT}{T} = m_2 c \ln\left(\frac{323}{273}\right) = 50 \text{ g} \times 1 \text{ cal·g}^{-1}\text{·K deg}^{-1} \times 2.303 \times 0.0730$$

$$= 8.4 \text{ cal·K deg}^{-1}.$$

Since $S_1 = 0$, it follows that $S_2 = 8.4$ cal·K deg^{-1}.

When the water is mixed, the heat gained by the cold water is equal to the heat lost by the hot water. Therefore $m_1 c(t_3 - t_1) = m_2 c(t_2 - t_3)$.

$$\therefore \qquad 100 \text{ g} \times (t_3 - 0°\text{C}) = 50 \text{ g} \times (50°\text{C} - t_3). \qquad \therefore \qquad t_3 = \frac{2500°\text{C}}{150} = 16.67°\text{C}.$$

The entropy of the final mixture is

$$S_3 = \int_{273°\text{K}}^{289.67°\text{K}} \frac{dQ}{T} = \int_{273°\text{K}}^{289.67°\text{K}} (m_1 + m_2)c\frac{dT}{T} = (m_1 + m_2)c \ln\left(\frac{289.67}{273}\right)$$

$$= 150 \text{ g} \times 1 \text{ cal·g}^{-1}\text{·K deg}^{-1} \times 2.303 \times 0.0257 = 8.9 \text{ cal·K deg}^{-1}.$$

The increase in entropy is thus 0.5 cal·K deg^{-1}.

20

Molecular Properties of Matter

PROBLEM 20.1

Find the minimum radius for a planet of mean density $5500 \text{ kg} \cdot \text{m}^{-3}$ and temperature $400°C$ which has retained oxygen in its atmosphere.

Solution. We found in Problem 4.11 that the escape velocity from a planet was given by the relation

$$V = \sqrt{2gr} = \sqrt{\frac{2GM}{r}} = \sqrt{2}\sqrt{\frac{G \times \frac{4}{3}\pi r^3 \rho}{r}} = \sqrt{\frac{8}{3}G\pi\rho r^2},$$

where the symbols have their usual significance.

If most oxygen molecules have velocities greater than this, then, when they are traveling upward near the top of the atmosphere, they will escape into space and never return. A slow loss of oxygen from the atmosphere will therefore take place. In this case, however, we are told that the planet has retained its oxygen and we can assume that escape velocity from the planet is greater than the rms velocity of the oxygen molecules. When the two are equated, the minimum radius for the planet results. Thus $\sqrt{\frac{8}{3}G\pi\rho r_{min}^2} = \sqrt{3RT/M'}$ or

$$r_{min} = \sqrt{\frac{9RT}{8G\pi\rho M'}} = \sqrt{\frac{9 \times 8.315 \text{ J} \cdot \text{mole}^{-1} \cdot \text{K deg}^{-1} \times 673 \text{ K deg}}{8 \times 6.67 \times 10^{-11} \text{ N} \cdot \text{m}^2 \cdot \text{kg}^{-2} \times \pi \times 5500 \text{ kg} \cdot \text{m}^{-3} \times 32 \times 10^{-3} \text{ kg} \cdot \text{mole}^{-1}}}.$$

$$\therefore \quad r_{min} = \sqrt{1.708 \times 10^{11} \text{ m}^2} = 4.131 \times 10^5 \text{ m} = 413.1 \text{ km}.$$

Fortunately the earth is well over the minimum size for retaining the oxygen in its atmosphere.

PROBLEM 20.2

To what volume must a liter of oxygen be expanded if the mean free path of the molecules is to become 2 m? The molecules of oxygen have a diameter of 3 Å. Assume that the gas starts at STP.

Solution. The mean free path is given by the expression $L = 0.707/n\sigma$, where n is the number of molecules per unit volume and σ the collision cross section of a molecule. If L is 200 cm, then

$$n = \frac{0.707}{L\sigma} = \frac{0.707}{200 \text{ cm} \times \pi(3 \times 10^{-8})^2 \text{ cm}^2}.$$

The gas equation is $pV = n_0RT$, where n_0 is the number of moles present in the volume V. But $n_0/V = n/N_0$, where N_0 is Avogadro's number.

$$\therefore \quad p = \frac{n}{N_0}RT = \frac{0.707 \times 8.3 \times 10^7 \text{ dynes} \cdot \text{cm} \cdot \text{mole}^{-1} \cdot \text{K deg}^{-1} \times 273 \text{ K deg}}{200 \text{ cm} \times \pi(3 \times 10^{-8})^2 \text{ cm}^2 \times 6.02 \times 10^{23} \text{ mole}^{-1}} = 0.047 \text{ dyne} \cdot \text{cm}^{-2}.$$

But since the temperature remains unchanged, the expansion takes place according to Boyle's law.

Thus 1 liter changes to a volume V', while the pressure changes from 1 atm to 0.047 dyne·cm^{-2}, and

$$1.013 \times 10^6 \text{ dynes·cm}^{-2} \times 10^3 \text{ cm}^3 = 0.047 \text{ dyne·cm}^{-2} \times V'.$$

$$\therefore \quad V' = \frac{1.013 \times 10^9}{0.047} \text{ cm}^3 = 2.155 \times 10^{10} \text{ cm}^3.$$

PROBLEM 20.3

What is the diameter of a helium molecule, given that the viscosity of helium at 0°C is 1.88×10^{-4} P?

Solution. The formula for the viscosity in the usual notation is $\eta = 0.236(m\bar{v}/\sigma)$. But $\bar{v} = \sqrt{3kT/m}$.

$$\therefore \quad \eta = \frac{0.236}{\sigma} \sqrt{3kmT} = \frac{0.236}{\sigma} \sqrt{\frac{3kTM}{N_0}},$$

where M is the molecular weight of helium and N_0 is Avogadro's number. If d is the diameter of a helium molecule, then

$$d^2 = \frac{0.236}{\pi\eta} \sqrt{\frac{3kTM}{N_0}}$$

$$= \frac{0.236}{\pi \times 1.88 \times 10^{-4} \text{ P}} \sqrt{\frac{3 \times 1.38 \times 10^{-16} \text{ erg·K deg}^{-1} \times 273 \text{ K deg} \times 4 \text{ g·mole}^{-1}}{6.02 \times 10^{23} \text{ mole}^{-1}}}$$

$$= 3.46 \times 10^{-16} \text{ cm}^2.$$

$$\therefore \quad d = 1.86 \times 10^{-8} \text{ cm} = 1.86 \text{ Å}.$$

PROBLEM 20.4

The constant b in van der Waals' equation for helium is 23.4 cm^3·mole^{-1}. Obtain an estimate of the diameter of a helium molecule and compare it with the answer given in the previous example.

Solution. The equation linking the constant b in van der Waals' equation to the molecular diameter is $b = \frac{2}{3}N_0\pi d^3$.

$$\therefore \quad d^3 = \frac{3b}{2\pi N_0} = \frac{3 \times 23.4 \text{ cm}^3 \cdot \text{mole}^{-1}}{2\pi \times 6.02 \times 10^{23} \text{ mole}^{-1}} \quad \text{or} \quad d = \sqrt[3]{\frac{3 \times 23.4}{2\pi \times 6.02 \times 10^{23}}} \text{ cm} = 2.65 \text{ Å}.$$

This differs from the result obtained in the preceding problem. It should be clear that the equations from which these answers were obtained are only first approximations to the situations existing. It is therefore not surprising that the answers differ quite markedly.

21

Traveling Waves

PROBLEM 21.1

The sound of a factory whistle reaches a particular worker 7 s after it starts to blow. Calculate the frequency of the factory whistle. The distance between worker and factory is 49,000 wavelengths of the emitted sound.

Solution. Since the distance from whistle to worker is 49,000 wavelengths, and it takes the sound 7 s to cover the distance, in 1 s the sound travels 7000 wavelengths. This means that the whistle must emit 7000 cycles in one second, in order that the wave train shall be continuous. Hence the frequency of the whistle is 7000 cycles·s^{-1}.

PROBLEM 21.2

A sonar device emits waves of frequency 40,000 cycles·s^{-1}. The velocities of the wave in air and water are 1100 ft·s^{-1} and 4200 ft·s^{-1}, respectively. What are the frequency of the wave in air and the wavelengths in air and water?

Suppose that the device is fixed to the bottom of a ship. It emits a signal and the echo from the ocean bed returns 0.8 s later. What is the depth of the ocean at that point?

Solution. The frequency of the waves emitted is the same in air or water. The surrounding medium has no influence on the vibration mechanism. Since $\lambda = c/f$, (a) in air

$$\lambda = \frac{1100 \text{ ft·s}^{-1}}{4 \times 10^4 \text{ s}^{-1}} = 2.75 \times 10^{-2} \text{ ft}$$

and (b) in water

$$\lambda' = \frac{4200 \text{ ft·s}^{-1}}{4 \times 10^4 \text{ s}^{-1}} = 10.50 \times 10^{-2} \text{ ft.}$$

Since the velocity of sound in water is 4200 ft·s^{-1} and the echo returns in 0.8 s after traversing $2d$, where d is the ocean depth at that point, we have $s = ct$ or $2d = 4200$ ft·s$^{-1} \times 0.8$ s.

$$\therefore \quad d = 1680 \text{ ft.}$$

PROBLEM 21.3

To what tension must a brass wire of cross-sectional area 10^{-2} cm^2 be subjected so that the speed of longitudinal and transverse waves along it may be the same? Young's modulus for brass is 9.1×10^{11} dynes·cm^{-2}. Is this situation physically realizable?

Solution. The speed of transverse waves in the wire is $\sqrt{S/\mu}$ and of longitudinal waves $\sqrt{Y/\rho}$ in the usual notation. In this problem $\sqrt{S/\mu} = \sqrt{Y/\rho}$.

$$\therefore \quad S = \frac{\mu}{\rho}\, Y = \frac{\text{mass per unit length}}{\text{mass per unit volume}}\, Y = AY,$$

where A is the cross-sectional area of the wire. Therefore

$$S = 10^{-2}\,\text{cm}^2 \times 9.1 \times 10^{11}\,\text{dynes}\cdot\text{cm}^{-2} = 9.1 \times 10^{9}\,\text{dynes}.$$

Since the formula for Young's modulus is $Y = (S/A)/(\Delta l/l)$, then $S = AY$ implies $\Delta l/l = 1$. The elastic limit would have been passed long before this point. The situation is therefore physically unrealizable and longitudinal waves will always travel faster than transverse ones in the wire.

PROBLEM 21.4

Considering air to be an ideal gas to a first approximation, calculate the ratio of the specific heats of air, given that at sea level and STP the velocity of sound in air is 334 m·s^{-1}, and that the molecular weight of air is 28.8 g·mole^{-1}.

Solution. Using the relation for the speed in terms of the temperature in the usual notation,

$$c = \sqrt{\frac{\gamma RT}{M}}, \qquad \gamma = \frac{Mc^2}{RT} = \frac{28.8\ \text{g}\cdot\text{mole}^{-1} \times 33{,}400^2\ \text{cm}^2\cdot\text{s}^{-2}}{8.31 \times 10^7\ \text{ergs}\cdot\text{mole}^{-1}\cdot\text{K deg}^{-1} \times 273\ \text{K deg}} = 1.415.$$

22

Vibrating Bodies

PROBLEM 22.1

One end of a horizontal wire is fixed and the other passes over a smooth pulley and has a heavy body attached to it. The frequency of the fundamental note emitted when the wire is plucked is 392 cycles·s⁻¹. When the body is totally immersed in water the frequency drops to 343 cycles·s⁻¹. Calculate the density of the body.

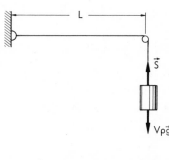

Solution. Let the density of the body be ρ and its volume be V. The density of water is $1 \text{ g·cm}^{-3} = \rho_0$. In the first case, the weight of the body is balanced by the tension S in the wire. In the second case a third force, the upthrust, enters into the calculation. The weight of the body is balanced partly by the new tension in the wire, S_0, and partly by the upthrust, U, acting on it according to Archimedes' principle. Thus

$$S = V\rho g \quad \text{and} \quad S_0 + U = S_0 + V\rho_0 g = V\rho g,$$

the upthrust due to the air in the first case being ignored.

The frequencies of the fundamental notes emitted in the two cases are

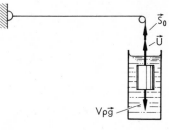

$$f_1 = \frac{1}{2L}\sqrt{\frac{S}{\mu}} \quad \text{and} \quad f_0 = \frac{1}{2L}\sqrt{\frac{S_0}{\mu}},$$

where μ is the mass of the wire per unit length. Thus

$$\frac{f_0^2}{f_1^2} = \frac{S_0}{S} = \frac{V\rho g - V\rho_0 g}{V\rho g} = \frac{\rho - \rho_0}{\rho}.$$

$$\therefore \quad \rho = \frac{f_1^2 \rho_0}{f_1^2 - f_0^2} = \frac{392^2 \text{ s}^{-2} \times 1 \text{ g·cm}^{-3}}{(392^2 - 343^2) \text{ s}^{-2}} = 4.27 \text{ g·cm}^{-3}.$$

PROBLEM 22.2

When a Kundt's tube contains air, the distance between several nodes is 25 cm. When the air is pumped out and replaced by a gas, the distance between the same number of nodes is 35 cm. The velocity of sound in air is 340 m·s⁻¹. What is the velocity of sound in the gas?

Solution. Let the number of nodes involved be $2n + 1$. There are $2n$ intervals between these $2n + 1$ nodes, and the total distance thus corresponds to $2n$ half-wavelengths.

The frequency of the emitted sound is the same in both cases. Thus $c_A = f\lambda_A$ and $c_G = f\lambda_G$.

$$\therefore \quad \frac{c_G}{c_A} = \frac{\lambda_G}{\lambda_A} = \frac{(35/n)\text{ cm}}{(25/n)\text{ cm}} = \frac{7}{5}. \quad \therefore \quad c_G = \frac{7}{5} \times 340 \text{ m·s}^{-1} = 476 \text{ m·s}^{-1}.$$

PROBLEM 22.3

A vibrating tuning fork of frequency 384 cycles·s⁻¹ is held over the end of a vertical glass tube, the other end of which dips into water. Resonance occurs when the top of the tube is 21.9 cm and also 66.4 cm above the water surface. Calculate the speed of sound in air and the end correction of the tube.

Assuming that the temperature is 13°C, what is the velocity of sound at 0°C?

Solution. An antinode never occurs quite at the end of an open pipe. Its position is just beyond the end of the pipe, the maximum displacement slightly overshooting the end. Thus for the first resonance the length of the tube will be almost a quarter of a wavelength, and $\lambda/4 = L + E$, where L is the length of the air column and E is the end correction. Similarly, for the second resonance, $3\lambda/4 = L' + E$, where L' is the length of the air column when the second resonance occurs. Thus

$$\frac{\lambda}{2} = L' - L = (66.4 - 21.9)\ \text{cm} = 44.5\ \text{cm} \qquad \text{or} \qquad \lambda = 89\ \text{cm}.$$

Therefore the velocity of sound is

$$c = f\lambda = 384\ \text{s}^{-1} \times 89\ \text{cm} = 34176\ \text{cm·s}^{-1} = 341.8\ \text{m·s}^{-1}.$$

Further, $E = \lambda/4 - L = (22.25 - 21.9)\ \text{cm} = 0.35\ \text{cm}.$

The velocity of sound in a gas is proportional to the square root of the absolute temperature. Hence $c_0/c = \sqrt{T_0/T} = \sqrt{273°\text{K}/286°\text{K}} = 0.977.$

$$\therefore \qquad c_0 = 0.977 \times 341.8\ \text{m·s}^{-1} = 333.9\ \text{m·s}^{-1}.$$

PROBLEM 22.4

A brass rod of density 8.5 g·cm⁻³ and length 100 cm is clamped at the center. When set into longitudinal vibration it emits a note two octaves above the fundamental note emitted by a wire also of 100-cm length weighing 0.295 g and under a tension of 20 kg weight which is vibrating transversely. What is Young's modulus for brass?

Solution. The rod vibrates with its center clamped. Its fundamental frequency of vibration is thus such that the center of the rod is a node and each of the ends an antinode. The length of the rod is half a wavelength. Thus $\lambda = 2L$. Further, the speed of sound in the rod is $c = \sqrt{Y/\rho}$, where Y is Young's modulus for brass and ρ its density. Hence the frequency of vibration is

$$f = \frac{c}{\lambda} = \frac{1}{2L}\sqrt{\frac{Y}{\rho}}.$$

For the vibrating wire the length is the same and, in the usual notation, the frequency of the fundamental vibration is

$$f_1 = \frac{1}{2L}\sqrt{\frac{S}{\mu}} = \frac{1}{2L}\sqrt{\frac{SL}{m}},$$

where m is the mass of the wire. But $f = 4f_1$, since one frequency is two octaves above the other. Hence

$$\frac{1}{2L}\sqrt{\frac{Y}{\rho}} = \frac{4}{2L}\sqrt{\frac{SL}{m}}$$

or

$$Y = \frac{16\rho SL}{m} = \frac{16 \times 8.5\ \text{g·cm}^{-3} \times 2 \times 10^4\ \text{kg} \times 981\ \text{cm·s}^{-2} \times 100\ \text{cm}}{0.295\ \text{g}} = 9.04 \times 10^{11}\ \text{dynes·cm}^{-2}.$$

23

Acoustical Phenomena

PROBLEM 23.1

In an attempt to break down a prisoner, the interrogators from the secret police beam intermittent pulses of sound into his cell at an intensity level of 130 db. What is the pressure amplitude of the sound during these pulses? The density of air is 1.23×10^{-3} g·cm^{-3} and the velocity of sound in air is 340 m·s^{-1}.

Solution. The intensity level is given by the expression $\beta = 10 \log (I/I_0)$, where I_0 is the zero intensity level of 10^{-16} W·cm^{-2}. Here $\log (I/I_0) = 13$.

$$\therefore \quad I = 10^{13} I_0 = 10^{-3} \text{ W·cm}^{-2} = 10^4 \text{ ergs·s}^{-1} \cdot \text{cm}^{-2}.$$

But $I = P^2/2\rho c$ in the usual notation. Thus

$$P = \sqrt{2I\rho c} = \sqrt{2 \times 10^4 \text{ ergs·s}^{-1} \cdot \text{cm}^{-2} \times 1.23 \times 10^{-3} \text{ g·cm}^{-3} \times 3.4 \times 10^4 \text{ cm·s}^{-1}}$$
$$= 915 \text{ dynes·cm}^{-2}.$$

The pressure amplitude is well above the threshold of pain.

PROBLEM 23.2

Two identical wires are stretched by the same tension of 100 N, and each emits a note of frequency 200 cycles·s^{-1}. The tension in one wire is increased by 1 N. Calculate the number of beats heard per second when the wires are plucked.

Solution. The fundamental frequency of transverse vibration of a stretched wire is $f_1 = (1/2L)\sqrt{S_1/\mu}$. When the tension in one wire is increased to S, the frequency changes to $f = (1/2L)\sqrt{S/\mu}$.

$$\therefore \quad \frac{f}{f_1} = \sqrt{\frac{S}{S_1}} = \sqrt{\frac{101 \text{ N}}{100 \text{ N}}} = 1.005. \quad \therefore \quad f = 1.005 \times 200 \text{ s}^{-1} = 201 \text{ cycles·s}^{-1}.$$

The number of beats heard per second is $f - f_1 = 1$.

PROBLEM 23.3

Our friend, the observant physics student, notices that the frequency of a note emitted by an automobile horn appears to drop from 284 cycles·s^{-1} to 266 cycles·s^{-1} as the automobile passes him. From this observation he is able to calculate the speed of the car, knowing that the speed of sound in air is 1100 ft·s^{-1}. What value does he obtain for the speed?

Solution. When there is no movement of the surrounding medium the relation between the frequency as heard by a moving observer and that emitted by a moving source is, in the usual notation,

$$\frac{f_L}{u + v_L} = \frac{f_s}{u + v_s}.$$

In this case the frequencies heard by the stationary listener will be $f_L = uf_s/(u \pm v_s)$, the plus or minus sign depending on whether the source is moving away from or toward the observer. Thus

$$284 \text{ s}^{-1} = \frac{uf_s}{u - v_s} \quad \text{and} \quad 266 \text{ s}^{-1} = \frac{uf_s}{u + v_s}.$$

$$\therefore \quad \frac{u + v_s}{u - v_s} = \frac{284}{266} \quad \text{or} \quad \frac{v_s}{u} = \frac{18}{550}.$$

$$\therefore \quad v_s = \frac{18}{550} \times 1100 \text{ ft} \cdot \text{s}^{-1} = 36 \text{ ft} \cdot \text{s}^{-1} = 24.5 \text{ mph}.$$

PROBLEM 23.4

Two trains moving along parallel tracks in opposite directions converge on a stationary observer, each sounding its whistle of frequency 350 cycles·s^{-1}. One train is traveling at 50 mph. What must be the speed of the other if the observer hears 5 beats per second? The speed of sound in air is 750 mph.

Solution. When a source is moving toward a stationary observer, the latter hears a frequency for the emitted note which is related to the frequency of the source by the expression $f = uf_s/(u - v_s)$. If one of the trains is moving toward the observer with speed v_1 and the other with speed v_2, then

$$f_1 = \frac{uf_s}{u - v_1} \quad \text{and} \quad f_2 = \frac{uf_s}{u - v_2} = \frac{750 \text{ mph} \times 350 \text{ s}^{-1}}{(750 - 50) \text{ mph}} = 375 \text{ cycles} \cdot \text{s}^{-1}.$$

But the observer hears 5 beats per second, so that f_1 is either 5 cycles·s^{-1} above or 5 cycles·s^{-1} below f_2. Hence $f_1 = 370$ cycles·s^{-1} or 380 cycles·s^{-1}.

$$\therefore \quad \frac{uf_s}{u - v_1} = 370 \text{ s}^{-1} \quad \text{or} \quad 380 \text{ s}^{-1}.$$

$$\therefore \quad u - v_1 = \frac{750 \text{ mph} \times 350 \text{ s}^{-1}}{370 \text{ s}^{-1}} \quad \text{or} \quad \frac{750 \text{ mph} \times 350 \text{ s}^{-1}}{380 \text{ s}^{-1}} = 709.5 \text{ mph} \quad \text{or} \quad 690.8 \text{ mph}.$$

$$\therefore \quad v_1 = 40.5 \text{ mph} \quad \text{or} \quad 59.2 \text{ mph}.$$

24

Coulomb's Law

PROBLEM 24.1

An electron has a mass of 9.1×10^{-31} kg and an electric charge of 1.6×10^{-19} coulombs (C). Suppose that two electrons are placed near one another. Compare the gravitational and electrical forces between them.

Solution. Given that the distance between the electrons is r, then the gravitational force of attraction between them is

$$F_G = G \frac{m^2}{r^2} = \frac{6.6 \times 10^{-11} \, \text{N} \cdot \text{m}^2 \cdot \text{kg}^{-2} \times 9.1^2 \times 10^{-62} \, \text{kg}^2}{r^2} = \frac{54.6 \times 10^{-72}}{r^2} \, \text{N} \cdot \text{m}^2.$$

The electrical force of repulsion between the electrons is

$$F_e = \frac{1}{4\pi\epsilon_0} \frac{q^2}{r^2} = \frac{9 \times 10^9 \, \text{N} \cdot \text{m}^2 \cdot \text{C}^{-2} \times 1.6^2 \times 10^{-38} \, \text{C}^2}{r^2} = \frac{23.04 \times 10^{-29}}{r^2} \, \text{N} \cdot \text{m}^2.$$

Thus

$$\frac{F_e}{F_G} = \frac{23.04 \times 10^{-29}}{54.6 \times 10^{-72}} = 4.2 \times 10^{42}.$$

It is clear that the gravitational force between the electrons is negligible in comparison with the electrical force.

PROBLEM 24.2

Two equal conducting spheres of negligible size are charged with 16.0×10^{-14} C and -6.4×10^{-14} C, respectively, and are placed 20 cm apart. They are then moved to a distance of 50 cm apart. Compare the forces between them in the two positions.

The spheres are connected by a thin wire. What force does each now exert on the other?

Solution. The equation giving the force between the spheres, which may be considered as point charges, is

$$F = \frac{1}{4\pi\epsilon_0} \frac{q_1 q_2}{r^2}.$$

Thus

$$F_1 = \frac{1}{4\pi\epsilon_0} \frac{q_1 q_2}{(0.2)^2 \, \text{m}^2} \quad \text{and} \quad F_2 = \frac{1}{4\pi\epsilon_0} \frac{q_1 q_2}{(0.5)^2 \, \text{m}^2}$$

$$\therefore \quad \frac{F_1}{F_2} = \frac{(0.5)^2}{(0.2)^2} = 6\tfrac{1}{4}.$$

If the spheres are joined by a wire, the charges, which are attracted to one another, can flow in the wire under the influence of the forces acting on them. The charges will neutralize as far as possible and $(16.0 \times 10^{-14} - 6.4 \times 10^{-14}) = 9.6 \times 10^{-14}$ C will be left distributed over the system. Neglecting the effect of the wire, by symmetry 4.8×10^{-14} C will reside on each sphere. The force between the two spheres is now

$$F = \frac{1}{4\pi\epsilon_0} \frac{q^2}{r^2} = 9 \times 10^9 \text{ N}\cdot\text{m}^2\cdot\text{C}^{-2} \times \frac{(4.8 \times 10^{-14})^2 \text{ C}^2}{(0.5)^2 \text{ m}^2} = 8.29 \times 10^{-17} \text{N}.$$

PROBLEM 24.3

Two small conducting balls, each of mass 0.25 g, are hanging from the roof on insulating threads of length 50 cm so that they just touch. A charge, which they share equally, is given to them and each takes up a position such that the thread by which it hangs makes an angle of 45° with the vertical. What is the charge on each?

Solution. There are three forces acting on each ball, the weight $m\mathbf{g}$ acting downward, the Coulombian repulsive force $\mathbf{F}$ acting horizontally, and the tension $\mathbf{T}$ in the supporting thread. Since the ball is in equilibrium, horizontal and vertical components must separately balance. Thus

$$mg = T\cos 45° \quad \text{and} \quad F = T\sin 45°$$

or

$$F = mg\tan 45° = mg.$$

But

$$F = \frac{q^2}{4\pi\epsilon_0 r^2} = \frac{q^2}{4\pi\epsilon_0(2h\sin 45°)^2},$$

where q is the charge on each ball.

$$\therefore \quad q^2 = 4\pi\epsilon_0(2h\sin 45°)^2 mg = \frac{[2 \times 0.5 \text{ m} \times (1/\sqrt{2})]^2 \times 2.5 \times 10^{-4} \text{ kg} \times 9.8 \text{ m}\cdot\text{s}^{-2}}{9 \times 10^9 \text{ N}\cdot\text{m}^2\cdot\text{C}^{-2}}$$

$$= 13.6 \times 10^{-14} \text{ C}^2.$$

$$\therefore \quad q = 3.7 \times 10^{-7} \text{ C}.$$

PROBLEM 24.4

Point charges of magnitude 2.5×10^{-14} C, 1.0×10^{-14} C, -3.5×10^{-14} C, and 2.0×10^{-14} C are placed in sequence at the corners A, B, C, and D of a rectangle in which AB has length 8 cm and BC has length 6 cm. What force is acting on the charge at D due to the other three?

Solution. Let the charges at A, B, C, and D be q_1, q_2, $-q_3$, and q_4, respectively. The forces exerted on q_4 by the other three are shown in the diagram as the vectors $\mathbf{F}_1$, $\mathbf{F}_2$, and $\mathbf{F}_3$, respectively. The x- and y-axes have been selected in the directions shown.

The three forces acting on q_4 will combine into a single force $\mathbf{F}$ with components (F_x, F_y) along the two chosen axes. Splitting $\mathbf{F}_2$ into its components along the x- and y-axes, and noting that

$$BD = \sqrt{8^2 \text{ cm}^2 + 6^2 \text{ cm}^2} = 10 \text{ cm},$$

we obtain

$$F_x = F_3 - F_2\sin\theta,$$

$$F_y = F_1 + F_2\cos\theta.$$

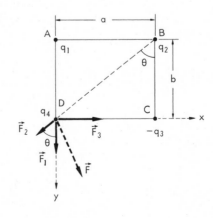

From these equations, it follows that

$$F_x = \frac{q_3 q_4}{4\pi\epsilon_0 a^2} - \frac{q_2 q_4}{4\pi\epsilon_0 (a^2 + b^2)} \times \frac{a}{\sqrt{a^2 + b^2}} = \frac{q_4}{4\pi\epsilon_0}\left[\frac{q_3}{a^2} - \frac{q_2 a}{(a^2 + b^2)^{3/2}}\right]$$

$$= 2.0 \times 10^{-14}\,\text{C} \times 9.0 \times 10^9\,\text{N} \cdot \text{m}^2 \cdot \text{C}^{-2}\left[\frac{3.5 \times 10^{-14}\,\text{C}}{64 \times 10^{-4}\,\text{m}^2} - \frac{1.0 \times 10^{-14}\,\text{C} \times 8 \times 10^{-2}\,\text{m}}{10^{-3}\,\text{m}^3}\right]$$

$$= 8.40 \times 10^{-16}\,\text{N}.$$

Similarly,

$$F_y = \frac{q_4}{4\pi\epsilon_0}\left[\frac{q_1}{b^2} + \frac{q_2 b}{(a^2 + b^2)^{3/2}}\right] = 13.58 \times 10^{-16}\,\text{N}.$$

The vector **F** has components $(8.40 \times 10^{-16}\,\text{N}, 13.58 \times 10^{-16}\,\text{N})$ and is thus a vector of magnitude $\sqrt{8.41^2 + 13.58^2} \times 10^{-16}\,\text{N} = 15.97 \times 10^{-16}\,\text{N}$ at an angle of $\tan^{-1}(13.58/8.40) = 58°16'$ to the direction of the x-axis.

25

The Electric Field. Gauss's Law

PROBLEM 25.1

A small conducting ball of mass 10^{-3} g is suspended from an insulating thread whose other end is attached to a large conducting plate which is standing vertically. When the sheet carries an electric charge of surface density 5×10^{-8} C·m^{-2}, the ball is repelled from the surface and the thread is found to make an angle of 30° with the vertical. What charge has passed to the ball?

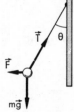

Solution. There are three forces acting on the ball, the weight $m\mathbf{g}$ acting downward, the force $\mathbf{F}$ exerted by the plate acting horizontally, and the tension $\mathbf{T}$ in the thread. Since the ball has settled in equilibrium, the horizontal and vertical components of the forces must balance separately. Thus

$$mg = T \cos \theta \quad \text{and} \quad F = T \sin \theta \quad \text{or} \quad F = mg \tan \theta.$$

But $F = Eq$, where E is the electric intensity due to the plate and q is the charge on the ball. Further, $F = mg \tan \theta = Eq = \sigma q / \epsilon_0$, where σ is the charge density on the plate. Thus

$$q = \frac{\epsilon_0\, mg \tan \theta}{\sigma} = \frac{8.85 \times 10^{-12}\ \text{C}^2 \cdot \text{m}^{-2} \cdot \text{N}^{-1} \times 10^{-6}\ \text{kg} \times 9.8\ \text{m} \cdot \text{s}^{-2} \times (1/\sqrt{3})}{5 \times 10^{-8}\ \text{C} \cdot \text{m}^{-2}} = 1.00 \times 10^{-9}\ \text{C}.$$

PROBLEM 25.2

A charged oil drop of mass 2.5×10^{-4} g is in the space between the two plates, each of area 175 cm^2, of a parallel-plate capacitor. When the upper plate has a charge of 4.5×10^{-7} C and the lower plate an equal negative charge, the drop remains stationary. What charge does it carry?

Solution. The electric intensity between equal and oppositely charged parallel plates is given by the equation $E = \sigma/\epsilon_0 = Q/A\epsilon_0$, where Q and A are the charge on, and area of, the positive plate. The force on the oil drop is $F = qE = qQ/A\epsilon_0$, and since this balances the weight of the drop, $mg = qQ/A\epsilon_0$ or

$$q = \frac{mg\, A\epsilon_0}{Q} = \frac{2.5 \times 10^{-7}\ \text{kg} \times 9.8\ \text{m} \cdot \text{s}^{-2} \times 175 \times 10^{-4}\ \text{m}^2 \times 8.85 \times 10^{-12}\ \text{C}^2 \cdot \text{m}^{-2} \cdot \text{N}^{-1}}{4.5 \times 10^{-7}\ \text{C}}$$

$$= 8.43 \times 10^{-13}\ \text{C}.$$

PROBLEM 25.3

By direct calculation, determine the value of the electric intensity at any distance from an infinite plane sheet of uniformly distributed charge. Show that the result follows at once from an application of Gauss's law.

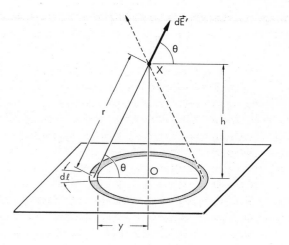

Solution. Consider any point X at a perpendicular distance h from the plane sheet of charge density ρ. Drop the perpendicular from the point to the sheet, cutting the latter at O, and draw two circles, centered at O, at radii of y and $y + dy$. Take a small portion of the annulus so formed, of length dl, and consider the electric intensity dE' at the point X due to the small element of charge. Then

$$dE' = \frac{dq}{4\pi\epsilon_0 r^2} = \frac{\rho \, dl \, dy}{4\pi\epsilon_0 r^2}.$$

The direction of dE' is the same as that of **r**, and dE' may therefore be resolved into components along OX and at right angles to it. The component along OX has the same value, no matter what position on the annulus dl occupies. But the element of the annulus diametrically opposite dl produces a component perpendicular to OX equal but opposite to that produced by dl. These two components thus cancel out, as do all components from diametrically opposite elements. The electric intensity from the whole annulus is thus perpendicular to the sheet and has magnitude

$$dE = \oint dE' = \frac{\rho \, dy}{4\pi\epsilon_0 r^2} \sin\theta \oint dl = \frac{\rho \, dy}{4\pi\epsilon_0 r^2} \cdot \frac{h}{r} \cdot 2\pi y = \frac{h\rho y \, dy}{2\epsilon_0 (h^2 + y^2)^{3/2}}.$$

For the whole sheet of charge the electric intensity is thus

$$E = \int dE = \int_0^\infty \frac{h\rho y \, dy}{2\epsilon_0 (h^2 + y^2)^{3/2}} = -\frac{h\rho}{2\epsilon_0}\left[(h^2 + y^2)^{-1/2} \right]_0^\infty = -\frac{h\rho}{2\epsilon_0}\left[0 - \frac{1}{h} \right] = \frac{\rho}{2\epsilon_0}.$$

To apply Gauss's law to the same problem, construct a cylinder of small and uniform cross-sectional area dA at right angles to the sheet and bisected by the sheet. Since the sheet is infinite and the charge uniformly distributed, the electric intensity must be the same at all points equidistant from the sheet, and thus by symmetry must be everywhere perpendicular to the sheet. Hence **E** is everywhere parallel to the sides of the cylinder and thus the flux of **E** from the cylinder through its sides is zero. The magnitude of **E** at each end of the cylinder will be the same if the cylinder is bisected by the sheet, and **E** will be perpendicular to each end. Hence, applying Gauss's law, we obtain

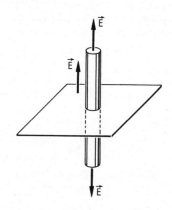

$$2E \, dA = (\rho \, dA/\epsilon_0).$$

Therefore $E = \rho/2\epsilon_0$. Thus **E** is everywhere perpendicular to the sheet and has the same value $\rho/2\epsilon_0$ at all points.

PROBLEM 25.4

Charge is uniformly distributed over a spherical volume. Show that the electric intensity at any point inside the volume is the same as if all the charge closer to the center were concentrated there, and the rest of the charge removed.

How does this justify the information given in Problem 11.4 concerning the gravitational force on a particle dropped down a shaft drilled along a diameter of the earth?

Solution. Consider any sphere concentric with the charged volume and of lesser radius r than the charged volume. By symmetry the electric intensity must be the same at all points on the surface of a sphere of radius r, and thus must be purely radial in direction. Hence the flux of intensity from such a sphere is E times the area of the sphere. Let ρ be the charge density. We apply Gauss's law to obtain

$$4\pi r^2 E = \frac{4}{3}\pi r^3 \frac{\rho}{\epsilon_0} = \frac{Q}{\epsilon_0}.$$

Therefore $E = Q/4\pi\epsilon_0 r^2$, where Q is the total charge inside the sphere.

But the same equation would have been obtained if all the charge inside a radius r were concentrated at the center and the rest removed, which proves the first part of the problem.

Gravitational and electrostatic forces are of the same type, obeying an inverse-square law, the constant of proportionality in the force equation in one case being G, and in the other $1/4\pi\epsilon_0$. A gravitational intensity may be defined in the same way as an electric intensity, and will obey a Gauss's law also. Hence, by the same argument as above, the gravitational intensity at any point inside the earth at distance r from the center is $E = GM/r^2$, where M is the total mass inside a sphere of radius r. Hence the force on a body of mass m a distance r from the center of the earth is $F = GMm/r^2$, where M is the mass of the portion of the earth nearer the center than the body. This was the result quoted in Problem 11.4.

PROBLEM 25.5

Two point charges of magnitude q are placed a distance $2a$ apart. Find the electric intensity at a point P on their perpendicular bisector a distance $2a$ from the line joining the two charges. Where must a charge of magnitude $\sqrt{5}q$ be placed so that the electric intensity at P is zero?

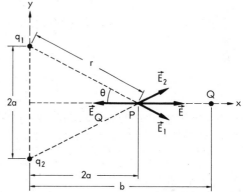

Solution. The diagram shows the two charges q_1 and q_2 and the electric intensities $\mathbf{E}_1$ and $\mathbf{E}_2$ produced by the two charges at the point P.

It is obvious from symmetry that the y-components of $\mathbf{E}_1$ and $\mathbf{E}_2$ cancel each other out; so that the net intensity $\mathbf{E}$ due to the charges is in the x-direction and has magnitude

$$E = 2 \times \frac{q}{4\pi\epsilon_0 r^2}\cos\theta$$

$$= \frac{q}{2\pi\epsilon_0 r^2}\cdot\frac{2a}{r} = \frac{qa}{\pi\epsilon_0(a^2 + 4a^2)^{3/2}} = \frac{q}{5\sqrt{5}\pi\epsilon_0 a^2}.$$

In order to make the electric intensity at P zero, the electric intensity due to the added charge $Q = \sqrt{5}q$ must have magnitude E and point in the negative x-direction. Therefore Q must obviously lie on the x-axis to the right of P. If the x-coordinate of the position of Q is b, the magnitude of the electric intensity at P due to Q is

$$E' = \frac{Q}{4\pi\epsilon_0(b - 2a)^2}$$

But $E = E'$, and therefore

$$\frac{q}{5\sqrt{5}\pi\epsilon_0 a^2} = \frac{\sqrt{5}q}{4\pi\epsilon_0(b - 2a)^2}$$

$$\therefore \quad (b - 2a)^2 = \frac{25a^2}{4} \quad \text{or} \quad b - 2a = \frac{5a}{2}. \quad \therefore \quad b = 4.5a.$$

PROBLEM 25.6

Point charges of q, $-q$, $2Q$, and Q are placed in sequence at the corners A, B, C, D of a square of side $2a$. Find the magnitude and direction of the electric intensity at the midpoint of CD.

What is the relation between q and Q if the electric intensity is zero at that point?

Solution. The situation is shown clearly in the diagram, where x-and y-axes have been drawn in. Each of the charges at A, B, C, and D produces an electric intensity at F, the midpoint of CD, these being shown in the diagram as $\mathbf{E}_A$, $\mathbf{E}_B$, $\mathbf{E}_C$, and $\mathbf{E}_D$. We can obtain $\mathbf{E}$, the total electric intensity at F, by adding vectorially the intensities produced by the separate charges. The vector $\mathbf{E}$ will have components (E_x, E_y) along the two axes chosen, where

$$E_x = E_D - E_C + E_B \cos \theta + E_A \cos \theta,$$

$$E_y = E_B \sin \theta - E_A \sin \theta.$$

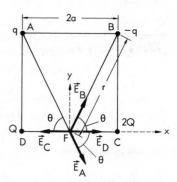

But $E_A = E_B = q/4\pi\epsilon_0 r^2$. Therefore $E_y = 0$ and $\mathbf{E}$ lies in the x-direction. Thus

$$E = E_x = \frac{Q}{4\pi\epsilon_0 a^2} - \frac{2Q}{4\pi\epsilon_0 a^2} + \frac{2q}{4\pi\epsilon_0 r^2} \cos \theta$$

$$= \frac{2q}{4\pi\epsilon_0 r^2} \cdot \frac{a}{r} - \frac{Q}{4\pi\epsilon_0 a^2}$$

$$= \frac{1}{4\pi\epsilon_0} \left[\frac{2aq}{(5a^2)^{3/2}} - \frac{Q}{a^2} \right] = \frac{1}{4\pi\epsilon_0 a^2} \left[\frac{2q}{5\sqrt{5}} - Q. \right]$$

If $E = 0$, then

$$\frac{2q}{5\sqrt{5}} - Q = 0 \quad \text{or} \quad q = 2.5\sqrt{5}Q.$$

26

Potential

PROBLEM 26.1

Calculate the work that must be done against electrostatic forces in moving a charge of -100 pC* from a position 10 cm below a charge of 10 μC to a position 1 m below it. In the final position the negatively charged body remains suspended, the electrostatic and gravitational forces on it being equal and opposite. What is the mass of the body?

Solution. The problem may be tackled either by calculating the potential at the two points and subtracting or by calculating the intensity at a general point and integrating. The former is by far the easier method.

The potential at a point a distance r from a point charge is $V = q/4\pi\epsilon_0 r$. Hence 10 cm below the charge

$$V_1 = \frac{10^{-5}\,\text{C} \times 9 \times 10^9\,\text{N} \cdot \text{m}^2 \cdot \text{C}^{-2}}{0.1\,\text{m}} = 9 \times 10^5\,\text{V},$$

and 1 m below the charge

$$V_2 = \frac{10^{-5}\,\text{C} \times 9 \times 10^9\,\text{N} \cdot \text{m}^2 \cdot \text{C}^{-2}}{1\,\text{m}} = 9 \times 10^4\,\text{V}.$$

The difference in potential between the points is

$$V_2 - V_1 = -8.1 \times 10^5\,\text{V}.$$

The work done in moving -100 pC through this potential difference is thus

$$Q(V_2 - V_1) = (-10^{-10}\,\text{C}) \times (-8.1 \times 10^5\,\text{V}) = 8.1 \times 10^{-5}\,\text{J}.$$

In the final position the upward force of attraction just balances the weight of the body. Hence

$$mg = q_1 q_2/4\pi\epsilon_0 r^2$$

or

$$m = \frac{10^{-5}\,\text{C} \times 10^{-10}\,\text{C} \times 9 \times 10^9\,\text{N} \cdot \text{m}^2 \cdot \text{C}^{-2}}{1^2\,\text{m}^2 \times 9.8\,\text{m} \cdot \text{s}^{-2}} = \frac{9}{9.8} \times 10^{-6}\,\text{kg} = 9.18 \times 10^{-4}\,\text{g}.$$

PROBLEM 26.2

Two hollow spherical shells are mounted concentrically, but are insulated from one another. The inner shell has a charge Q and the outer shell is grounded. What is the electric intensity and potential in the space between them?

When the outer shell is not grounded, why does a charge outside the system experience a force when the inner shell is charged?

---

*The notation pC indicates a picocoulomb, which is equal to 10^{-12} coulomb, or one $\mu\mu$C.

Solution. In the region between the shells, because of the symmetry of the arrangement, the electric intensity **E** must have the same magnitude at all points a distance r from the common center, and must thus be everywhere radial in direction. Hence, applying Gauss's law to a region bounded by a spherical surface of radius r, we have

$$4\pi r^2 E = \frac{Q}{\epsilon_0} \quad \text{or} \quad E = \frac{Q}{4\pi\epsilon_0 \, r^2} \, .$$

But $E = -dV/dr$;

$$\therefore \quad dV = -\frac{Q}{4\pi\epsilon_0 \, r^2} dr \quad \text{or} \quad V = \frac{Q}{4\pi\epsilon_0 \, r} + C,$$

where C is a constant of integration. But at the outer spherical shell of radius b, $V = 0$.

$$\therefore \quad 0 = \frac{Q}{4\pi\epsilon_0 b} + C \quad \text{or} \quad C = -\frac{Q}{4\pi\epsilon_0 b} \, .$$

$$\therefore \quad V = \frac{Q}{4\pi\epsilon_0} \left(\frac{1}{r} - \frac{1}{b} \right) .$$

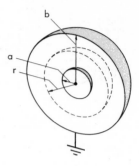

Lines of force come from the inner shell and all end on the outer shell. The same number of lines of force end on the outer shell as start on the inner shell; hence the charge induced on the inside of the outer shell is equal and opposite to that on the inner shell. Thus a charge $-Q$ is induced on the inside of the outer shell. But this shell was initially uncharged. Hence a charge $+Q$ must be left on the outside of the outer shell.

If the outer shell is grounded, electrons flow from the earth to neutralize this positive charge. In the absence of grounding, the positive charge remains on the outside of the shell and produces a field of force around the system which affects any other charge in the vicinity.

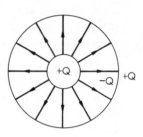

PROBLEM 26.3

A child's circular metal hoop of radius 0.3 m is dumped in the cellar where it is in contact with the battery powering the electric doorbell. The hoop receives a charge of 0.2 pC. Determine the potential and the field strength at the center of the hoop and at a point on the axis of the hoop 0.4 m from the center. Where on the axis is the field strength a maximum?

Solution. Consider a small element dl of the hoop carrying a charge dq. The potential at a point a distance z along the axis of the hoop is

$$dV = \frac{dq}{4\pi\epsilon_0 r} = \frac{dq}{4\pi\epsilon_0 \sqrt{y^2 + z^2}} \, .$$

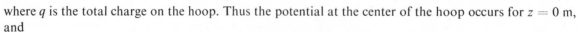

The total potential at the point is thus

$$V = \int dV = \int \frac{dq}{4\pi\epsilon_0 \sqrt{y^2 + z^2}} = \frac{q}{4\pi\epsilon_0 \sqrt{y^2 + z^2}} \, ,$$

where q is the total charge on the hoop. Thus the potential at the center of the hoop occurs for $z = 0$ m, and

$$V_0 = \frac{0.2 \times 10^{-12} \, \text{C} \times 9 \times 10^9 \, \text{N} \cdot \text{m}^2 \cdot \text{C}^{-2}}{0.3 \, \text{m}} = 6 \times 10^{-3} \, \text{V}.$$

Also when $z = 0.4$ m,

$$V_{0.4} = \frac{0.2 \times 10^{-12} \, \text{C} \times 9 \times 10^9 \, \text{N} \cdot \text{m}^2 \cdot \text{C}^{-2}}{\sqrt{0.3^2 + 0.4^2} \, \text{m}} = \frac{1.8 \times 10^{-3}}{0.5} \, \text{V} = 3.6 \times 10^{-3} \, \text{V}.$$

The electric intensity at the general point on the axis is

$$E = -\frac{dV}{dz} = +\frac{qz}{4\pi\epsilon_0 (y^2 + z^2)^{3/2}} \, ,$$

since from symmetry considerations the direction of **E** must be along the z-axis. Thus at the center of the hoop E is zero and at the position where $z = 0.4$ m,

$$E_{0.4} = \frac{0.2 \times 10^{-12} \text{ C} \times 0.4 \text{ m} \times 9 \times 10^9 \text{ N} \cdot \text{m}^2 \cdot \text{C}^{-2}}{(0.5)^3 \text{ m}^3} = 5.76 \times 10^{-3} \text{ V} \cdot \text{m}^{-1}.$$

Note that when z is positive, E is positive, and when z is negative, E is negative. The direction of **E** is thus always along the axis away from the hoop.

The electric intensity E is zero when $z = 0$ and also when $z = \infty$; E must therefore pass through a maximum value somewhere between these two points. For a maximum $dE/dz = 0$, or

$$\frac{q}{4\pi\epsilon_0 (y^2 + z^2)^{3/2}} - \frac{3qz^2}{4\pi\epsilon_0 (y^2 + z^2)^{3/2}} = 0.$$

$$\therefore \quad y^2 + z^2 - 3z^2 = 0 \quad \text{or} \quad z = \pm \frac{y}{\sqrt{2}}.$$

Thus at a distance along the axis of $(0.3/\sqrt{2})$ m $= 0.21$ m, E has its maximum value of

$$E_{\text{max}} = \frac{0.2 \times 10^{-12} \text{ C} \times 0.21 \text{ m} \times 9 \times 10^9 \text{ N} \cdot \text{m}^2 \cdot \text{C}^{-2}}{(0.3^2 + 0.21^2)^{3/2} \text{ m}^3} = 7.70 \times 10^{-3} \text{ V} \cdot \text{m}^{-1}.$$

PROBLEM 26.4

An electron travels from one to the other of two plates, between which is maintained a potential difference of 1000 V. With what speed and with what energy does the electron arrive at the positive plate?

A positively charged particle with equal and opposite charge but 3680 times the mass is then released at the positive plate. With what velocity and what energy does it reach the negative plate?

Solution. The electron travels through a potential difference of 1000 V. The energy acquired is thus 1000 eV $= 1.60 \times 10^{-16}$ J. Further,

$$\frac{1}{2} mv^2 = 1.60 \times 10^{-16} \text{ J} \quad \text{or} \quad v^2 = \frac{3.20 \times 10^{-16} \text{ J}}{9.1 \times 10^{-31} \text{ kg}}.$$

$$\therefore \quad v = 1.88 \times 10^7 \text{ m} \cdot \text{s}^{-1}.$$

For the positively charged particle, the charge it possesses is the same in magnitude as that of the electron and it moves through the same potential difference in the opposite direction. Hence it acquires the same energy of 1.60×10^{-16} J. The velocity, however, is different because of the much larger mass. Thus

$$\frac{1}{2} m_1 v_1^2 = 1.60 \times 10^{-16} \text{ J} \quad \text{or} \quad v_1^2 = \frac{3.20 \times 10^{-16} \text{ J}}{9.1 \times 10^{-31} \times 3680 \text{ kg}}.$$

$$\therefore \quad v_1 = 3.10 \times 10^5 \text{ m} \cdot \text{s}^{-1}.$$

PROBLEM 26.5

The air pressures inside and outside a soap bubble are the same. To what potential has the soap bubble, of radius 2 cm, been charged? The surface tension of the soap solution is 0.0265 N·m^{-1}.

Solution. In an uncharged soap bubble the effect of the surface tension is to produce a contraction of the bubble which continues until a pressure difference of $4\gamma/R$ is set up between the inside and outside of the bubble, γ being the surface tension of the soap solution and R the radius of the bubble. This counteracts the inward pressure due to the surface tension. If the soap bubble is charged, an outward force opposes the contraction due to the surface tension and, if large enough, can prevent any compression of the air inside the bubble.

Assume that such a state of equilibrium has been reached, and that V and Q are, respectively, the potential of and the charge carried by the bubble. The energy of a charged conductor is $W = \frac{1}{2} VQ$, and in this case, $V = Q/4\pi\epsilon_0 R$. Thus $W = Q^2/8\pi\epsilon_0 R$.

If the radius is increased by an amount dR, the electrical energy changes by an amount dW, where $dW = -(Q^2/8\pi\epsilon_0 R^2)\,dR$.

At the same time the surface tension energy increases by an amount equal to the surface tension times the increase in area. Hence

$$dW' = 2 \times \gamma \times \{4\pi(R + dR)^2 - 4\pi R^2\} = 16\pi R\gamma\,dR,$$

since the bubble has two surfaces, and we are ignoring terms in dR^2. But $-dW = dW'$, and therefore $Q^2/8\pi\epsilon_0 R^2 = 16\pi R\gamma$.

$$\therefore \quad V^2 = \frac{Q^2}{16\pi^2\epsilon_0^2 R^2} = \frac{8\gamma R}{\epsilon_0}.$$

$$\therefore \quad V = \sqrt{\frac{8 \times 0.0265\ \text{N}\cdot\text{m}^{-1} \times 0.02\ \text{m}}{8.85 \times 10^{-12}\ \text{C}^2\cdot\text{N}^{-1}\cdot\text{m}^{-2}}} = 2.19 \times 10^4\ \text{V}.$$

PROBLEM 26.6

Show that, for a given dipole, V and E cannot have the same magnitude in MKS units at distances less than 2 m from the dipole. Suppose that the distance is $\sqrt{5}$ m; determine the positions at which V and E are equal in magnitude, and find the direction of E at these positions.

Solution. The expression for the magnitudes of the potential and electric intensity due to a dipole are, in the usual notation,

$$V = \frac{p\cos\theta}{4\pi\epsilon_0 r^2}$$

and

$$E = \frac{p}{4\pi\epsilon_0 r^3}\sqrt{4\cos^2\theta + \sin^2\theta}$$

If these are equal in magnitude,

$$\cos\theta = \frac{\sqrt{4\cos^2\theta + \sin^2\theta}}{r}$$

or

$$r^2 = \frac{4\cos^2\theta + \sin^2\theta}{\cos^2\theta} = 4 + \tan^2\theta.$$

The minimum value of r^2 occurs when $\tan\theta = 0$. Hence the minimum value of r for V and E to be equal in magnitude occurs for $r^2 = 4$; that is, $r = 2$ m, in MKS units.

If $r = \sqrt{5}$ m, then $5\cos^2\theta = 4\cos^2\theta + \sin^2\theta$ or $\cos^2\theta = \sin^2\theta$. Thus $\theta = 45°$, $135°$, $225°$, or $315°$.

In these directions at a distance of $\sqrt{5}$ m, E makes an angle with the radial direction of ϕ, where

$$\tan\phi = \frac{\sin\theta}{2\cos\theta} = \tfrac{1}{2} \quad \text{for } \theta = 45° \text{ or } 225° \text{ and} \quad -\tfrac{1}{2} \quad \text{for } \theta = 135° \text{ or } 315°.$$

PROBLEM 26.7

An oil drop carries a net charge of three times the electronic charge and has a radius of 10^{-4} cm. What is its terminal velocity when it falls between two horizontal plates kept at a potential difference of 1000 V and 2 cm apart, the positive plate being uppermost? The densities of the oil and of air are 800 kg·m⁻³ and 1.29 kg·m⁻³ and the viscosity of air is 1.80×10^{-5} N·s·m⁻².

Solution. Between two parallel plates, separated by a distance d and maintained at a difference of potential V, the electric intensity E is $E = V/d$. The electrostatic force acting on the drop is upward, and of magnitude $qE = qV/d$. Three other forces are acting on the drop: its weight downward and two upward forces, the viscous retarding force and the buoyant upthrust. When the terminal velocity is achieved, the forces balance and

$$\frac{4}{3}\pi r^3 \rho g = \frac{4}{3}\pi r^3 \sigma g + 6\pi \eta r v + \frac{qV}{d},$$

where r is the radius of the drop, ρ its density, σ and η the density and viscosity of air, and v the terminal velocity. Hence

$$v = \frac{\frac{4}{3}\pi r^3 g(\rho - \sigma) - (qV/d)}{6\pi \eta r}$$

$$= \frac{\frac{4}{3}\pi \times 10^{-18}\ \text{m}^3 \times 9.8\ \text{m}\cdot\text{s}^{-2}\ (800 - 1.29)\ \text{kg}\cdot\text{m}^{-3} - \dfrac{3 \times 1.6 \times 10^{-19}\ \text{C} \times 10^3\ \text{V}}{0.02\ \text{m}}}{6\pi \times 1.80 \times 10^{-5}\ \text{N}\cdot\text{s}\cdot\text{m}^{-2} \times 10^{-6}\ \text{m}}$$

$$= \frac{(3.27 - 2.40) \times 10^{-14}}{3.40 \times 10^{-10}}\ \text{m}\cdot\text{s}^{-1} = 2.56 \times 10^{-5}\ \text{m}\cdot\text{s}^{-1}.$$

PROBLEM 26.8

In a Van de Graaff accelerator, protons are accelerated through a potential difference of 5×10^6 V. What is the final energy of the protons in electron volts and joules, and what is their mass and their velocity?

Solution. A proton carries an elementary positive charge. The energy acquired in traveling through a potential difference of 5 MV is

$$E = 5\ \text{MeV} = 5 \times 10^6\ \text{eV} \times 1.6 \times 10^{-19}\ \text{J}\cdot\text{eV}^{-1} = 8.0 \times 10^{-13}\ \text{J}.$$

To determine the mass at this energy, use the equation $E = mc^2$.

$$\therefore \quad m = \frac{E}{c^2} = \frac{8 \times 10^{-13}\ \text{J}}{(3 \times 10^8)^2 \text{m}^2 \cdot \text{s}^{-2}} = 0.89 \times 10^{-29}\ \text{kg}.$$

This is the mass equivalent of the energy acquired. The total mass the particle now possesses is obtained by adding this mass to the rest mass. That is,

$$M = m + m_0 = (0.89 \times 10^{-29} + 1.672 \times 10^{-27})\ \text{kg} = 1.681 \times 10^{-27}\ \text{kg}.$$

Also

$$\frac{v}{c} = \sqrt{1 - \frac{m_0}{M}} = \sqrt{1 - \frac{1.672}{1.681}} = 0.074.$$

$$\therefore \quad v = 0.074 \times 3 \times 10^8\ \text{m}\cdot\text{s}^{-1} = 2.22 \times 10^7\ \text{m}\cdot\text{s}^{-1}.$$

PROBLEM 26.9

The spherical shell of a Van de Graaff generator is to be charged to a potential of 10^6 V. Calculate the minimum radius the shell can have if the dielectric strength of air is 3×10^6 V·m^{-1}.

Solution. The potential and electric intensity at the surface of a sphere of radius R are

$$V = \frac{Q}{4\pi \epsilon_0 R} \quad \text{and} \quad E = \frac{Q}{4\pi \epsilon_0 R^2} = \frac{V}{R}.$$

Therefore $R = V/E$. But the maximum acceptable value of E is 3×10^6 V·m^{-1}. Hence the maximum radius for the spherical shell is

$$R = \frac{10^6\ \text{V}}{3 \times 10^6\ \text{V}\cdot\text{m}^{-1}} = \frac{1}{3}\ \text{m}.$$

PROBLEM 26.10

Calculate the power required to drive the belt of a Van de Graaff generator which is transferring charge to the collector at a rate of 10^{-3} C·s^{-1} when the potential difference between the collector and the delivery point is 10^6 V. Ignore frictional effects in the calculation, even though these may be large.

Solution. The work done in transporting 10^{-3} C through a potential difference of 10^6 V is

$$W = 10^{-3} \, \text{C} \times 10^6 \, \text{V} = 10^3 \, \text{J}.$$

This work is done in 1 s. Hence the rate of working is

$$P = \frac{W}{\tau} = 10^3 \, \text{J·s}^{-1} = 1 \, \text{kW}.$$

27

Capacitance. Properties of Dielectrics

PROBLEM 27.1

A 1-μF capacitor charged to 200 V and a 2-μF capacitor charged to 400 V are connected; the positive plate of each is connected to the negative plate of the other. Find the difference of potential and charge on each capacitor and the loss of energy that has taken place.

Solution. The charge on a charged capacitor in the usual notation is $Q = CV$. Thus the charge on the 1-μF capacitor before connection is 200 μC and on the 2-μF capacitor is 800 μC. If the two capacitors are now connected positive to negative, a charge of $+800$ μC and one of -200 μC are joined, as are charges of -800 μC and $+200$ μC. The composite capacitor thus has charges of ± 600 μC on its plates, since charge cannot be created or destroyed, but only neutralized. These charges will be shared between the individual capacitors, with $\pm Q_1$ on the first capacitor and $\pm Q_2$ on the second, since the charge flows from one to the other until a common potential V_0 is achieved. Thus

$$Q_1 = C_1 V_0 \quad \text{and} \quad Q_2 = C_2 V_0, \quad \text{where} \quad Q_1 + Q_2 = 600 \ \mu\text{C}.$$

$$\therefore \quad 600 \times 10^{-6} \ \text{C} = (1 \times 10^{-6} \ \text{F} + 2 \times 10^{-6} \ \text{F}) V_0 \quad \text{or} \quad V_0 = \frac{600 \times 10^{-6} \ \text{C}}{3 \times 10^{-6} \ \text{F}} = 200 \ \text{V}.$$

$$\therefore \quad Q_1 = 200 \ \mu\text{C}, \quad Q_2 = 400 \ \mu\text{C}.$$

The initial energy of the charged capacitors minus the final energy is

$$W = \tfrac{1}{2} C_1 V_1^2 + \tfrac{1}{2} C_2 V_2^2 - \tfrac{1}{2} C_1 V_0^2 - \tfrac{1}{2} C_2 V_0^2$$

$$= \tfrac{1}{2} \times 10^{-6} \ \text{F} \times (200)^2 \ \text{V}^2 + \tfrac{1}{2} \times 2 \times 10^{-6} \ \text{F} \times (400)^2 \ \text{V}^2$$

$$- \tfrac{1}{2} \times 10^{-6} \ \text{F} \times (200)^2 \ \text{V}^2 - \tfrac{1}{2} + 2 \times 10^{-6} \ \text{F} \times (200)^2 \ \text{V}^2$$

$$= 12 \times 10^4 \times 10^{-6} \ \text{J} = 0.12 \ \text{J}.$$

This energy is lost as heat in the connecting wires when the two capacitors are joined.

PROBLEM 27.2

How should 5 capacitors, each of capacitance 1 μF, be connected so as to produce a total capacitance of $\tfrac{3}{7}$ μF?

Solution. If all capacitors are joined in parallel, the resultant capacitance is 5 μF, and if connected in series, the resultant capacitance is $\tfrac{1}{5}$ μF. The connection is thus more complicated.

Suppose that n capacitors are connected in parallel and $5 - n$ in series. The resultant capacitances are thus such that

$$C_1 = \sum_n (1 + 1 + \cdots) \, \mu F = n \, \mu F \qquad \text{and} \qquad \frac{1}{C_2} = \sum_{5-n} \left(\frac{1}{1} + \frac{1}{1} + \cdots \right) = (5 - n) \, \mu F^{-1}$$

or

$$C_2 = \frac{1}{5 - n} \, \mu F.$$

If C_1 and C_2 are connected in parallel, then

$$C_1 + C_2 = \left(n + \frac{1}{5 - n} \right) \mu F = \tfrac{3}{7} \, \mu F.$$

$$\therefore \quad 5n - n^2 + 1 = \frac{15 - 3n}{7}. \qquad \therefore \quad 7n^2 - 38n + 8 = 0,$$

which has no integral solution for n. But if C_1 and C_2 are connected in series, then

$$\frac{1}{C_1} + \frac{1}{C_2} = \left(\frac{1}{n} + 5 - n \right) \mu F^{-1} = \tfrac{7}{3} \, \mu F^{-1}.$$

$$\therefore \quad 3 + 15n - 3n^2 = 7n \qquad \text{or} \qquad 3n^2 - 8n - 3 = 0.$$

$$\therefore \quad (3n + 1)(n - 3) = 0.$$

This has an integral solution for n, $n = 3$. Thus the required capacitance is given if 3 capacitors are connected in parallel, and the combination is connected in series with the other two.

PROBLEM 27.3

A radio capacitor consists of a stack of five equally spaced plates each of area 0.01 m², the separation between neighbors being 2.0 mm. Calculate the capacitance (a) if the top and bottom plates are connected to form one conductor and the center three are connected to form the other, and (b) if the top, center, and bottom plates are connected to form one conductor and the other two plates are connected to form the other conductor.

Solution. (a) Since the middle three plates are at the same potential, no field exists between them. The capacitor essentially consists of two capacitors of equal capacitance in parallel, one formed from the top two plates, the other from the bottom two plates. Thus

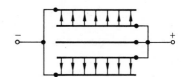

$$C_1 = 2\epsilon_0 \frac{A}{d} = \frac{2 \times 8.85 \times 10^{-12} \, \text{C}^2 \cdot \text{N}^{-1} \cdot \text{m}^{-2} \times 0.01 \, \text{m}^2}{0.002 \, \text{m}} = 8.85 \times 10^{-11} \, \text{F}.$$

(b) Here a field exists between any pair of plates. Each of the two connected plates acts as the positive plate for each of two capacitors formed between itself and the outer and middle plates. There are effectively four equal capacitors all connected in parallel. Hence

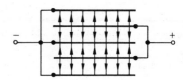

$$C_2 = 4\epsilon_0 \frac{A}{d} = 17.7 \times 10^{-11} \, \text{F},$$

which is twice the capacitance of the previous arrangement.

PROBLEM 27.4

A capacitor of capacitance 0.1 μF is charged until the difference in potential between its plates is 25 V. Then the charge is shared with a second capacitor which has air as the dielectric between its plates; the potential difference falls to 15 V. The experiment is repeated with a dielectric between the plates of the second capacitor, and the final potential difference is 8 V. What is the dielectric coefficient of the dielectric used?

Solution. The charge possessed by the first capacitor initially is

$$Q = C_1 V_1 = 10^{-7} \text{ F} \times 25 \text{ V} = 2.5 \ \mu\text{C}.$$

This charge is shared with a second capacitor of capacitance C_2, no charge being lost. Hence

$$Q = (C_1 + C_2)V_2 \quad \text{or} \quad C_2 = \frac{Q}{V_2} - C_1 = \frac{2.5 \times 10^{-6}\text{C}}{15 \text{ V}} - 10^{-7} \text{ F} = \frac{2}{3} \times 10^{-7} \text{ F}.$$

If a dielectric of coefficient K is placed between the plates of capacitor C_2 and the experiment is repeated, $Q = (C_1 + KC_2)V_3$.

$$\therefore \quad K = \frac{1}{C_2}\left(\frac{Q}{V_3} - C_1\right) = \frac{3}{2} \times 10^7 \text{ F}^{-1}\left(\frac{2.5 \times 10^{-6}\text{ C}}{8 \text{ V}} - 10^{-7} \text{ F}\right) = \frac{3}{2} \times 10^7 \times \frac{17}{8} \times 10^{-7} = 3.2.$$

PROBLEM 27.5

A particular type of x-ray equipment discharges a capacitor to obtain its electrical energy. The capacitor of capacitance 0.25 μF is charged to 100 kV and discharged to 40 kV during a 0.1-s exposure. Calculate the quantity of charge supplied to the x-ray tube, the average current through it, and the energy dissipated.

Solution. The charge possessed by the capacitor initially is

$$Q_1 = CV_1 = 0.25 \times 10^{-6} \text{ F} \times 10^5 \text{ V} = 0.025 \text{ C}.$$

At the end of the exposure the capacitor is left with charge

$$Q_2 = CV_2 = 0.25 \times 10^{-6} \text{ F} \times 4 \times 10^4 \text{ V} = 0.01 \text{ C}.$$

The charge supplied to the x-ray set is thus $Q_1 - Q_2 = 0.015$ C. This charge is supplied in 0.1 s. The average current flowing is thus

$$i = \frac{Q_1 - Q_2}{\tau} = \frac{0.015 \text{ C}}{0.1 \text{ s}} = 150 \text{ mA}.$$

The energy dissipated in this time is

$$W = \tfrac{1}{2}CV_1^2 - \tfrac{1}{2}CV_2^2 = \tfrac{1}{2} \times 0.25 \times 10^{-6} \text{ F}(10^{10} - 16 \times 10^8) \text{ V}^2 = 1050 \text{ J}.$$

PROBLEM 27.6

The space between the plates of a parallel-plate capacitor is filled with dielectric of coefficient 2.5 and strength 5 $\times$ 10^6 V·m^{-1}. The plates are 2 mm apart. What is the maximum voltage which can be applied between the plates? What area of plates will give a capacitance of 10^{-3} μF, and at maximum voltage what are the free and bound charges per unit area of the plate and dielectric surface?

Solution. If the dielectric strength is 5 $\times$ 10^6 V·m^{-1}, the electric intensity E must not exceed this value. Hence the maximum voltage across the plates is

$$V_{\text{max}} = E_{\text{max}} d = 5 \times 10^6 \text{ V·m}^{-1} \times 2 \times 10^{-3} \text{ m} = 10^4 \text{ V}.$$

The capacitance of a parallel-plate capacitor with dielectric between the plates is $C = K\epsilon_0(A/d)$.

$$\therefore \quad A = \frac{Cd}{K\epsilon_0} = \frac{10^{-9} \text{ F} \times 2 \times 10^{-3} \text{ m}}{2.5 \times 8.85 \times 10^{-12} \text{ C}^2 \cdot \text{N}^{-1} \cdot \text{m}^{-2}} = 0.09 \text{ m}^2.$$

The free charge density on the plates of the capacitor is given by the equation $E = \sigma/\epsilon = \sigma/K\epsilon_0$ or

$$\sigma = EK\epsilon_0 = 5 \times 10^6 \text{ V·m}^{-1} \times 2.5 \times 8.85 \times 10^{-12} \text{ C}^2 \cdot \text{N}^{-1} \cdot \text{m}^{-2} = 110.6 \ \mu\text{C·m}^{-2}.$$

The bound charge density on the dielectric surface is

$$\sigma_b = \chi E = (\epsilon - \epsilon_0)\frac{\sigma}{K\epsilon_0} = \sigma\frac{K-1}{K} = 110.6 \times \frac{1.5}{2.5} = 66.4 \ \mu\text{C·m}^{-2}.$$

PROBLEM 27.7

What is the equivalent capacitance between the points A and B in diagram (a)? The charge on the 6-μF capacitor is 90 μC. What potential difference exists between the points A and R?

Solution. In the arrangement shown in diagram (a) there are two sets of capacitors in parallel. In each case the capacitances add, and so the arrangement is equivalent to that shown in diagram (b).

In each branch there are now two capacitors in series. For each branch,

$$\frac{1}{C} = \frac{1}{C_1} + \frac{1}{C_2}.$$

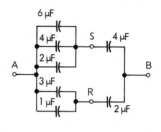

(a)

Thus the arrangement is equivalent to that shown in diagram (c). Here we have two capacitors in parallel. Their capacitances add. Hence the equivalent capacitance between A and B is

$$C = \left(3 + \frac{4}{3}\right) \mu F = 4\frac{1}{3} \mu F.$$

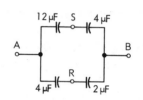

(b)

The charge on the 6-μF capacitor is 90 μC. Hence the potential across it is

$$V_1 = \frac{Q_1}{C_1} = \frac{90 \times 10^{-6} \text{ C}}{6 \times 10^{-6} \text{ F}} = 15 \text{ V}.$$

This potential is common to all the capacitors between A and S. Hence the total charge on the equivalent 12-μF capacitor is

$$Q_2 = C_2 V_1 = 12 \times 10^{-6} \text{ F} \times 15 \text{ V} = 180 \text{ } \mu C.$$

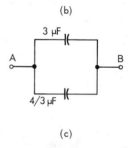

(c)

The conductors connected to S are isolated and initially must have been uncharged. If a charge of -180 μC appears on the negative plate of the equivalent 12-μF capacitor connected to S, a corresponding charge of $+180$ μC must be induced on the positive plate of the 4-μF capacitor connected to S, leaving the net charge at S zero. A corresponding -180-μC charge is induced on the negative terminal of the 4-μF capacitor, and the voltage between the plates is thus

$$V_3 = \frac{Q_3}{C_3} = \frac{180 \times 10^{-6} \text{ C}}{4 \times 10^{-6} \text{ F}} = 45 \text{ V}.$$

The total potential difference between A and B is thus

$$V = V_{AS} + V_{SB} = (15 + 45) \text{ V} = 60 \text{ V}.$$

This is the potential difference between A and B by either branch. Referring to diagram (c), the charge on the equivalent $\frac{4}{3}$-μF capacitor is thus

$$Q_4 = C_4 V = \tfrac{4}{3} \times 10^{-6} \text{ F} \times 60 \text{ V} = 80 \text{ } \mu C.$$

This is the charge on the plate attached to A in either the equivalent circuit or the original circuit, since the two produce identical effects. Hence the equivalent 4-μF capacitor between A and R has charges of ± 80 μC on each of its plates. Hence the potential difference across it is

$$V_{AR} = \frac{Q_4}{C_5} = \frac{80 \times 10^{-6} \text{ C}}{4 \times 10^{-6} \text{ F}} = 20 \text{ V}.$$

28

Current, Resistance, and Electromotive Force

PROBLEM 28.1

Protons of mass 1.67×10^{-27} kg and moving with a velocity of 2×10^7 m·s^{-1} strike a target of mass 1 g and specific heat capacity 0.334 cal·g^{-1}·C deg^{-1}. The proton stream corresponds to a current of 4.8 μA. At what rate does the temperature of the target initially rise if one-third of the energy of the protons is converted into heat?

Solution. Each proton carries a charge of 1.60×10^{-19} C. If the current flowing is 4.8 μA, the number of protons striking the target in 1 s must be n, where

$$\frac{n \times 1.60 \times 10^{-19} \text{ C}}{1 \text{ s}} = 4.8 \times 10^{-6} \text{ A}. \qquad \therefore \qquad n = 3.00 \times 10^{13} \text{ protons.}$$

In one second the total kinetic energy lost by the protons is $n \times \frac{1}{2} m_p v^2$, in the usual notation, and one-third of this energy is converted into heat in the target. If in one second the temperature rise of the target is t, the heat gained by the target is mct, in the usual notation. Therefore $mct = \frac{1}{3} \times \frac{1}{2} nm_p v^2$ or

$$t = \frac{nm_p v^2}{6mc} = \frac{3.00 \times 10^{13} \times 1.67 \times 10^{-27} \text{ kg} \times 4 \times 10^{14} \text{ m}^2 \cdot \text{s}^{-2}}{6 \times 1 \text{ g} \times 4.18 \text{ J} \cdot \text{cal}^{-1} \times 0.334 \text{ cal} \cdot \text{g}^{-1} \cdot \text{C deg}^{-1}} = 2.39 °\text{C}.$$

PROBLEM 28.2

In order to find how much insulated wire he has left on a bobbin a technician measures the total resistance of the wire, finding it to be 5.18 Ω*. He then cuts off a 200-cm length and finds the resistance of this to be 0.35 Ω. What was initially the length of wire on the bobbin?

Solution. The resistance of the wire on the bobbin is related to its length by the formula $R_0 = \rho l_0 / A$, in the usual notation. The cut-off length has the same resistivity and cross-sectional area. Hence its resistance is $R = \rho l / A$.

$$\therefore \qquad \frac{l_0}{l} = \frac{R_0}{R} \qquad \text{or} \qquad l_0 = 200 \text{ cm} \times \frac{5.18 \ \Omega}{0.35 \ \Omega} = 2960 \text{ cm.}$$

PROBLEM 28.3

Our enquiring physics student connects a cell to a circuit and measures the current drawn from the cell to be I_1. When he joins a second, identical cell in series with the first, the current becomes I_2. When he connects the cells in parallel, the current through the circuit is I_3. Show that the relation he finds between the currents is $3I_2 I_3 = 2I_1(I_2 + I_3)$.

---

*The International Union of Pure and Applied Physics has decreed that the Greek letter omega (Ω) be used to represent ohm.

Solution. Let the emf of any of the cells be $\mathscr{E}$ and its internal resistance be r. Let the external circuit have a resistance R. When a single cell is used, we apply the circuit equation,

$$I_1 = \frac{\mathscr{E}}{R + r}.$$

(a)

If two identical cells are connected in series, their emf's act in the same sense. Hence

$$I_2 = \frac{2\mathscr{E}}{R + 2r}.$$

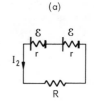

When the cells are connected in parallel, since they are identical, by the symmetry of the arrangement identical currents I_0 must flow through each cell. Further, since no charge accumulates at point A in this circuit,

$$I_3 = I_0 + I_0 = 2I_0.$$

(b)

Considering the passage of current through either cell, we have

$$V_{AB} = \mathscr{E} - I_0 r = \mathscr{E} - \frac{I_3}{2} r.$$

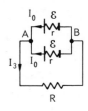

When we consider the passage of current through the external circuit, then $V_{AB} = I_3 R$.

$$\therefore \quad \mathscr{E} = I_3 \left(R + \frac{r}{2} \right).$$

(c)

Rewriting the three equations obtained, we find that

$$R + r = \frac{\mathscr{E}}{I_1}, \qquad R + 2r = \frac{2\mathscr{E}}{I_2}, \qquad \text{and} \qquad R + \frac{r}{2} = \frac{\mathscr{E}}{I_3}.$$

Eliminating r between the first two equations gives

$$R = 2\mathscr{E} \left(\frac{1}{I_1} - \frac{1}{I_2} \right),$$

and between the first and third yields

$$R = \mathscr{E} \left(\frac{2}{I_3} - \frac{1}{I_1} \right).$$

Dividing these last two equations one by the other gives

$$1 = \frac{2[(1/I_1) - (1/I_2)]}{(2/I_3) - (1/I_1)}.$$

$$\therefore \quad 2I_1 I_2 - I_2 I_3 = 2I_2 I_3 - 2I_1 I_3. \qquad \therefore \quad 3I_2 I_3 = 2I_1(I_2 + I_3).$$

PROBLEM 28.4

A battery of 50 cells is being charged from a dc supply of 230 V and negligible internal resistance. The emf of each cell on charge is 2.3 V, its internal resistance is 0.1 Ω and the necessary charging current is 6 A. What extra resistance must be inserted in the circuit?

Solution. Let R be the extra resistance needed in the circuit. The 50 cells have a total emf of 115 V and a total internal resistance of 5 Ω. We apply the circuit equation $\mathscr{E} = I(R + r)$ to obtain

$$(230 - 115)\ \text{V} = 6\ \text{A}(R + 5\ \Omega).$$

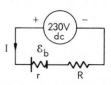

$$\therefore \quad R = \frac{115\ \text{V}}{6\ \text{A}} - 5\ \Omega = 14.2\ \Omega.$$

PROBLEM 28.5

A wire of diameter 1 mm carrying a heavy current has a temperature of 1200°K when equilibrium has been achieved. We assume that the heat lost from the wire is purely by radiation. The temperature of the surroundings is 300°K, the resistivity of the wire at this temperature is $5 \times 10^{-8}\ \Omega \cdot$m, and the temperature coefficient of resistance of the wire is 4×10^{-3} per C deg. What is the magnitude of the current in the wire?

Solution. Since the heat is being lost by radiation only, the energy lost per second by a 1-m length of the wire is $W = A\sigma(T^4 - T_0^4)$, where A is the surface area of the length of wire and σ is Stefan's constant, the wire being assumed to radiate as a blackbody.

But this energy is supplied by the current flowing. Thus, if R is the resistance of 1 m of the wire, then $I^2 R = W = A\sigma(T^4 - T_0^4)$. But

$$R = \frac{\rho l}{A'} = \frac{\rho_0\,[1 + \alpha\,(T - T_0)]\,l}{A'},$$

where A' is the cross-sectional area, l is the length, ρ_0 is the resistivity at 300°K, and α is the temperature coefficient of resistance. Hence

$$I^2 = \frac{AA'\sigma\,(T^4 - T_0^4)}{\rho_0[1 + \alpha(T - T_0)]\,l}$$

$$= \frac{1\text{m} \times 2\pi \times \frac{1}{2} \times 10^{-3}\text{m} \times \pi(\frac{1}{2} \times 10^{-3})^2\text{m}^2 \times 5.67 \times 10^{-8}\ \text{W} \cdot \text{m}^{-2}(\text{K deg})^{-4}(1200^4 - 300^4)\,(\text{K deg})^4}{5 \times 10^{-8}\ \Omega \cdot \text{m}\,[1 + 4 \times 10^{-3}\,(\text{K deg})^{-1}\,(1200 - 300)\,\text{K deg}] \times 1\ \text{m}}$$

$$= 1258\ \text{A}^2.$$

$$\therefore \qquad I = 35.5\ \text{A}.$$

PROBLEM 28.6

An electric kettle contains 2 liters of water which it heats from 20°C to boiling point in 5 min. The supply voltage is 200 V and a kWh* unit costs 2 cents. Calculate (a) the power consumed (assume that heat losses are negligible), (b) the cost of using the kettle under these conditions six times, (c) the resistance of the heating element, and (d) the current in the element.

Solution. The heat gained by the water in being raised to the boiling point is given by the expression $H = mc(t_2 - t_1)$, in the usual notation.

(a) $\therefore \qquad H = 2 \times 10^3\ \text{cm}^3 \times 1\ \text{g} \cdot \text{cm}^{-3} \times 4.18\ \text{J} \cdot \text{g}^{-1} \cdot \text{C deg}^{-1} \times (100 - 20)\ \text{C deg} = 6.69 \times 10^5\ \text{J},$

and since heat losses are neglected, this is the electrical energy consumed by the kettle.

The power is the energy consumed per second, which is thus

$$P = \frac{H}{\tau} = \frac{6.69 \times 10^5\ \text{J}}{5 \times 60\ \text{s}} = 2.23 \times 10^3\ \text{J} \cdot \text{s}^{-1} = 2.23\ \text{kW}.$$

(b) The kettle uses 2.23 kW for 5 min each time the water is boiled. When it is used six times, 2.23 kW is used for 30 min $= \frac{1}{2}$ hr. The cost is thus

$$2.23\ \text{kW} \times \tfrac{1}{2}\ \text{hr} \times 2\ \text{cents} \cdot \text{kWh}^{-1} = 2.23\ \text{cents}.$$

(c) The power consumed is 2.23 kW and the supply voltage is 200 V. But $P = V^2/R$ or

$$R = \frac{V^2}{P} = \frac{200^2\ \text{V}^2}{2.23 \times 10^3\ \text{W}} = 17.9\ \Omega.$$

---

*The letters kWh, under the system adopted by the International Union of Pure and Applied Physics, denote kilowatt-hour.

(d) But one may also write the power as $P = IV$.

$$\therefore \quad I = \frac{P}{V} = \frac{2.23 \times 10^3 \text{ W}}{200 \text{ V}} = 11.2 \text{ A}.$$

PROBLEM 28.7

A dynamo driven by a steam engine which uses 10^3 kg of coal per day produces a current of 200 A at an emf of 240 V. What is the efficiency of the system if the calorific value of coal is $6.6 \times 10^3 \text{ cal} \cdot \text{g}^{-1}$?

Solution. The energy supplied by the coal per second is

$$E_0 = \frac{6.6 \times 10^3 \text{ cal} \cdot \text{g}^{-1} \times 10^6 \text{ g}}{24 \times 60 \times 60 \text{ s}} = \frac{4.2 \times 6.6 \times 10^9}{24 \times 60 \times 60} \text{ J} \cdot \text{s}^{-1} = 3.2 \times 10^5 \text{ W}.$$

The electrical power supplied by the dynamo is

$$P = IV = 200 \text{ A} \times 240 \text{ V} = 4.8 \times 10^4 \text{ W}.$$

The efficiency of the system is thus

$$\frac{P}{E_0} \times 100\% = \frac{4.8 \times 10^4}{3.2 \times 10^5} \% = 15\%.$$

29

Direct-Current Circuits and Instruments

PROBLEM 29.1

Two conductors of the same length and material but of different cross-sectional areas are connected (a) in series, and (b) in parallel. When a potential difference is applied across the combinations, in which conductor will the heating be greater in each case?

Solution. The resistance of each conductor has the form $R = \rho l/A$. Since the resistivity and length are the same in each case, $R_1/R_2 = A_2/A_1$.

(a) When the conductors are in series, the same current passes through each. Hence the ratio of the heating produced in the wires is

$$\frac{H_1}{H_2} = \frac{i^2 R_1}{i^2 R_2} = \frac{R_1}{R_2} = \frac{A_2}{A_1}.$$

The heating is thus greater in the conductor with the smaller cross-sectional area.

(b) When the conductors are in parallel, different currents pass through them but the potential difference across each is the same. Hence

$$\frac{H_1'}{H_2'} = \frac{V^2/R_1}{V^2/R_2} = \frac{R_2}{R_1} = \frac{A_1}{A_2}.$$

In this case the heating is greater in the conductor with the larger cross-sectional area.

PROBLEM 29.2

Five resistors, each of resistance 10 Ω, are connected to form a letter H, a 2-V cell of internal resistance 1.86 Ω being connected across the upper ends and an ammeter of resistance 5 Ω across the lower ends. What current passes through the ammeter?

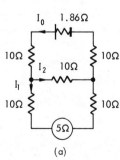

(a)

Solution. The circuit is shown in diagram (a) and is equivalent to the circuit shown in diagram (b). The resistances of 10 Ω and 25 Ω are in parallel. Hence the equivalent resistance is R, where

$$\frac{1}{R} = \frac{1}{10\ \Omega} + \frac{1}{25\ \Omega} = \frac{5 + 2}{50\ \Omega}.$$

$$\therefore \quad R = \frac{50}{7}\ \Omega = 7\frac{1}{7}\ \Omega = 7.14\ \Omega.$$

The circuit is therefore equivalent to the one shown in diagram (c) (see page 126). It is now possible to find the current I_0 in the battery circuit, for

$$I_0 = \frac{\mathscr{E}}{R} = \frac{2\ \text{V}}{(10 + 10 + 7.14 + 1.86)\ \Omega} = \frac{2}{29}\ \text{A}.$$

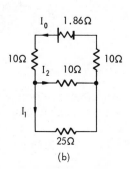

(b)

This current splits up into currents I_1 and I_2 through the lower parts of the circuit, as shown in diagrams (a) and (b), where

$$\frac{I_1}{I_2} = \frac{R_2}{R_1} = \frac{10\ \Omega}{25\ \Omega}. \qquad \therefore \qquad \frac{I_1}{I_1 + I_2} = \frac{10}{35}.$$

Since no charge can accumulate in the circuit, then $I_1 + I_2 = I_0$.

$$\therefore \qquad I_1 = \frac{10}{35} I_0 = \frac{10}{35} \times \frac{2}{29}\ A = 0.0197\ A,$$

which is the current flowing through the ammeter.

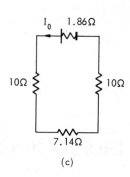

(c)

PROBLEM 29.3

A bank of cells having a total emf of 12 V and negligible internal resistance is connected in series with two resistors. A voltmeter of resistance 5000 Ω is connected across the resistors in turn, and measures 4 V and 6 V, respectively. What are the resistances of the two resistors?

Solution. The voltmeter is connected across R_1 as in diagram (a), and the circuit is equivalent to that shown in diagram (b), where

$$\frac{1}{R} = \frac{1}{R_1} + \frac{1}{5000\ \Omega}.$$

$$\therefore \qquad R = \frac{5000\ R_1\ \Omega}{5000\ \Omega + R_1}.$$

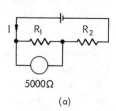

(a)

Since 4 V are dropped across the resistance R and thus 8 V across resistance R_2, $4\ V = IR$ and $8\ V = IR_2$.

$$\therefore \qquad R = \frac{5000\ R_1\ \Omega}{5000\ \Omega + R_1} = \frac{R_2}{2}.$$

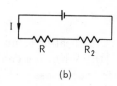

(b)

Similarly, from diagrams (c) and (d), showing the second connection of the voltmeter and the equivalent circuit, we have

$$R' = \frac{5000\ R_2\ \Omega}{5000\ \Omega + R_2} \qquad \text{and} \qquad 6\ V = I'R_1 = I'R'.$$

$$\therefore \qquad R' = \frac{5000\ R_2\ \Omega}{5000\ \Omega + R_2} = R_1.$$

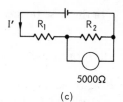

(c)

Hence, from the two equations obtained, we have

$$10{,}000\ R_1\ \Omega = 5000\ R_2\ \Omega + R_1 R_2 \qquad \text{and} \qquad 5000\ R_2\ \Omega = 5000\ R_1\ \Omega + R_1 R_2.$$

Subtracting these equations, we obtain

$$15{,}000\ R_1 = 10{,}000\ R_2 \qquad \text{or} \qquad R_1 = \tfrac{2}{3} R_2.$$

Substituting back into the equations, we get

$$R_1 = \frac{5000\ \Omega}{3} = 1667\ \Omega \qquad \text{and} \qquad R_2 = \frac{5000\ \Omega}{2} = 2500\ \Omega.$$

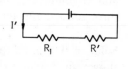

(d)

PROBLEM 29.4

A piece of uniform wire is made up into two squares with a common side of length 4 in. A current enters the rectangular system at one of the corners and leaves at the diagonally opposite corner. Show that the current in the common side is one-fifth of the entering current. What length of wire connected between input and output terminals would have an equivalent resistive effect?

Solution. Let each side of the double square have resistance R, and let the lettering of the diagram and the currents flowing be as shown. Applying the first Kirchhoff rule, $\Sigma I = 0$, to the points A, B, and E in turn gives

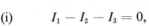

(i) $I_1 - I_2 - I_3 = 0,$

(ii) $I_2 - I_4 - I_5 = 0,$

(iii) $I_3 + I_4 - I = 0.$

Applying the second Kirchhoff rule to circuits $ABED$ and $BCFE$ gives

(iv) $I_2 R + I_4 R - I_3 \times 2R = 0,$

(v) $I_5 \times 2R - I_6 R - I_4 R = 0.$

Eliminating I_5 and I_6 from Eqs. (ii), (iii), and (v), we obtain

(i) $I_1 - I_2 - I_3 = 0,$

(iv) $I_2 - 2I_3 + I_4 = 0,$

(vi) $2I_2 - I_3 - 4I_4 = 0.$

Eliminating I_2 from these three equations gives

(vii) $I_1 - 3I_3 + I_4 = 0,$

and

(viii) $2I_1 - 3I_3 - 4I_4 = 0,$

or

(ix) $I_4 = \tfrac{1}{5} I_1.$

Further, the potential drop from A to F by route $ADEF$ is

$$V_{AF} = I_3 \times 2R + I_6 \times R = R(2I_3 + I_3 + I_4) = R(I_1 + 2I_4) = I_1 R(1 + \tfrac{2}{5}) = \tfrac{7}{5} RI_1,$$

employing Eqs. (iii), (vii), and (ix).

The equivalent effect is therefore obtained if a wire $\tfrac{7}{5}$ times the length of any side of the square is connected between A and F, because it produces the same potential drop as the double square between these points.

PROBLEM 29.5

Two cells, one of emf 1.2 V and internal resistance 0.5 Ω, the other of emf 2 V and internal resistance 0.1 Ω, are connected in parallel and the combination connected in series with an external resistance of 5 Ω. What current passes through this external resistance?

Solution. The diagram is labeled and current values have been inserted in each part of the circuit. Applying Kirchhoff's first law to point A, we have

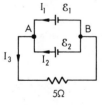

$$I_1 + I_2 = I_3.$$

Applying Kirchhoff's second law to the closed circuit containing both cells and then to the closed circuit through the lower cell and the external resistance, we have

$$\mathscr{E}_2 - \mathscr{E}_1 = (2 - 1.2) \text{ V} = I_2 \times 0.1 \, \Omega - I_1 \times 0.5 \, \Omega \quad \text{and} \quad \mathscr{E}_2 = 2 \text{ V} = I_2 \times 0.1 \, \Omega + I_3 \times 5 \, \Omega.$$

$$\therefore \quad I_2 - 5I_1 = 8 \text{ A} \quad \text{and} \quad I_2 + 50(I_1 + I_2) = 20 \text{ A}$$

or

$$10I_2 - 50I_1 = 80 \text{ A} \quad \text{and} \quad 51I_2 + 50I_1 = 20 \text{ A}.$$

$$\therefore \quad I_2 = \frac{100 \text{ A}}{61} = 1.64 \text{ A} \quad \text{and} \quad I_1 = -\frac{388}{355} = -1.27 \text{ A}.$$

$$\therefore \quad I_3 = I_2 + I_1 = 0.37 \text{ A}.$$

PROBLEM 29.6

A galvanometer of resistance 20 Ω gives a full-scale deflection when a current of 1 mA passes through it. What modification must be made to the instrument so that it will give full-scale deflection for (a) a current of 0.5 A, and (b) a potential difference of 500 V?

Solution. If a galvanometer has a resistance of 20 Ω and gives full-scale deflection for a current of 1 mA, then the voltage drop across it under these circumstances is

$$V = IR = 10^{-3} \text{A} \times 20 \ \Omega = 0.02 \text{ V.}$$

(a) To allow the galvanometer to read up to 0.5 A, a shunt resistor must be added. This resistor must take 499 mA, allowing only 1 mA through the galvanometer. But the potential difference across each is the same. Thus if r is the resistance of the shunt, then

$$1 \text{ mA} \times 20 \ \Omega = 499 \text{ mA} \times r. \qquad \therefore \qquad r = \frac{20 \ \Omega}{499} = 0.0401 \ \Omega.$$

(b) To convert to a voltmeter reading up to 500 V, one must add a series resistor. Only 0.02 V is dropped across the galvanometer for the maximum current of 1 mA. Thus 499.98 V must be dropped across the resistor of resistance R. The same current flows through both resistor and galvanometer. Hence

$$R = \frac{499.98 \text{ V}}{10^{-3} \text{ A}} = 499{,}980 \ \Omega.$$

PROBLEM 29.7

A coil of wire is connected across one gap of a Wheatstone bridge and a temperature-controlled standard 1-Ω resistor across the other. If the temperature of the coil is 0°C, the other arms of the bridge have resistances in the ratio 0.923. If the temperature of the coil is 100°C the ratio is 1.338. What is the temperature coefficient of resistance of the wire?

Solution. From the Wheatstone-bridge equation, the resistances of the coil, R_0 at 0°C and R_t at 100°C, are $R_0 = 0.923 \times 1 \ \Omega$ and $R_t = 1.338 \times 1 \ \Omega$. But $R_t = R_0(1 + \alpha t)$, where α is the temperature coefficient of resistance of the wire. Thus

$$\alpha = \frac{(R_t/R_0) - 1}{t} = \frac{(1.338/0.923) - 1}{100°\text{C}} = 0.0045 \text{ per } °\text{C.}$$

PROBLEM 29.8

A variable resistor in series with a 2-V cell and an ammeter is adjusted to give a full-scale deflection on the meter, which occurs for a current of 1 mA. What resistance placed in series in the circuit will reduce the meter reading by $1/f$?

The meter is calibrated to measure resistance on this basis, but the emf of the cell drops by 5% and the variable resistor is readjusted so that the full-scale deflection again corresponds to the zero of the resistance scale. What percentage error is now given on a resistor which has a true resistance of 3800 Ω?

Solution. The total resistance in the circuit when the meter is giving full-scale deflection is

$$R = \frac{\mathscr{E}}{I} = \frac{2 \text{ V}}{10^{-3} \text{A}} = 2000 \ \Omega.$$

If an unknown resistance X is added to the circuit and produces a meter reading of $(1/f)$ mA, then

$$R + X = \frac{2 \text{ V}}{(1/f) \times 10^{-3} \text{A}} = 2000 f \ \Omega.$$

$$\therefore \qquad X = (2000f - 2000) \ \Omega = 2000(f - 1) \ \Omega.$$

The emf of the cell now drops to $\frac{95}{100}$ of 2 V = 1.9 V. For full-scale deflection the resistance in the circuit is now

$$R' = \frac{1.9 \text{ V}}{10^{-3} \text{A}} = 1900 \, \Omega,$$

and if a further resistance of 3800 Ω is inserted in the circuit, the current is 1.9 V/(1900 + 3800) $\Omega = \frac{1}{3}$ mA.

But from the meter calibration, when the current drops to one-third of its value, the inserted resistance should have a value

$$X = [2000 \, (3 - 1)] \, \Omega = 4000 \, \Omega.$$

The error in the reading is thus 200 Ω, and the percentage error is

$$\frac{200}{3800} \times 100\% = 5.3\%.$$

PROBLEM 29.9

A length of 300 cm of a potentiometer wire is required to balance the emf of a cell. When a 10-Ω resistor is connected across the cell, the length required for balance is 250 cm. Calculate the internal resistance of the cell.

Solution. The potentiometer wire is uniform and thus the potential drop along it is regular. Hence length along the wire is directly proportional to the potential drop across it. Thus $\mathscr{E} = k \times 300$ cm, where k is the constant of proportionality between potential and length, having units of V·cm^{-1}.

When a 10-Ω resistor is put across the terminals of the cell, the potential across the resistor is $V = k \times 250$ cm.

$$\therefore \quad \frac{\mathscr{E}}{V} = \frac{300}{250} = \frac{6}{5}.$$

But when a resistor is across the terminals of the cell, a current I will flow in that circuit, where $V = IR$ and $\mathscr{E} = I(R + r)$.

$$\therefore \quad \frac{\mathscr{E}}{V} = \frac{6}{5} = \frac{R + r}{R} = \frac{10 \, \Omega + r}{10 \, \Omega}. \qquad \therefore \quad r = 2 \, \Omega.$$

PROBLEM 29.10

A conductor of capacitance 10^{-2} μF to the ground is insulated from the ground by a silica plate 2.5 mm thick and 5 cm^2 in cross-sectional area. What is the minimum resistivity of the silica if the rate of decrease of potential is to be no greater than 0.1% per min?

Solution. The silica plate has a large resistance R and the conductor discharges slowly through it. Thus the charge on the conductor at any time is $q = Q_0 e^{-t/RC}$, or the potential of the conductor is $V = V_0 e^{-t/RC}$.

$$\therefore \quad \ln V = \ln V_0 - \frac{t}{RC}. \qquad \therefore \quad \frac{\Delta V}{V} = -\frac{\Delta t}{RC}.$$

After 60 s, $\Delta V/V$ is to be no more than $-0.1/100$. Thus R must have a value of at least

$$R = -\frac{\Delta t}{C} \frac{V}{\Delta V} = \frac{60 \text{ s}}{10^{-8} \text{F} \times 10^{-3}} = 6 \times 10^{12} \, \Omega.$$

But $R = \rho l/A$, in the usual notation. Thus the resistivity of the silica must be at least

$$\rho = \frac{AR}{l} = \frac{5 \times 10^{-4} \text{ m}^2 \times 6 \times 10^{12} \, \Omega}{2.5 \times 10^{-3} \text{ m}} = 1.2 \times 10^{12} \, \Omega \cdot \text{m}.$$

30

The Magnetic Field

PROBLEM 30.1

A particle is projected horizontally with a velocity of 10^4 m·s^{-1} in such a direction that it moves at right angles to a horizontal magnetic field of induction, of magnitude 4.9×10^{-5} Wb·m^{-2}. The particle, which carries a single electronic charge, stays in the same horizontal plane. What is its mass?

Solution. Since the particle stays in the same horizontal plane during its motion, the magnetic force on it must just balance its weight. Since the motion is at right angles to the direction of the magnetic induction, it follows that $-mg = q(\mathbf{v} \times \mathbf{B})$, and thus $mg = qvB$ or $m = qvB/g$.

$$\therefore \quad m = \frac{1.6 \times 10^{-19}\,\text{C} \times 10^4\,\text{m·s}^{-1} \times 4.9 \times 10^{-5}\,\text{Wb·m}^{-2}}{9.8\,\text{m·s}^{-2}} = 8.0 \times 10^{-21}\,\text{kg.}$$

PROBLEM 30.2

The energy of the doubly charged α-particles of mass 6.64×10^{-27} kg emitted from ThC is 6.048 MeV. What is their velocity and what magnetic field applied perpendicular to a collimated beam of such particles would bend the beam into a circle of radius 40 cm?

Solution. If the energy of the α-particles is 6.048 MeV $= 6.048 \times 1.602 \times 10^{-13}$ J $= 9.689 \times 10^{-13}$ J, then $\frac{1}{2}mv^2 = 9.689 \times 10^{-13}$ J, or

$$v = \sqrt{\frac{19.378 \times 10^{-13}\,\text{J}}{6.64 \times 10^{-27}\,\text{kg}}} = 1.709 \times 10^7\,\text{m·s}^{-1}.$$

In the magnetic field the magnetic force supplies the centripetal force necessary to keep the particles moving in a circle. Hence $qvB = mv^2/R$ or $v = qBR/m$. Therefore $B = mv/qR$.
The α-particles carry twice the electronic charge.

$$\therefore \quad B = \frac{6.64 \times 10^{-27}\,\text{kg} \times 1.709 \times 10^7\,\text{m·s}^{-1}}{2 \times 1.602 \times 10^{-19}\,\text{C} \times 0.40\,\text{m}} = 0.885\,\text{Wb·m}^{-2}.$$

PROBLEM 30.3

A set of positive-ray parabolas are examined and it is found that for the same horizontal displacement y, the corresponding vertical displacements for the three parabolas observed are 3.24 mm, 3.00 mm, and 2.81 mm. The parabola with the largest displacement is known to correspond to C^{12} and all ions are singly charged. What are the other ions present?

Solution. The equation linking the horizontal and vertical displacements in any parabola is, in the usual notation,

$$z^2 = \frac{q}{m} \frac{B^2 L D}{E} y.$$

For all the ions present the quantities q, B^2, L, D, and E are the same, and thus for fixed y, $z^2 = k/m$, where k is constant for all ions.

Since, when $z = 3.24$ mm, m is 12.000 amu, then $k = 3.24^2$ mm$^2 \times$ 12.000 amu $=$ 126 mm$^2 \cdot$ amu. Thus when $z = 3.00$ mm,

$$m = \frac{k}{z^2} = \frac{126 \text{ mm}^2 \cdot \text{amu}}{9 \text{ mm}^2} = 14.00 \text{ amu.}$$

The ion is thus N^{14}.

When $z = 2.81$ mm,

$$m = \frac{k}{z^2} = \frac{126 \text{ mm}^2 \cdot \text{amu}}{2.81^2 \text{ mm}^2} = 15.96 \text{ amu.}$$

This ion is thus O^{16}.

PROBLEM 30.4

In one type of mass spectrometer the charged particles pass through a velocity selector before entering the magnetic field. In another the particles pass through a strong electric field before entering the magnetic field. Compare the ratio of the radii of singly charged lithium ions of masses 6 amu and 7 amu in the two cases.

Solution. In the magnetic field an ion moves in a circle, the centripetal force necessary being provided by the magnetic force on it. Thus $qvB = mv^2/R$ or $v = qBR/m$. When the ions have passed through a velocity selector, both lithium ions have the same velocity in the field. Further, they have the same charge and are in the same magnetic flux density. Thus $R_6/m_6 = R_7/m_7$.

$$\therefore \quad \frac{R_6}{R_7} = \frac{m_6}{m_7} = \frac{6}{7} = 0.857.$$

If the ions have passed through a strong electric field, they have both acquired the same energy. But, from the previous equation, we have $\frac{1}{2}mv^2 = q^2B^2r^2/2m$.

$$\therefore \quad \frac{r_6^2}{m_6} = \frac{r_7^2}{m_7} \quad \text{or} \quad \frac{r_6}{r_7} = \sqrt{\frac{m_6}{m_7}} = 0.926.$$

PROBLEM 30.5

A cyclotron has an oscillator frequency of 11.4 Mc$\cdot$s^{-1} and a radius of 60 cm. What magnetic intensity is required to accelerate protons of mass 1.67×10^{-27} kg and charge 1.6×10^{-19} C, and what is the final energy that they acquire?

What error is made by assuming that the mass of the protons remains constant?

Solution. The angular frequency of the protons in the cyclotron is, in the usual notation, $\omega = Bq/m$ or $f = Bq/2\pi m$.

$$\therefore \quad B = \frac{2\pi f m}{q} = \frac{2\pi \times 11.4 \times 10^6 \text{ s}^{-1} \times 1.67 \times 10^{-27} \text{ kg}}{1.6 \times 10^{-19} \text{ C}} = 0.748 \text{ Wb} \cdot \text{m}^{-2}.$$

The final energy of the protons is

$$\frac{1}{2}mv^2 = \frac{q^2 B^2 R^2}{2m} = \frac{(1.6 \times 10^{-19})^2 \text{ C}^2 \times (0.748)^2 \text{ Wb}^2 \cdot \text{m}^{-4} \times 0.6^2 \text{ m}^2}{2 \times 1.67 \times 10^{-27} \text{ kg}}$$

$$= 0.154 \times 10^{-11} \text{ J} = \frac{0.154 \times 10^{-11} \text{ J}}{1.6 \times 10^{-13} \text{ J} \cdot \text{MeV}^{-1}} = 9.64 \text{ MeV.}$$

Since $E = mc^2$, this energy is equivalent to an increase of mass

$$\Delta m = \frac{0.154 \times 10^{-11}\,\text{J}}{9 \times 10^{16}\,\text{m}^2 \cdot \text{s}^{-2}} = 0.017 \times 10^{-27}\,\text{kg}.$$

The error is thus

$$\frac{\Delta m}{m} \times 100 = \frac{0.017}{1.67} \times 100 = 1.02\%.$$

31

Magnetic Forces on Current-Carrying Conductors

PROBLEM 31.1

A scientifically minded Prince Charming has found a method of sending secret messages to a beautiful princess who is immured by a wicked ogre in the top floor of his castle 50 ft from the ground. The prince places two light metal rods (too light to use for climbing up) against her windowsill, and between the rods he mounts a wire 10 cm long, to which is attached the message and a magnet so placed that the wire is permanently in a magnetic field of strength 0.049 Wb·m⁻², at right angles to the plane of the rods. When he passes a current of 10 A up one rod, through the connecting wire and back down the other rod, the message, wire, and magnet travel at uniform speed up the rods. The moving assembly weighs 0.25 kg. Neglecting friction, calculate what the length of the rods must be.

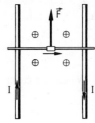

Solution. From the first diagram, we see that the magnetic field must be at right angles to the plane of the rods and acting downward. The magnitude of the force experienced by the wire and attachments is

$$F = IlB = 0.1 \text{ m} \times 10 \text{ A} \times 0.049 \text{ Wb·m}^{-2} = 0.049 \text{ N}.$$

Considering the second diagram, we see that the forces acting on the wire and attachments are three in number: the weight acting vertically downward, the force **F** acting up the plane of the rods, and **N**, the normal reaction of the rods on the wire acting at right angles to the plane of the rods. Since the assembly moves up the rods at uniform speed, $N = mg \cos \theta$ and $F = mg \sin \theta$.

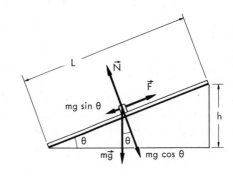

$$\therefore \quad \sin \theta = \frac{0.049 \text{ N}}{0.25 \text{ kg} \times 9.8 \text{ m·s}^{-2}} = 0.02.$$

From the diagram, $h/L = 0.02$.

$$\therefore \quad L = \frac{h}{0.02} = \frac{50 \text{ ft}}{0.02} = 2500 \text{ ft}.$$

Carrying such rods around would be quite a feat. Prince Charming would do better to engage the services of a good witch!

PROBLEM 31.2

Calculate the angular velocity of precession of an electron in a magnetic field of strength 0.75 Wb·m⁻².

Solution. The magnetic moment of the electron is $\mu_B = eh/4\pi m$, and the velocity of precession is

$$\Omega = \frac{\Gamma}{L} = \frac{\mu_B B}{L} = \frac{eh/4\pi m}{h/4\pi} B = \frac{eB}{m}.$$

$$\therefore \quad \Omega = \frac{1.6 \times 10^{-19}\, \text{C} \times 0.75\, \text{Wb} \cdot \text{m}^{-2}}{9.1 \times 10^{-31}\, \text{kg}} = 13.2 \times 10^{10}\, \text{rad} \cdot \text{s}^{-1} = 2.1 \times 10^{10}\, \text{cycles} \cdot \text{s}^{-1}.$$

PROBLEM 31.3

The coil of a galvanometer has 150 turns of mean area 1 cm² and the restoring couple of the suspension is 10^{-6} N·m per radian. The magnitude of the radial magnetic induction in which the coil swings is 0.2 Wb·m⁻². What deflection will be produced when a current of 10 μA passes through the coil?

The plates of a 1-μF capacitor are charged to a potential difference of 1 V and then discharged through the galvanometer coil, the resultant deflection being 0.1 rad. What is the moment of inertia of the coil?

Solution. The magnitude of the torque acting on the 150 turns of the coil due to the magnetic field is, in the usual notation, $\Gamma = 150\, AIB$, the field being a radial one.

The coil swings until this torque is counterbalanced by the restoring torque of the suspension $k\theta$. Thus at the equilibrium position of deflection, $k\theta = 150\, AIB$ or

$$\theta = \frac{150\, AIB}{k} = \frac{150 \times 10^{-4}\, \text{m}^2 \times 10^{-5}\, \text{A} \times 0.2\, \text{Wb} \cdot \text{m}^{-2}}{10^{-6}\, \text{N} \cdot \text{m}} = 0.03\, \text{rad}.$$

When the capacitor is discharged, the charge flowing through the galvanometer coil is

$$Q = CV = 10^{-6}\, \text{F} \times 1\, \text{V} = 10^{-6}\, \text{C}.$$

But the charge and the resultant maximum deflection of the galvanometer are related by the equation $Q = (\sqrt{kI'}/nAB)\, \theta_{\text{max}}$, where I' is the moment of inertia of the coil. Thus

$$I' = \frac{n^2 A^2 B^2 Q^2}{k\theta_{\text{max}}^2} = \frac{150^2 \times 10^{-8}\, \text{m}^4 \times 0.2^2\, \text{Wb}^2 \cdot \text{m}^{-4} \times 10^{-12}\, \text{C}^2}{10^{-6}\, \text{N} \cdot \text{m} \times 10^{-2}} = 9 \times 10^{-10}\, \text{kg} \cdot \text{m}^2.$$

PROBLEM 31.4

A current-carrying wire in the form of a semicircle lies in a plane at right angles to the direction of a uniform magnetic induction. Show that the force on the wire is the same as that experienced by a straight wire lying along the diameter between the ends of the semicircle.

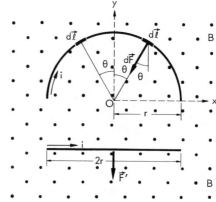

Solution. Let the semicircle carrying a current i have radius r, and let the magnetic induction have magnitude B. Consider the diagram, in which a vector element $d\mathbf{l}$ of the current-carrying wire is shown in a direction from the center O of the semicircle making an angle θ with the radius of symmetry. The force on that element due to the magnetic field is $d\mathbf{F} = i(d\mathbf{l} \times \mathbf{B})$. Here $d\mathbf{l}$ and $\mathbf{B}$ are at right angles, and thus $d\mathbf{F}$ lies along the radius from $d\mathbf{l}$ to O. Also $d\mathbf{F}$ has components, in the x- and y-directions shown, of $-i\, dlB \sin \theta$ and $-i\, dlB \cos \theta$, respectively. But there is a corresponding element $d\mathbf{l}$ in a direction from O making an angle $-\theta$ with the radius of symmetry. This element is subjected to a force which has x- and y-components of $+i\, dlB \sin \theta$ and $-i\, dlB \cos \theta$, respectively. The x-components of the forces of these two elements thus cancel out, and this is true of all pairs of elements chosen at all possible angles θ on the semicircle. It follows that the total force $\mathbf{F}$ on the semicircle has a y-component only. Now $dl = r\, d\theta$, and therefore

$$F = \int_0^l -i\, dlB \cos \theta = \int_{-\pi/2}^{\pi/2} -ir\, d\theta B \cos \theta = -iBr \left[\sin \theta \right]_{-\pi/2}^{\pi/2} = -2iBr.$$

Consider the straight wire: the force $\mathbf{F}'$ on it is $\mathbf{F}' = i(2\mathbf{r} \times \mathbf{B})$. Thus $\mathbf{F}'$ has magnitude $2iBr$ and points in the negative y-direction. This is the same force as that which acts on the semicircle.

One may arrive at this result and a more general result very simply by noting that a closed current-carrying loop lying in a plane at right angles to the magnetic field experiences no net force. If the semicircular loop is closed by allowing the current to return along a wire occupying the vacant diameter (or by any loop whatsoever lying in the plane and joining the two ends of the semicircle), the complete circuit so formed experiences no net force. It follows that the forces on the semicircle and on the return wire are equal and opposite. Since reversing the direction of the current reverses the magnetic force on it, it immediately follows that the force on the semicircle is equal to the force on any current-carrying conductor lying in the plane and having the same endpoints.

32

Magnetic Field of a Current

PROBLEM 32.1

The current from a dc supply is carried to an instrument by two long parallel wires, 10 cm apart. What is the magnetic flux density midway between the wires when the current carried is 100 A?

Solution. The magnetic field due to each wire in the diagram at the point midway between them will be into the paper. The effects due to the wires are therefore additive at that point and the total effect is twice the effect of either alone. Hence, midway between the wires,

$$B = 2 \times \frac{\mu_0}{2\pi} \frac{I}{r} = 2 \times 2 \times 10^{-7}\,\text{N} \cdot \text{A}^{-2} \times \frac{100\,\text{A}}{0.05\,\text{m}} = 8 \times 10^{-4}\,\text{Wb} \cdot \text{m}^{-2}.$$

PROBLEM 32.2

A long, horizontal, rigidly supported wire carries a current of 50 A. Directly above it and parallel to it is a fine wire, the weight of which is 0.075 N per meter, which carries a current of 25 A. How far above the first wire should the second wire be strung in order for it to be supported by magnetic repulsion?

Solution. If the upper wire is to be supported by magnetic repulsion, the magnetic force per unit length must just equal the weight of a unit length of the wire. Further, the currents in the two wires must be in opposite directions in order for the force between the wires to be one of repulsion. Hence

$$\frac{mg}{l} = \frac{F}{l} = \frac{\mu_0}{2\pi} \frac{II'}{r}.$$

$$\therefore \quad r = \frac{\mu_0 l II'}{2\pi mg} = \frac{2 \times 10^{-7}\,\text{N} \cdot \text{A}^{-2} \times 50\,\text{A} \times 25\,\text{A}}{0.075\,\text{N} \cdot \text{m}^{-1}} = 0.33 \times 10^{-2}\,\text{m} = 0.33\,\text{cm}.$$

The wires must therefore be very thin in order to allow their centers to be so close together.

PROBLEM 32.3

Determine the value of the magnetic induction at the center of a rectangular coil of length a and width b, which carries a current I.

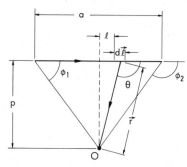

Solution. Consider the wire of length a in the first diagram. Any element $d\mathbf{l}$ is in the direction of current flow and $d\mathbf{l} \times \mathbf{r}$ gives a vector, whatever $d\mathbf{l}$, into the paper. Thus the contribution from all

$d\mathbf{l}$ is in the same direction and the magnitudes are directly additive. For the element $d\mathbf{l}$ shown, the magnitude of the magnetic induction produced at O a distance p from the wire is

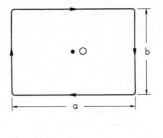

$$dB = \frac{\mu_0}{4\pi} \frac{I\,dl}{r^2} \sin\theta.$$

But $p/r = \sin\theta$, $p/l = -\tan\theta$, and therefore $dl = p\csc^2\theta\,d\theta$.

$$\therefore \quad dB = \frac{\mu_0 I}{4\pi} \frac{p\csc^2\theta\,d\theta \times \sin\theta}{p^2/\sin^2\theta} = \frac{\mu_0 I}{4\pi p}\sin\theta\,d\theta.$$

For the whole wire,

$$B = \frac{\mu_0 I}{4\pi p}\int_{\phi_1}^{\phi_2}\sin\theta\,d\theta = -\frac{\mu_0 I}{4\pi p}(\cos\phi_2 - \cos\phi_1) = \frac{\mu_0 I}{2\pi p}\frac{a/2}{\sqrt{(a/2)^2 + p^2}}.$$

When we consult the second diagram, it is obvious that, since the currents go in different directions in the two wires of length a, the induction due to each wire at O is the same and p has the value $b/2$. It is also obvious that the value of B' due to each of the other wires of length b is

$$B' = \frac{\mu_0 I}{2\pi(a/2)}\frac{b/2}{\sqrt{(a/2)^2 + (b/2)^2}}.$$

The total value of the magnetic induction at O is thus

$$2(B + B') = \frac{\mu_0 I}{\pi b}\frac{a}{\sqrt{(a/2)^2 + (b/2)^2}} + \frac{\mu_0 I}{\pi a}\frac{b}{\sqrt{(a/2)^2 + (b/2)^2}} = \frac{2\mu_0 I}{\pi\sqrt{a^2 + b^2}}\left(\frac{a}{b} + \frac{b}{a}\right) = \frac{2\mu_0 I}{\pi ab}\sqrt{a^2 + b^2}.$$

PROBLEM 32.4

Two 250-turn circular Helmholtz coils are placed parallel to one another and separated by a distance equal to their common radius. Find the value of the magnetic induction at a point on the axis between them when current flows through both coils in the same sense, and show that the field is almost uniform about the midpoint.

Solution. The magnetic induction due to a single coil at a point along the axis a distance y from the plane of the coil is

$$B_1 = \frac{\mu_0}{2}\frac{Ia\sin\alpha}{r^2} = \frac{\mu_0}{2}\frac{Ia^2}{r^3} = \frac{\mu_0}{2}\frac{Ia^2}{(a^2 + y^2)^{3/2}}.$$

Similarly, at the same point the magnetic induction due to a single turn of the second coil is

$$B_2 = \frac{\mu_0}{2}\frac{Ia^2}{[a^2 + (a - y)^2]^{3/2}}.$$

These act in the same direction, and thus the total effect at O due to the n turns of both coils is

$$B = n(B_1 + B_2) = \frac{250\mu_0 Ia^2}{2}\left\{\frac{1}{(a^2 + y^2)^{3/2}} + \frac{1}{[a^2 + (a - y)^2]^{3/2}}\right\}.$$

If $y = a/2$, then $B = (8 \times 250\,\mu_0 I)/5^{3/2}a$. Further,

$$\frac{dB}{dy} = \frac{250\mu_0 Ia^2}{2}\left\{\frac{-3y}{(a^2 + y^2)^{5/2}} + \frac{3(a - y)}{[a^2 + (a - y)^2]^{5/2}}\right\} = 0 \quad \text{if } y = \frac{a}{2}.$$

Also

$$\frac{d^2B}{dy^2} = \frac{250\mu_0 Ia^2}{2}\left\{\frac{-3}{(a^2 + y^2)^{5/2}} - \frac{3}{[a^2 + (a - y)^2]^{5/2}} + \frac{15y^2}{(a^2 + y^2)^{7/2}} + \frac{15(a - y)^2}{[a^2 + (a - y)^2]^{7/2}}\right\}$$

$$= \frac{250\mu_0 Ia^2}{2}\left\{\frac{15y^2 - 3(a^2 + y^2)}{(a^2 + y^2)^{7/2}} + \frac{15(a - y)^2 - 3[a^2 + (a - y)^2]}{[a^2 + (a - y)^2]^{7/2}}\right\} = 0 \quad \text{if } y = \frac{a}{2}.$$

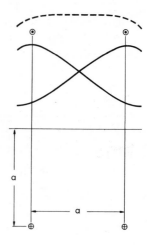

Thus dB/dy and d^2B/dy^2 are each equal to zero at the point $y = a/2$, midway between the coils. Hence B hardly varies around that point, giving a large region of uniform field midway between the coils.

With this particular spacing of the coils, the dropping off in the value of B due to one coil as we move away from it is compensated for by the increase in B due to the other coil for much of the region between them. The situation is illustrated in the diagram. The solid lines give the magnitude of B due to each coil separately at various distances along the axis. The dashed line shows the combined effect of the two coils, and the region of uniform field around the midpoint of the system is clearly seen.

33

Induced Electromotive Force

PROBLEM 33.1

A wire of length 1 m is moving at a speed of 2 m·s⁻¹ perpendicular to a magnetic field of induction of 0.5 Wb·m⁻². What is the potential difference induced between the ends of the wire? The ends are joined by a circuit of total resistance 6 Ω. At what rate is work being done to keep the wire moving at constant velocity?

Solution. Since the direction of motion and the magnetic induction are at right angles, the induced emf will have magnitude

$$\mathscr{E} = vBl = 2 \text{ m·s}^{-1} \times 0.5 \text{ Wb·m}^{-2} \times 1 \text{ m} = 1 \text{ V}.$$

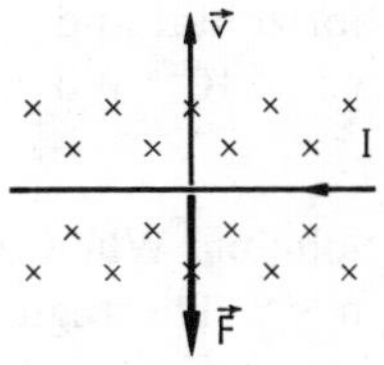

The power dissipated in the external circuit is

$$P = \frac{\mathscr{E}^2}{R} = \frac{1^2 \text{V}^2}{6 \,\Omega} = \frac{1}{6} \text{ W},$$

and this must equal the rate at which work is being done to keep the wire moving at constant velocity.

This can be checked by considering that a current

$$I = \frac{\mathscr{E}}{R} = \frac{1}{6} \text{ A}$$

will flow in the wire in the direction shown in the diagram. When a current flows in a wire in a magnetic field, the wire experiences a force of magnitude

$$F = IlB,$$

which will be in this case in the direction shown. The work done per second to keep the wire traveling at uniform speed v is

$$Fv = IlvB = \tfrac{1}{6} \text{A} \times 1 \text{ m} \times 2 \text{ m·s}^{-1} \times 0.5 \text{ Wb·m}^{-2} = \tfrac{1}{6} \text{ W},$$

in agreement with the result obtained above.

PROBLEM 33.2

A metal bar of length 1 m falls from rest under gravity while remaining horizontal with its ends pointing toward the magnetic east and west. What is the potential difference between its ends when it has fallen 10 m? The horizontal component of the earth's magnetic induction is 1.7×10^{-5} Wb·m⁻².

Solution. The direction of motion is vertical, and thus the vertical component of the earth's magnetic induction produces no effect. An induced emf will, however, be produced due to motion relative to the horizontal component of the earth's magnetic induction.

The equation of motion of the bar is $v^2 = v_0^2 + 2\,gs$, where v_0 is the initial velocity of zero. When s is 10 m,

$$v^2 = 2 \times 9.8\ \text{m} \cdot \text{s}^{-2} \times 10\ \text{m} \qquad \text{or} \qquad v = 14\ \text{m} \cdot \text{s}^{-1}.$$

The magnitude of the induced emf may now be calculated in two ways.

(a) The formula for the induced emf is

$$\mathscr{E} = vBl = 14\ \text{m} \cdot \text{s}^{-1} \times 1.7 \times 10^{-5}\ \text{Wb} \cdot \text{m}^{-2} \times 1\ \text{m} = 2.38 \times 10^{-4}\ \text{V}.$$

(b) The flux of magnetic induction swept through by the bar in time Δt seconds at a speed of $14\ \text{m} \cdot \text{s}^{-1}$ is B times an area of width 1 m and length $14\ \Delta t$ m. Thus

$$\dot{\phi} = \frac{B \times 1\ \text{m} \times 14\ \Delta t\ \text{m}}{\Delta t\ \text{s}} = 2.38 \times 10^{-4}\ \text{Wb} \cdot \text{s}^{-1}.$$

But $\mathscr{E} = -\dot{\phi}$, and thus the magnitude of $\mathscr{E}$ is

$$\mathscr{E} = 2.38 \times 10^{-4}\ \text{V}.$$

PROBLEM 33.3

An anemometer is made by attaching cups to each end of a metal rod 50 cm long fixed rigidly to a central vertical column which can rotate freely. A square vertical coil of side 10 cm is attached to the column and the wind speed is measured by finding the emf induced in the coil due to rotation in the earth's magnetic field. Given that the maximum wind velocity to be measured is 120 mph and the maximum induced emf cannot exceed 15 mV, how many turns must the coil have?

Calculate the emf induced in the metal rod during rotation at maximum speed. Assume that the horizontal and vertical components of the earth's magnetic induction are $1.5 \times 10^{-5}\ \text{Wb} \cdot \text{m}^{-2}$ and $5.5 \times 10^{-5}\ \text{Wb} \cdot \text{m}^{-2}$, respectively.

Solution. When the anemometer is moving at maximum speed, the cups are moving at 120 mph $= 53.64$ $\text{m} \cdot \text{s}^{-1}$. The angular velocity of rotation of the cups is thus

$$\omega = \frac{v}{r} = \frac{53.64\ \text{m} \cdot \text{s}^{-1}}{0.25\ \text{m}} = 214.6\ \text{rad} \cdot \text{s}^{-1}.$$

The plane of the coil is vertical, and thus the vertical component of the earth's magnetic induction produces no effect during rotation. Only the horizontal component is involved. The maximum emf induced during rotation of a coil in a magnetic field of induction B is $\mathscr{E}_{\max} = n\omega AB$, where n is the number of turns of the coil and A is its area. In this case $\mathscr{E}_{\max}$ must not exceed 15 mV. Hence the number of turns on the coil is

$$n = \frac{\mathscr{E}_{\max}}{\omega AB} = \frac{15 \times 10^{-3}\ \text{V}}{214.6\ \text{s}^{-1} \times 10^{-2}\ \text{m}^2 \times 1.5 \times 10^{-5}\ \text{Wb} \cdot \text{m}^{-2}} = 470\ \textbf{turns.}$$

The rod which holds the cups is rotating at right angles to the vertical component of the earth's magnetic induction, and is therefore acting as a crude form of Faraday disk dynamo. (The horizontal component is in the plane of rotation and thus has no effect.)

Any element of the rod dy is moving at any instant with speed v at right angles to its length in a magnetic induction of strength B'. A motional field E_n is set up in the element, acting in a radial direction and of magnitude $E_n = vB' = y\omega B'$.

An emf is thus established between the center and either end, of magnitude

$$\mathscr{E} = \int_0^a E_n \cdot dy = \omega B' \int_0^a y\, dy = \tfrac{1}{2}\,\omega B' a^2 = \tfrac{1}{2} \times 214.6\ \text{s}^{-1} \times 5.5 \times 10^{-5}\ \text{Wb} \cdot \text{m}^{-2} \times (0.25)^2\ \text{m}^2$$

$$= 3.69 \times 10^{-4}\ \text{V}.$$

PROBLEM 33.4

A current of 10 A is flowing in a long straight wire situated near a rectangular loop, as indicated in the diagram. The current is switched off and falls to zero in 0.02 s. Find the emf induced in the loop and indicate the direction in which the induced current flows.

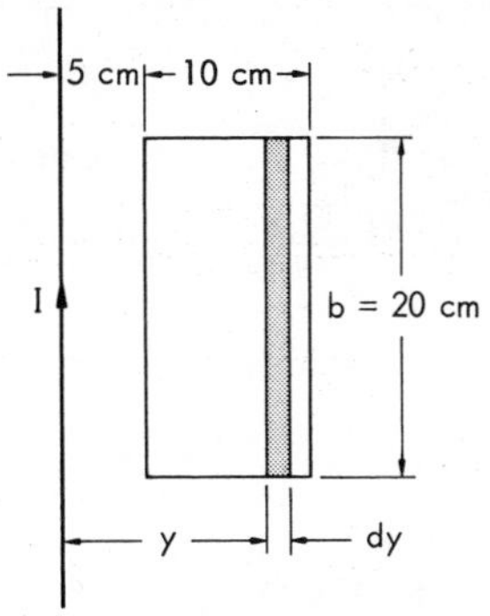

Solution. Consider the diagram, and in particular the shaded portion of width dy situated distance y from the straight current-carrying wire. The magnetic induction at all points of the shaded portion has the value

$$dB = \frac{\mu_0}{2\pi} \frac{I}{y},$$

and therefore the flux through the shaded area is

$$d\phi = \frac{\mu_0}{2\pi} \frac{I}{y} b \, dy.$$

The flux through the whole loop is thus

$$\phi = \int d\phi = \frac{\mu_0}{2\pi} Ib \int_{0.05\mathrm{m}}^{0.15\mathrm{m}} \frac{dy}{y} = \frac{\mu_0}{2\pi} Ib \ln 3.$$

The emf induced in the loop is $\mathscr{E} = -\dot\phi$. Thus the magnitude of the induced emf is

$$\mathscr{E} = \frac{\phi}{\tau} = \frac{\mu_0 Ib}{2\pi} \ln 3 \times \frac{1}{\tau} = \frac{4\pi \times 10^{-7} \, \mathrm{N \cdot A^{-2}} \times 10 \, \mathrm{A} \times 0.2 \, \mathrm{m} \times \ln 3}{2\pi \times 0.02 \, \mathrm{s}} = 22.0 \times 10^{-6} \, \mathrm{V}.$$

The flux through the loop is decreasing. The induced current must produce effects tending to oppose the change causing it. The current must therefore be in such a direction as to produce a flux through the loop in the same direction as that produced by the current in the straight wire, i.e., into the plane of the paper. Thus the induced current traverses the loop in a clockwise direction.

PROBLEM 33.5

A search coil of 100 turns, each of mean area 4 cm², is placed between the poles of an electromagnet with its plane perpendicular to the field of induction of strength 0.5 Wb·m⁻². When it is removed quickly to a position of zero field, what charge passes through a galvanometer connected to it? (Assume that the total resistance of the circuit is 20 Ω.) The resultant maximum galvanometer deflection is 0.2 radian. What is the galvanometer constant?

Solution. The magnetic induction and the charge flowing through the search-coil circuit are related by the equation $B = RQ/NA$, in the usual notation.

$$\therefore \quad Q = \frac{NAB}{R} = \frac{100 \times 4 \times 10^{-4} \, \mathrm{m} \times 0.5 \, \mathrm{Wb \cdot m^{-2}}}{20 \, \Omega} = 10^{-3} \, \mathrm{C}.$$

The charge passing through the galvanometer is related to the resulting deflection by the equation,

$$Q = \frac{\sqrt{k'I'}}{N'A'B'} \theta_{\max},$$

in the usual notation. The expression $\sqrt{k'I'}/N'A'B'$ is called the galvanometer constant, c. Thus

$$c = \frac{Q}{\theta_{\max}} = \frac{10^{-3} \, \mathrm{C}}{0.2 \, \mathrm{rad}} = 5 \times 10^{-3} \, \mathrm{C \cdot rad^{-1}}.$$

PROBLEM 33.6

Electrons with energies of 1 MeV are injected into the vacuum tube of a betatron of radius 1 m, through the center of which is a magnetic flux which changes at the rate of $100\,\text{Wb}\cdot\text{s}^{-1}$. The electrons make 250,000 revolutions before being ejected from the betatron. What is their final energy?

Solution. The force due to the changing magnetic flux acting on the electrons is $E_n = \dot{\phi}/2\pi r$, where r is the radius of the evacuated tube. The energy gained in one revolution is thus

$$2\pi r \times qE_n = q\dot{\phi}\,\text{J} = \dot{\phi}\,\text{eV} = 100\,\text{eV}.$$

The total energy the electrons acquire while in the betatron is thus the energy gained per revolution times the number of revolutions performed.

$$\therefore \quad W = 100 \times 250{,}000\,\text{eV} = 25\,\text{MeV}.$$

The final energy is thus $E = 1\,\text{MeV} + W = 26\,\text{MeV}.$

PROBLEM 33.7

A long air-cored solenoid is wound with 500 turns per meter and has a cross-sectional area of $20\,\text{cm}^2$. Around the middle of the solenoid are wound 400 turns of wire. What is the mutual inductance between the solenoid and the secondary winding?

Solution. The magnetic induction at the center of a long air-cored solenoid carrying a current I_1 is $B = \mu_0 N I_1/l$. The flux through a section of the solenoid of cross-sectional area A is $\phi = BA$, and thus the total flux through a secondary winding of n turns wound round the center of the solenoid is

$$n\phi = nBA = \mu_0 n N A I_1/l.$$

The emf induced in the secondary winding is

$$\mathscr{E}_2 = -\frac{d(n\phi)}{dt} = -\mu_0 n N A \frac{dI_1/dt}{l}.$$

But the formula linking $\mathscr{E}_2$ to dI_1/dt is $\mathscr{E}_2 = -M(dI_1/dt)$.

$$\therefore \quad M = \mu_0 n N A/l = 4\pi \times 10^{-7}\,\text{N}\cdot\text{A}^{-2} \times 400 \times 500\,\text{m}^{-1} \times 20 \times 10^{-4}\,\text{m}^2$$

$$= 503 \times 10^{-6}\,\text{H}^* = 503\,\mu\text{H}.$$

PROBLEM 33.8

A solenoid switch is activated when the magnetic induction on the axis is $5 \times 10^{-4}\,\text{Wb}\cdot\text{m}^{-2}$. The solenoid has 50 turns per cm and an inductance of 180 mH, and is operated by a 12-V battery. Find the time lag when it is employed in a circuit of resistance $90\,\Omega$.

Solution. When the magnetic induction in the solenoid has the value B, the current i passing through the coil is given by the equation $B = \mu_0 n i$, where n is the number of turns per unit length of the solenoid.

Further, the current at any time t after the solenoid circuit is switched on is given by the relation

$$i' = \frac{V}{R}\left[1 - \exp\left(-\frac{Rt}{L}\right)\right].$$

---

*A capital H, in roman type, is the symbol adopted by the International Union of Pure and Applied Physics to denote a henry.

When these two currents i and i' are equal, the solenoid switch operates and

$$\frac{B}{\mu_0 n} = \frac{V}{R}\left[1 - \exp\left(-\frac{Rt}{L}\right)\right].$$

$$\therefore \quad t = -\frac{L}{R}\ln\left(1 - \frac{RB}{\mu_0 nV}\right) = -\frac{180 \times 10^{-3}\,\text{H}}{90\,\Omega}\ln\left(1 - \frac{90\,\Omega \times 5 \times 10^{-4}\,\text{Wb·m}^{-2}}{4\pi \times 10^{-7}\,\text{N·A}^{-2} \times 5 \times 10^3\,\text{m}^{-1} \times 12\,\text{V}}\right)$$

$$= -2 \times 10^{-3} \times 2.303 \log(1 - 0.597)\,\text{s} = +4.606 \times 10^{-3} \log\left(\frac{1}{0.403}\right)\,\text{s} = 1.818 \times 10^{-3}\,\text{s}.$$

The time lag is thus 1.82×10^{-3} s.

34

Magnetic Properties of Matter

PROBLEM 34.1

A Rowland ring made of iron has a mean circumferential length of 50 cm and a cross-sectional area of 4 cm². It is wound with 450 turns of wire which carry a current of 1.2 A. The relative permeability of iron under these conditions is 550. What is the magnetic flux through the ring? What would be the flux through the ring if a gap of 2 cm were to be cut in its length, assuming that the flux did not spread from the gap?

Solution. The magnetic induction through a Rowland ring is given by the formula

$$B = \mu H = \mu \frac{NI_c}{l} = K_m \mu_0 \frac{NI_c}{l},$$

where I_c is the conduction current in the wire. Hence

$$\phi = K_m \mu_0 A \frac{NI_c}{l},$$

where A is the cross-sectional area of the ring. Therefore

$$\phi = 550 \times 4\pi \times 10^{-7}\,\text{N} \cdot \text{A}^{-2} \times 4 \times 10^{-4}\,\text{m}^2 \times \frac{450 \times 1.2\,\text{A}}{0.5\,\text{m}} = 2.99 \times 10^{-4}\,\text{Wb}.$$

When a gap is cut in the ring, the flux may be obtained by use of the magnetic circuit relation

$$\phi = \frac{\mathcal{M}}{\mathcal{R}_1 + \mathcal{R}_2},$$

where $\mathcal{M}$ is the magnetomotive force and $\mathcal{R}_1$ and $\mathcal{R}_2$ the reluctance of ring and gap, respectively. Thus

$$\phi = \frac{NI_c}{(l_1/\mu_1 A_1) + (l_2/\mu_2 A_2)}$$

$$= \frac{450 \times 1.2\,\text{A}}{[0.48\,\text{m}/(550 \times 4\pi \times 10^{-7}\text{N} \cdot \text{A}^{-2} \times 4 \times 10^{-4}\text{m}^2)] + [0.02\,\text{m}/(4\pi \times 10^{-7}\text{N} \cdot \text{A}^{-2} \times 4 \times 10^{-4}\text{m}^2)]}$$

$$= \frac{450 \times 1.2 \times 4\pi \times 10^{-7} \times 4 \times 10^{-4}}{[(0.48/550) + 0.02]}\,\text{Wb} = 1.30 \times 10^{-5}\,\text{Wb}.$$

PROBLEM 34.2

A bar of iron to be used in an experiment is found to be magnetized and to have a coercive force of 10^3 A·m⁻¹. In order to demagnetize it, the experimenter places it in a solenoid 20 cm long carrying 50 turns of wire. What current must be passed through the solenoid?

144

Solution. The magnetizing field set up inside the solenoid must be as great as the coercive force possessed by the iron. If the current to be passed is I, then

$$\frac{NI}{l} = 10^3 \text{ A·m}^{-1} \qquad \text{or} \qquad I = \frac{l \times 10^3 \text{ A·m}^{-1}}{N} = \frac{0.20 \text{ m} \times 10^3 \text{ A·m}^{-1}}{50} = 4 \text{ A}.$$

35

Alternating Currents

PROBLEM 35.1

A flat coil consisting of 500 turns, each of area 50 cm², rotates about a diameter in a uniform field of intensity 0.14 Wb·m⁻², the axis of rotation being perpendicular to the field and the angular velocity of rotation being 150 rad·s⁻¹. The coil has a resistance of 5 Ω, and the induced emf is connected via slip rings and brushes to an external resistance of 10 Ω.

Calculate the peak current flowing and the average power supplied to the 10-Ω resistor.

Solution. The emf generated by the motion is given, in the usual notation, by the equation

$$\mathscr{E} = NAB\omega \sin \omega t.$$

The current flowing is thus

$$I = \frac{\mathscr{E}}{R} = \frac{NAB\omega}{R} \sin \omega t.$$

The peak value of the current is

$$I_{max} = \frac{NAB\omega}{R} = \frac{500 \times 50 \times 10^{-4}\,\text{m}^2 \times 0.14\,\text{Wb·m}^{-2} \times 150\,\text{s}^{-1}}{15\,\Omega} = 3.5\,\text{A}.$$

The average power supplied to the external resistor is thus

$$P = I_{rms}^2 R = \left(\frac{3.5}{\sqrt{2}}\right)^2 \text{A}^2 \times 10\,\Omega$$

$$= 61.25\,\text{W}.$$

PROBLEM 35.2

When a 2-V cell is connected in series with two electrical elements, the current in the circuit is 200 mA. If a 50-cycle·s⁻¹, 2-V ac source replaces the cell, the current becomes 100 mA. What are the values of the circuit elements? Suppose that the frequency is increased to 1000 cycle·s⁻¹. What is the new value of the current?

Solution. Since a dc current can flow through the elements, neither of them can be a capacitor which offers an infinite resistance to direct current. The resistance of the elements is

$$R = \frac{V}{I} = \frac{2\,\text{V}}{200 \times 10^{-3}\,\text{A}} = 10\,\Omega.$$

Since the current changes when alternating current is supplied, the circuit must also contain an inductor of inductance L, where

$$Z = \sqrt{R^2 + \omega^2 L^2} = \frac{V'}{I'} = \frac{2\ V}{100 \times 10^{-3}\ A} = 20\ \Omega.$$

$$\therefore \quad 100\ \Omega^2 + \omega^2 L^2 = 400\ \Omega^2 \quad \text{or} \quad L^2 = \frac{300\ \Omega^2}{\omega^2}.$$

$$\therefore \quad L = \frac{17.32\ \Omega}{2\pi \times 50\ s^{-1}} = 0.055\ H.$$

When the frequency is increased to 10^3 cycles $\cdot$ s^{-1},

$$I' = \frac{V'}{Z'} = \frac{2\ V}{\sqrt{100\ \Omega^2 + (2\pi \times 10^3 \times 0.055)^2\ \Omega^2}} = \frac{2}{346}\ A = 5.77\ mA.$$

PROBLEM 35.3

When a cathode-ray tube has its deflector plates connected across a 100-V battery, the spot on the fluorescent screen is deflected 12 cm. If the plates are now connected across a resistance of 20 Ω in parallel with an ac voltmeter and in series with a 50-cycle $\cdot$ s^{-1} ac generator, the length of trace on the screen is 17 cm and the voltmeter reads 50 V. How can these apparently contradictory figures be explained?

Suppose that the resistance is replaced by a coil of resistance 5 Ω and reactance 0.1 H, and that the current drawn from the generator is adjusted to the same value as before. What length of trace will be obtained and what is the rate of heat production in the coil?

Solution. When the 100-V battery is applied to the deflector plates, a deflection of 12 cm is obtained. The displacement per volt is thus 1.2 mm.

When the ac voltage across the resistor is applied to the cathode ray tube, a trace of length 17 cm is obtained and the voltmeter reads only 50 V. At first sight this might appear to give a different displacement per volt, but this is not so. The reading on the voltmeter is the rms value of the voltage. The peak value is thus $50\sqrt{2} = 70.7$ V. The trace on the screen marks a movement of the spot from the position where it is subjected to the peak value to the position where it is subjected to minus the peak voltage. In other words the length of the trace corresponds to a deflection due to a change of $70.7 - (-70.7) = 141.4$ V. The displacement per volt is 17 cm/141.4 = 1.2 mm, in agreement with the dc measurement.

The current through the resistor is

$$I = \frac{V}{R} = \frac{50\ V}{20\ \Omega} = 2.5\ A.$$

When the resistor is replaced by a coil, the current remains the same and the voltage across the coil is

$$V = IZ = 2.5\ A \times \sqrt{5^2\ \Omega^2 + (2\pi \times 50 \times 0.1)^2\ \Omega^2} = 2.5 \times 31.8\ V = 79.5\ V.$$

This is the rms value of the voltage. The peak-to-peak value is thus $V' = 2\sqrt{2} \times 79.5 = 224.8$ V, from the discussion above, and the trace on the screen is 224.8 V $\times$ 0.12 cm $\cdot$ V^{-1} = 27 cm in length.

The rate of heat production in the coil is due solely to the resistive part of the impedance. Thus

$$W = I^2 R = 2.5^2\ A^2 \times 5\ \Omega = 31.25\ W.$$

PROBLEM 35.4

A coil of resistance 10 ohm and inductance 0.1 H is in series with a capacitor and a 100-V 60-cycle $\cdot$ s^{-1} source. The capacitor is adjusted to give resonance in the circuit. Calculate the capacitance of the capacitor and the voltages across coil and capacitor.

Solution. At resonance, $X_L = X_c$.

$$\therefore \quad C = \frac{1}{\omega^2 L} = \frac{1}{4\pi^2 \times 60^2 \text{ s}^{-2} \times 0.1 \text{ H}} = 70.4 \; \mu\text{F}.$$

Further, the circuit becomes purely resistive, and thus

$$I = \frac{V}{R} = \frac{100 \text{ V}}{10 \; \Omega} = 10 \text{ A}.$$

$$\therefore \quad V_L = IZ_L = 10 \text{ A} \times \sqrt{10^2 + (2\pi \times 60 \times 0.1)^2} \; \Omega = 390 \text{ V}$$

and

$$V_c = IZ_c = \frac{10 \text{ A}}{2\pi \times 60 \text{ s}^{-1} \times 70.4 \times 10^{-6} \text{ F}} = 377 \text{ V}.$$

PROBLEM 35.5

A 500-W fluorescent lamp takes a current of 2.5 A at a power factor of 1. Calculate the inductance of the coil required in series with it if the lamp is to work from 250-V 50-cycle·s^{-1} mains. What is the capacitance of the capacitor which, if connected across the mains, will now return the power factor to 1?

Solution. Since the lamp takes a current of 2.5 A at a power factor of 1, it must be purely resistive and its resistance is such that $W = I^2 R$ or

$$R = \frac{W}{I^2} = \frac{500 \text{ W}}{2.5^2 \text{ A}^2} = 80 \; \Omega.$$

Since the final arrangement is to work from the 250-V 50-cycle·s^{-1} mains, a coil of inductance L must be put in series, where

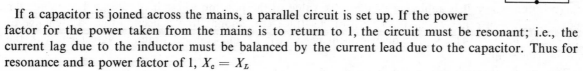

$$Z^2 = R^2 + \omega^2 L^2 = \frac{V^2}{I^2} = \frac{250^2 \text{ V}^2}{2.5^2 \text{ A}^2} = 10{,}000 \; \Omega^2.$$

$$\therefore \quad \omega^2 L^2 = 3600 \; \Omega^2 \quad \text{or} \quad L = \frac{60 \; \Omega}{2\pi \times 50 \text{ s}^{-1}} = 0.191 \text{ H}.$$

If a capacitor is joined across the mains, a parallel circuit is set up. If the power factor for the power taken from the mains is to return to 1, the circuit must be resonant; i.e., the current lag due to the inductor must be balanced by the current lead due to the capacitor. Thus for resonance and a power factor of 1, $X_c = X_L$

$$\therefore \quad \frac{1}{\omega C} = \omega L \quad \text{or} \quad C = \frac{1}{\omega^2 L} = \frac{1}{4\pi^2 \times 50^2 \text{ s}^{-2} \times 0.191 \text{ H}} = 53 \; \mu\text{F}.$$

PROBLEM 35.6

An ac source of internal resistance 9000 Ω is to supply current to a load of resistance 10 Ω. How should the source be matched to the load, and what is then the ratio of the currents passing through load and source?

Solution. The matching may be done by means of a transformer. If the numbers of turns on primary and secondary windings are N_1 and N_2, then the internal resistance of the source R_1 and load resistance R_2 are related by the equation $R_1 = (N_1/N_2)^2 R_2$.

$$\therefore \quad \left(\frac{N_1}{N_2}\right)^2 = \frac{R_1}{R_2} = 900 \quad \text{or} \quad \frac{N_1}{N_2} = 30.$$

Therefore a transformer with a turns ratio of 30 : 1 must be employed. The transformer lowers the voltage in the ratio 30 : 1, but correspondingly increases the current in the same ratio.

36

Electromagnetic Waves

PROBLEM 36.1

The solar constant, the power due to radiation from the sun falling on the earth's atmosphere, is $1.35 \text{ kW} \cdot \text{m}^{-2}$. What are the magnitudes of **E** and **B** for the electromagnetic waves emitted from the sun at the earth and at the surface of the sun?

Solution. Starting with the electromagnetic waves at the earth, it is possible to determine **E** and **B** by two methods. (a) The Poynting vector gives the energy flow across any section of the field per unit area per unit time. Thus $|1/\mu_0 \, \mathbf{E} \times \mathbf{B}| = EH = 1.35 \times 10^3 \text{ W} \cdot \text{m}^{-2}$.

But in the electromagnetic field in vacuum, $\epsilon_0 E^2 = \mu_0 H^2$.

$$\therefore \qquad E \times \sqrt{\epsilon_0/\mu_0} \, E = 1.35 \times 10^3 \text{ W} \cdot \text{m}^{-2}$$

or

$$E^2 = \sqrt{\mu_0/\epsilon_0} \times 1.35 \times 10^3 \text{ W} \cdot \text{m}^{-2} = 377 \, \Omega \times 1.35 \times 10^3 \text{ W} \cdot \text{m}^{-2}.$$

$$\therefore \qquad E = \sqrt{5.09 \times 10^5} \text{ V} \cdot \text{m}^{-1} = 0.71 \times 10^3 \text{ V} \cdot \text{m}^{-1}.$$

Similarly,

$$1.35 \times 10^3 \text{ W} \cdot \text{m}^{-2} = \sqrt{\mu_0/\epsilon_0} \, H^2 = \frac{1}{\sqrt{\epsilon_0 \mu_0}} \frac{B^2}{\mu_0}.$$

$$\therefore \qquad B^2 = \frac{4\pi \times 10^{-7} \text{ N} \cdot \text{A}^{-2} \times 1.35 \times 10^3 \text{ W} \cdot \text{m}^{-2}}{3 \times 10^8 \text{ m} \cdot \text{s}^{-1}} \qquad \text{or} \qquad B = 2.36 \times 10^{-6} \text{ Wb} \cdot \text{m}^{-2}.$$

(b) The energy density in an electromagnetic field in vacuum is $\mu_0 H^2 = \epsilon_0 E^2$. The energy falling on 1 m^2 of the earth's atmosphere in 1 s is the energy initially contained in a cylinder 1 m^2 in cross section and 3×10^8 m in length; for all this energy travels to the end of the cylinder in the space of 1 s. Hence the energy density near the earth is

$$\mu_0 H^2 = \epsilon_0 E^2 = \frac{1.35 \times 10^3 \text{ W} \cdot \text{m}^{-2}}{3 \times 10^8 \text{ m} \cdot \text{s}^{-1}}.$$

$$\therefore \qquad E^2 = \frac{1.35 \times 10^3 \text{ W} \cdot \text{m}^{-2}}{8.85 \times 10^{-12} \text{ C}^2 \cdot \text{N}^{-1} \cdot \text{m}^{-2} \times 3 \times 10^8 \text{ m} \cdot \text{s}^{-1}} = \frac{1.35}{26.55} \times 10^7 \text{ V}^2 \cdot \text{m}^{-2}.$$

$$\therefore \qquad E = 0.71 \times 10^3 \text{ V} \cdot \text{m}^{-1}.$$

Also

$$\mu_0 H^2 = \frac{B^2}{\mu_0} = \frac{1.35 \times 10^3 \text{ W} \cdot \text{m}^{-2}}{3 \times 10^8 \text{ m} \cdot \text{s}^{-1}} \qquad \text{or} \qquad B^2 = \frac{4\pi \times 10^{-7} \text{ N} \cdot \text{A}^{-2} \times 1.35 \times 10^3 \text{ W} \cdot \text{m}^{-2}}{3 \times 10^8 \text{ m} \cdot \text{s}^{-1}}.$$

$$\therefore \qquad B = 2.36 \times 10^{-6} \text{ Wb} \cdot \text{m}^{-2}.$$

The energy falling on 1 m² of the earth's atmosphere has passed through a much smaller area A at the sun's surface. The areas are related by

$$\frac{A}{1\ \text{m}^2} = \frac{r^2}{R^2},$$

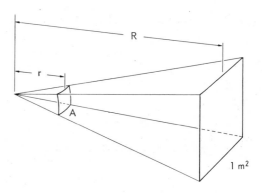

where r is the radius of the sun and R the distance of the earth from the sun. The energy density at the sun's surface is thus greater than that at the earth, the two being in the ratio R^2/r^2. It follows that the values of E^2 and B^2 at the sun's surface are greater than at the earth's by factors R^2/r^2. Thus at the sun's surface,

$$E = 0.71 \times 10^3 \frac{R}{r}\ \text{V}\cdot\text{m}^{-1} = 0.71 \times 10^3 \times \frac{1.5 \times 10^8}{7 \times 10^5}\ \text{V}\cdot\text{m}^{-1} = 1.52 \times 10^5\ \text{V}\cdot\text{m}^{-1}$$

and

$$B = 2.36 \times 10^{-6} \times \frac{1.5 \times 10^8}{7 \times 10^5}\ \text{Wb}\cdot\text{m}^{-2} = 5.06 \times 10^{-4}\ \text{Wb}\cdot\text{m}^{-2}.$$

PROBLEM 36.2

A circular parallel-plate capacitor has vacuum between its plates. Neglecting fringe effects, show that while the capacitor is being charged the Poynting vector points everywhere radially into the volume between the plates, and that the rate at which energy flows into this volume is equal to the rate at which the electrostatic energy increases.

Solution. A conduction current I_C is flowing into the lower plate of the capacitor in the diagram and from the upper plate. At any instant the charge on the plates will be $\pm Q$ and the charge densities $\pm\sigma = \pm(Q/A)$, where A is the area of either plate. A displacement current $I_D = I_C$ is flowing through the dielectric with current density vector $\mathbf{J}_D$ in the direction shown.

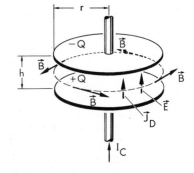

At any point between the plates the electric intensity vector $\mathbf{E}$ is in the same direction as $\mathbf{J}_D$ and has magnitude σ/ϵ_0. The magnetic induction vector $\mathbf{B}$ at any point due to the displacement current is everywhere at right angles to $\mathbf{J}_D$ and to the radius vector $\mathbf{r}$ from the center of the plates. It is thus everywhere tangential to circles concentric with the axis of the capacitor as shown. In particular at the edges $\mathbf{B}$ has everywhere the magnitude $(\mu_0/2\pi)(I_D/r)$, where r is the radius of either plate. It follows that $\mathbf{H}$ is in the same direction as $\mathbf{B}$ and has magnitude at the edges

$$\frac{1}{2\pi}\frac{I_D}{r} = \frac{1}{2\pi}\frac{I_C}{r}.$$

The Poynting vector is $\mathbf{S} = \mathbf{E} \times \mathbf{H}$. Hence the direction of $\mathbf{S}$ is everywhere radial toward the center of the capacitor, and at the edges

$$S = \frac{1}{2\pi}\frac{\sigma}{\epsilon_0}\frac{I_C}{r} = \frac{1}{2\pi\epsilon_0 r}\frac{Q}{A}\frac{dQ}{dt} = \frac{1}{4\pi\epsilon_0 rA}\frac{d}{dt}(Q^2) = \frac{A}{4\pi\epsilon_0 r}\frac{d}{dt}(\sigma^2) = \frac{\epsilon_0 A}{4\pi r}\frac{d}{dt}(E^2).$$

The total energy flow into the capacitor is thus

$$2\pi rhS = \frac{1}{2}\epsilon_0 Ah\frac{d}{dt}(E^2) = Ah\frac{d}{dt}\left(\frac{1}{2}\epsilon_0 E^2\right).$$

But Ah is the volume of the capacitor and $\frac{1}{2}\epsilon_0 E^2$ the electrostatic energy density at that instant at any point between the plates. Thus the total energy flow into the capacitor equals the rate at which the electrostatic energy in the capacitor increases. Therefore the energy stored in the dielectric of a capacitor may be considered as flowing into the dielectric from the electromagnetic field.

37

The Nature and Propagation of Light

PROBLEM 37.1

When journeys to the other planets have become a reality, communication between a space traveler and earth will become a problem, partly because of the finite speed of electromagnetic waves and partly because of the sun getting in the path of signals at certain times. It has been proposed that a relay station should be put into the earth's orbit at an angle of 90° to the earth so that communications should be possible at all times.

Given that Mars and the earth are on opposite sides of the sun and that a relay station has been set up, calculate the minimum time delay between the sending of a message by an astronaut on Mars and the receipt of the answer. Mars and the earth may be considered to be traveling in circular orbits of radii 230×10^6 km and 150×10^6 km, respectively.

Solution. The disposition of the planets and the relay station are as shown in the diagram. The minimum time delay occurs when earth receives the message by route MRE and relays the answer immediately by the same path.

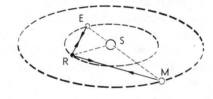

The total distance traveled is thus $2(MR + RE)$.

By the Pythagorean theorem,

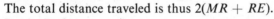

$$2(MR + RE) = 2(\sqrt{ES^2 + SR^2} + \sqrt{MS^2 + SR^2})$$

$$= 2[\sqrt{2} \times 150 \times 10^9 + \sqrt{150^2 + 230^2} \times 10^9] \text{ m}$$

$$= 2 \times 10^9 (212.1 + 274.6) \text{ m} = 973.4 \times 10^9 \text{ m}.$$

Electromagnetic waves travel with a constant speed of 2.998×10^8 m·s^{-1}, and thus the time taken is given by

$$t = 2(MR + RE)/c = 973.4 \times 10^9 \text{ m} / 2.998 \times 10^8 \text{ m·s}^{-1} = \frac{3245}{60} \text{ min} = 54.1 \text{ min}.$$

Casual conversation between astronaut and base is therefore out!

PROBLEM 37.2

Prove that when light goes from one point to another via a plane mirror, the path chosen is the one which takes the least time.

Solution. Let the points be A and B, and let C be any general point on the mirror. Orient the diagram so that the x- and y-axes are as shown. Draw the normals to the mirror surface passing through A, B, and C. By the laws of optics, A, B, and C must be in the same plane.

The coordinates of the three points are $A(x_1, 0)$; $B(x_2, y_0)$; $C(0, y)$.

The length of the path ACB is, by the Pythagorean theorem,

$$p = \sqrt{x_1^2 + y^2} + \sqrt{x_2^2 + (y_0 - y)^2}.$$

But the time of travel of light by this path, the velocity of light being c, is $t = p/c$. For the path to be traveled in minimum time, we must have $dt/dy = 0$, where y is the variable which changes with path. Thus

$$0 = \frac{1}{c} \left\{ \frac{y}{\sqrt{x_1^2 + y^2}} - \frac{y_0 - y}{\sqrt{x_2^2 + (y_0 - y)^2}} \right\}.$$

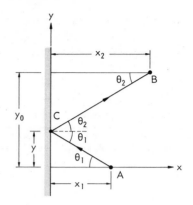

But since $c \neq \infty$, the quantity in the braces must be zero. Consulting the diagram we see that, in that case, $\sin \theta_1 - \sin \theta_2 = 0$.

$$\therefore \quad \theta_1 = \theta_2,$$

which is the law of reflection, and thus the path light would follow. Therefore the light ray follows the path which takes the least time.

PROBLEM 37.3

The easiest method of measuring the refracting angle of a prism is to direct a parallel beam of light on to the angle and measure the angular separation of the beams reflected from the two sides of the prism containing the refracting angle. Show that this angular separation is twice the angle of the prism.

Solution. Consider three incoming rays, all parallel and striking the prism at points A, B, and C. Erect normals to AB at A and B and to AC at A and C. Designate the angles as in the diagram.

The rays striking at B and C are reflected according to the laws of optics, as shown, and the reflected rays produced backward meet at D; E is the point at which the normals at B and C meet.

In the quadrilateral $ABEC$, since two of the angles are right angles,

$$(1) \quad \alpha + \gamma = 180°.$$

In the quadrilateral $BDCE$,

$$(2) \quad \beta + \gamma + \theta_1 + \theta_2 = 360°.$$

Since two of the angles surrounding A are right angles,

$$(3) \quad \alpha + \theta_1 + \theta_2 = 180°.$$

Add Eqs. (1) and (3) and subtract Eq. (2).

$$\therefore \quad 2\alpha - \beta = 0.$$

Thus the angle between the reflected beams is twice the refracting angle of the prism.

PROBLEM 37.4

A man standing symmetrically in front of a plane mirror with beveled edges can see three images of his eyes when he is 3 ft from the mirror. The mirror is silvered on the back, is 2 ft 6 in. wide, and is made of glass of refractive index 1.54. What is the angle of bevel of the edges?

Solution. The man can only see an image of his eyes if light leaves them, strikes the mirror, and is reflected back along the same path. The central image is thus formed by light traversing the perpendicular from his eyes to the mirror. The outer images are formed by light striking the beveled edges at the point A at an angle of incidence ϕ such that the angle of refraction ϕ' makes the refracted ray strike the silvered surface normally. The angle ϕ' lies between the normal to the beveled edge and the normal to the back surface. It must therefore be equal to the angle between the beveled edge and the back surface, i.e., the angle θ.

Draw BA a construction line at A parallel to the back of the mirror. Angle BAC is also equal to θ.

But $\sin \phi = n \sin \phi' = n \sin \theta$. Also $\alpha = \theta + (90 - \phi)$.

$$\therefore \quad \sin [90 - (\alpha - \theta)] = n \sin \theta.$$

$$\therefore \quad \cos (\alpha - \theta) = n \sin \theta.$$

$$\therefore \quad \cos \alpha \cos \theta + \sin \alpha \sin \theta = n \sin \theta.$$

$$\therefore \quad \tan \theta = \frac{\cos \alpha}{n - \sin \alpha}.$$

But $\alpha = \tan^{-1} (3 \text{ ft}/1\frac{1}{4} \text{ ft}) = \tan^{-1} (12/5)$.

$$\therefore \quad \tan \theta = \frac{5/13}{1.54 - (12/13)} = 0.625.$$

$$\therefore \quad \theta = 32°.$$

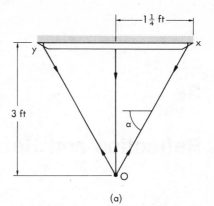

(a)

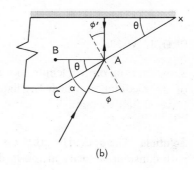

(b)

38

Reflection and Refraction at Plane Surfaces

PROBLEM 38.1

Show that the optical length of a light path, defined as the geometrical length times the refractive index of the medium in which the light is moving, is the equivalent distance which the light would have traveled in a vacuum.

Solution. The optical length $= nl = cl/v$, where v is the velocity of light in the medium. But light travels with constant velocity in the medium, and hence $l/v = t$, where t is the time taken to traverse the light path.

$$\therefore \quad nl = ct = l_0,$$

where l_0 is the distance the light would have traveled at velocity c, that is, in a vacuum. Thus the optical length is the equivalent distance which the light would have traveled in the same time in a vacuum.

PROBLEM 38.2

A man, who can run for short distances at a speed of 25 ft·s⁻¹, but can swim at a speed of only 10 ft·s⁻¹, is standing on the edge of a swimming pool when he observes that his wife is in difficulties at a distance of 20 yd in a direction making an angle of 30° with the edge of the pool. Assuming that he wishes to save her from drowning, what is the minimum time in which he can reach her?

How does the analysis of this problem tie in with the laws of optics?

Solution. Taking the x-axis as the edge of the pool and the y-axis at right angles to it through the original position of the man, the coordinates of the man and his wife will be $(0, 0)$ and (a, b), respectively. Take any point Q on the x-axis with coordinates $(f, 0)$. Then

$$QP = \sqrt{(a - f)^2 + b^2}.$$

The time taken to travel the path OQP is

$$t = \frac{f}{v_1} + \frac{\sqrt{(a - f)^2 + b^2}}{v_2},$$

where v_1 and v_2 are the speed of the man while running and swimming, respectively. For this time to be a minimum,

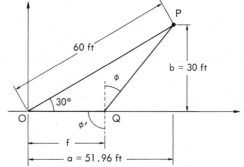

$$\frac{dt}{df} = \frac{1}{v_1} - \frac{a - f}{v_2\sqrt{(a - f)^2 + b^2}} = 0. \quad \therefore \quad \sqrt{(a - f)^2 + b^2} = \frac{v_1}{v_2}(a - f).$$

$$\therefore \quad \left(\frac{v_1^2}{v_2^2} - 1\right)(a - f)^2 = b^2 \quad \text{or} \quad f = a - \frac{b}{\sqrt{(v_1^2/v_2^2) - 1}}.$$

But $a = 60 \cos 30°$ ft and $b = 60 \sin 30°$ ft.

$$\therefore \quad f = 51.96 \text{ ft} - \frac{30 \text{ ft}}{\sqrt{[(25 \text{ ft} \cdot \text{s}^{-1})^2/(10 \text{ ft} \cdot \text{s}^{-1})^2] - 1}} = 38.86 \text{ ft.}$$

Thus

$$t_{\min} = \frac{38.86 \text{ ft}}{25 \text{ ft} \cdot \text{s}^{-1}} + \frac{\sqrt{(51.96 - 38.86)^2 \text{ ft}^2 + 30^2 \text{ ft}^2}}{10 \text{ ft} \cdot \text{s}^{-1}} = (1.55 + 3.27) \text{ s} = 4.82 \text{ s.}$$

In Chapter 37, Problem 2, it was shown that the actual path taken by a light ray in traveling between two points via a plane mirror was that path which took the shortest time. This is also true for the case of refraction at a plane surface.

Under these circumstances we should expect the minimum-time path found in the problem to be the path of a ray of light from P to O when the x-axis is the boundary between two media in which the velocities of light are in the ratio $v_2 : v_1$. Now, by the laws of optics, $n_2 \sin \phi = n_1 \sin \phi'$. That is,

$$(c/v_2) \sin \phi = (c/v_1) \sin \phi'.$$

But $\sin \phi' = 1$, and therefore $\sin \phi = v_2/v_1$.

But from the previous analysis, we know that

$$\sin \phi = \frac{a - f}{\sqrt{(a - f)^2 + b^2}},$$

and, for the minimum-time path,

$$\sin \phi = \frac{a - f}{(v_1/v_2)(a - f)} = \frac{v_2}{v_1}.$$

Hence the minimum-time path is the one which obeys Snell's law, and that in which ϕ is the critical angle.

PROBLEM 38.3

The crooks in a typical TV drama are attempting to recover a fortune in diamonds which they have earlier sunk in a chest in 24 ft of water. As a cover for the operation they have moored a floating oil-drilling rig above the position where they sank the chest. If the dimensions of the chest are small in comparison with the rig, determine the size of rig required in order that no passing sailor can see what is going on under the surface.

Solution. We can consider the sunken chest as a point source of light. If the oil rig is big enough for its purpose, then all rays of light from the chest which would be refracted into the air at the surface must be blocked off by the base of the rig, and all rays striking the surface of the water outside the rig must be totally internally reflected.

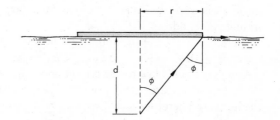

The rig must obviously be circular, and, if its center is moored directly above the chest, a ray of light striking the edge of the rig must do so at an angle $\geq$ the critical angle.

For the minimum radius, r, of the rig, $\sin \phi = 1/n_w$ or $r/\sqrt{r^2 + d^2} = 1/n_w$.

$$\therefore \quad r^2 + d^2 = n_w^2 r^2 \quad \text{or} \quad r^2 = \frac{d^2}{n_w^2 - 1}.$$

$$\therefore \quad r = \frac{24 \text{ ft}}{\sqrt{\frac{16}{9} - 1}} = \frac{72 \text{ ft}}{\sqrt{7}} = 27.2 \text{ ft.}$$

PROBLEM 38.4

A ray of light enters the face BA of a right-angled prism of refracting material at grazing incidence. It emerges from the adjacent face AC at an angle θ to the normal. If ϕ_c is the critical angle for the material, show that $\sin \theta = \cot \phi_c$.

Will a ray always emerge from AC? If not, explain what happens, and deduce for what values of the refractive index of the material the ray actually emerges.

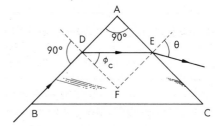

Solution. Since the ray strikes the prism at grazing incidence, the refracted ray DE must enter at the critical angle ϕ_c. Now angles DAE, ADF, and AEF are all right angles. Thus DFE must be a right angle also, since the four angles of a quadrilateral add up to $360°$.

The angles of a triangle must add up to $180°$, and therefore $\angle DEF = 90° - \phi_c$.

Applying Snell's law to the refraction at face AC, we have $n \sin \angle DEF = \sin \theta$. But $\sin \phi_c = 1/n$.

$$\therefore \quad \frac{1}{\sin \phi_c} \cdot \sin (90° - \phi_c) = \sin \theta. \qquad \therefore \quad \frac{\cos \phi_c}{\sin \phi_c} = \cot \phi_c = \sin \theta.$$

The ray will emerge from AC only if $\angle DEF$ is less than the critical angle. If it is greater, total internal reflection occurs and the ray is directed toward BC.

Thus, for the ray to emerge, $\angle DEF < \phi_c$. That is, $90° - \phi_c < \phi_c$ or $\phi_c > 45°$.

$$\therefore \quad \sin \phi_c = \frac{1}{n} > \sin 45° = \frac{1}{\sqrt{2}}. \qquad \therefore \quad n < \sqrt{2}.$$

PROBLEM 38.5

A parallel beam of light falls normally on the first face of a prism of small angle. At the second face it is partly transmitted and partly reflected, the reflected beam striking the first face again and emerging from it in a direction making an angle of $6°30'$ with the reversed direction of the incident beam. The refracted beam is found to have undergone a deviation of $1°15'$ from the original direction. Calculate the refractive index of the glass and the angle of the prism.

Solution. Let the angle of the prism be α and its refractive index n. Since α is small, we know from theory that $\delta_1 = (n - 1)\alpha$. Also $\angle ADC$ is a right angle as is $\angle ACE$. Thus $\angle ACD = 90° - \alpha$, since the three angles of a triangle must add to $180°$.

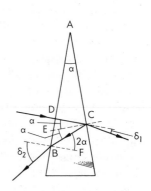

Therefore $\angle DCE = \alpha$, and, from the law of reflection, $\angle DCB = 2\alpha$.

Hence $\angle DBC = 90° - 2\alpha$ or $\angle CBF = 2\alpha$.

Applying Snell's law to the refraction at B, we have $n \sin 2\alpha = \sin \delta_2$.

But the angles are small, and we can replace the sines by the angles themselves. Therefore $\delta_2 = 2n\alpha$.

$$\therefore \quad \frac{\delta_1}{\delta_2} = \frac{n - 1}{2n} \quad \text{or} \quad \frac{2 \times 1\frac{1}{4}°}{6\frac{1}{2}°} = 1 - \frac{1}{n}.$$

$$\therefore \quad \frac{1}{n} = 1 - \frac{5}{13} \quad \text{or} \quad n = \frac{13}{8} = 1\frac{5}{8}.$$

Hence

$$\alpha = \frac{6\frac{1}{2}°}{2 \times 1\frac{5}{8}} = 2°.$$

PROBLEM 38.6

The spectrum from a hydrogen discharge tube contains the red C line and the violet F line. A parallel beam from the discharge tube is passed through a refracting prism of 60° angle with the red C light suffering minimum deviation. What are the deviations suffered by the red C light and the violet F light?

On emerging from the prism, the light is focused on a screen by an achromatic lens of focal length 30 cm. What is the separation of the C and F images on the screen? (Here $n_C = 1.604$ and $n_F = 1.620$.)

Solution. The red light is suffering minimum deviation. Thus

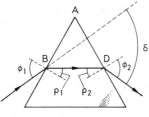

$$n_C = \frac{\sin \frac{1}{2}(A + \delta_C)}{\sin \frac{1}{2} A}.$$

That is,

$$\sin \tfrac{1}{2}(60° + \delta_C) = 1.604 \sin 30° = 0.802.$$

$$\therefore \quad \tfrac{1}{2}(60° + \delta_C) = 53.3° \quad \text{or} \quad \delta_C = 106.6° - 60° = 46.6°.$$

In fact the violet light is so close to minimum deviation that we could apply the same formula. If we replace n_C by n_F in the above, δ_F comes out as 48.2°.

But let us work the answer out from first principles. From textbook theory, $\delta_C = \phi_1 + \phi_2 - A$. But for minimum deviation, $\phi_1 = \phi_2$.

$$\therefore \quad \phi_1 = \tfrac{1}{2}(\delta_C + A) = 53.3°.$$

All colors are in the parallel beam striking the prism. Thus all colors have the same value for ϕ_1. Hence for the violet light,

$$\sin \rho_1 = \frac{1}{n_F} \sin \phi_1 = \frac{1}{1.620} \sin 53.3° = \frac{0.802}{1.620} = 0.495.$$

$$\therefore \quad \rho_1 = 29.67°.$$

But $A = \rho_1 + \rho_2$.

$$\therefore \quad \rho_2 = 60° - 29.67° = 30.33°.$$

Also

$$\sin \phi_2 = n_F \sin \rho_2 = 1.620 \times 0.505 = 0.818. \qquad \therefore \quad \phi_2 = 54.9°.$$

$$\therefore \quad \delta_F = \phi_1 + \phi_2 - A = 108.2° - 60° = 48.2°.$$

A parallel beam of red light is emerging from the prism at an angle of 48.2° − 46.6° = 1.6° to a similarly parallel beam of violet light. Parallel beams are brought to a focus in the focal planes of lenses, and thus both the red and violet beams give sharp images in the focal plane of the inserted lens.

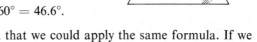

The real image of a point object is the place at which all rays converge. Hence if we can find the point at which *any* violet ray, and the point at which *any* red ray, strike the focal plane of the lens, we have located the images, and their separation gives us the answer required. The easiest rays to choose are the red and violet rays which pass through the center of the lens, since these are undeviated.

It is easy to see from the diagram that the separation of the images is PQ. Now 1.6° is a small angle and is 0.028 radian. Thus

$$PQ = OP \times 0.028 = 30 \text{ cm} \times 0.028 = 0.84 \text{ cm}.$$

39

Images Formed by a Single Reflection or Refraction

PROBLEM 39.1

A standard sight-testing chart measuring 50 cm by 18 cm, the longer dimension being vertical, should be viewed by the patient at a distance of 6 m. Because of lack of space in his office, an optician may place a reversed chart behind the patient and allow him to view the image in a plane mirror.

In such an office the patient is placed 2.5 m from the mirror with his eyes 1.2 m from the floor, the chart being 1 m behind him with its lower edge 2.0 m from the floor. What is the smallest size mirror the optician can install, and how far from the floor must its lower edge be?

Suppose that the chart is clipped to the patient's chair. Show that the size of the mirror and its positioning with respect to the floor are not dependent on the distance of the patient from the mirror.

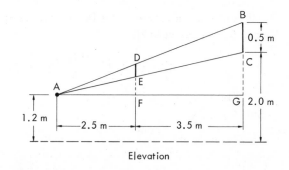

Elevation

Solution. The mirror is 2.5 m from the observer A, and the image of the chart is 3.5 m beyond the mirror. Thus the image of the chart is 6 m from the observer, as required.

Consider the situation in elevation and let the image of the chart be BC. Join AB and AC, cutting the plane of the mirror in D and E, respectively. Drop the perpendicular from A to the plane of the mirror, cutting it at F, and produce it to meet BC produced in G.

Triangles AFE and AGC are similar, and thus $EF/GC = AF/AG$. That is,

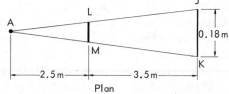

Plan

$$EF = \frac{AF}{AG} \cdot GC = \frac{2.5 \text{ m}}{6.0 \text{ m}} \times 0.8 \text{ m} = \frac{1}{3} \text{ m} = 33.3 \text{ cm}.$$

Similarly, in triangles AFD and AGB,

$$DF = \frac{AF}{AG} \cdot GB = \frac{2.5 \text{ m}}{6.0 \text{ m}} \times 1.3 \text{ m} = 54.2 \text{ cm}.$$

Thus the height of the mirror is $DF - EF = 20.9$ cm, because all rays from the chart reaching A via the mirror must strike the mirror between D and E, since all lines from the image of the chart to A pass through DE.

The height of the lower edge of the mirror from the floor is 1.2 m + EF = 153.3 cm.

Similarly, let us treat the situation in plan, and we find that $LM/JK = 2.5$ m/6.0 m. That is,

$$LM = \left(18 \times \frac{2.5}{6.0}\right) \text{ cm} = 7.5 \text{ cm}.$$

Thus the mirror has dimensions 20.9 cm by 7.5 cm and its lower edge is 153.3 cm from the floor.

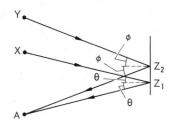

Let us assume that A and the chart are at the same distance from the mirror, and consider any point X on the chart. Draw the plane through AX at right angles to the plane of the mirror. Point X is seen by A by reflection in the mirror, and thus the ray from X to A must obey the law of reflection. Since A and X are at equal distances from the mirror, the point Z_1 must lie on the perpendicular bisector of AX, whatever the distance from AX to the mirror.

In particular, if X is the point on the bottom of the chart nearest to A and if Y is the corresponding point on the opposite side, Z_1 on the perpendicular bisector of AX and Z_2 on the perpendicular bisector of AY define a mirror height Z_1Z_2 which is independent of the position of the mirror. Point Z_1 is on the lower edge of the mirror, which is thus at a fixed distance from the floor wherever the mirror is positioned.

Similar considerations apply to the width of the mirror.

PROBLEM 39.2

Two mirrors are placed coaxially 32 cm apart with their reflecting surfaces facing one another. A small object is placed midway between them and its image after reflection of light from the mirrors in turn is also midway between them. One mirror is concave and of radius of curvature 24 cm. What kind of mirror is the other, and what is the magnification produced by the double reflection?

Solution. Consider the reflection in the concave mirror. We know that

$$\frac{1}{S_1} + \frac{1}{S_1'} = \frac{2}{R_1} = \frac{1}{f_1},$$

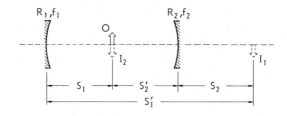

and in this case $S_1 = +16$ cm, $f_1 = 12$ cm.

$$\therefore \quad \frac{1}{S_1'} = \frac{1}{12 \text{ cm}} - \frac{1}{16 \text{ cm}} = \frac{1}{48 \text{ cm}}.$$

Therefore $S_1' = 48$ cm. Thus the first mirror forms a real image at I_1, and I_1 acts as a virtual object for the second mirror, producing a real image at I_2. For the second mirror,

$$\frac{1}{S_2} + \frac{1}{S_2'} = \frac{2}{R_2} = \frac{1}{f_2},$$

where $S_2 = (32 - 48)$ cm $= -16$ cm and $S_2' = 16$ cm.

$$\therefore \quad \frac{1}{f_2} = -\frac{1}{16 \text{ cm}} + \frac{1}{16 \text{ cm}} = 0. \quad \therefore \quad f_2 = \infty.$$

That is, the mirror is a plane mirror. The magnification produced by the first reflection is

$$m = -\frac{S_1'}{S_1} = -\frac{48 \text{ cm}}{16 \text{ cm}} = -3.$$

The magnification produced by the second is, of course, $+1$. Therefore the total magnification is -3.

PROBLEM 39.3

A man wishes to buy a shaving mirror which will allow him to see an upright image of his face magnified twice at a distance of 50 cm. What type of mirror should he buy and what should its radius of curvature be?

Solution. The mirror must be a concave spherical mirror. A convex mirror can never produce an image greater in size than its real object. A concave mirror can produce an upright image only if the distance of the object from the mirror is less than the focal distance.

These statements can be proved easily. Consider the first diagram, with an object PQ at any distance from the reflecting surface. To locate the image position, draw a ray from Q parallel to the axis. After reflection at the surface it must appear to have come from the focal point of the surface F and thus its path is as shown. Draw another ray from Q toward C. It strikes the surface at Y normally and is thus reflected back along the same path. Since Y is of necessity closer to the pole A than X is, these two reflected rays produced backward must meet somewhere along XF. Their intersection defines the image point Q' by definition. Hence $P'Q'$ is always less than PQ.

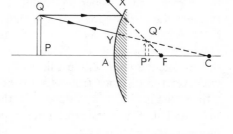

Using a similar construction for the concave case in the second diagram, we see that $P'Q'$ is always greater than PQ as long as P is closer to the mirror than F. For P further from the mirror than F, the image is real and inverted.

The mirror is therefore concave, with a positive focal length. The object distance S is less than f and S' is negative. Thus $|S| + |S'|$, that is, $S - S'$, $= 50$ cm. Hence

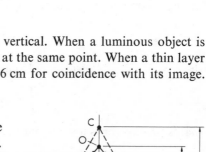

$$\frac{1}{S} + \frac{1}{S'} = \frac{1}{S} - \frac{1}{50\,\text{cm} - S} = \frac{1}{f}.$$

Also the image is magnified two times. Thus

$$m = -\frac{S'}{S} = \frac{50\,\text{cm} - S}{S} = 2.$$

$$\therefore \quad 50\,\text{cm} - S = 2S \quad \text{or} \quad S = \frac{50}{3}\,\text{cm}.$$

$$\therefore \quad f = \frac{S(50\,\text{cm} - S)}{50\,\text{cm} - 2S} = \frac{S \cdot 2S}{S} = 2S = \frac{100\,\text{cm}}{3} = 33\tfrac{1}{3}\,\text{cm}.$$

PROBLEM 39.4

A concave mirror is placed horizontally so that its optical axis is vertical. When a luminous object is placed on the axis and 24 cm above the mirror, its image is located at the same point. When a thin layer of liquid is poured into the mirror, the object has to be lowered 6 cm for coincidence with its image. What is the refractive index of the liquid?

Solution. With no liquid present, object and image in the concave mirror coincide at a distance of 24 cm from the pole of the mirror. Thus the radius of curvature of the mirror is 24 cm, since the light reflected at the mirror must have returned by the same path.

We can also show that this is correct by applying the mirror formula, $(1/S) + (1/S') = 2/R$.

In this case $S = S'$, and thus $R = S = S' = 24$ cm.

When liquid is poured into the mirror, object and final image coincide at 18 cm from the pole of the mirror. Once again the light reflected at the mirror surface must have struck the surface at right angles and been reflected back along the same path. This tells us that, after the refraction in the plane liquid surface, the light rays are normal to the mirror surface, and if produced backward must meet at the center of curvature of the mirror. Thus for the refraction in the plane surface the real object distance is $S = 18$ cm and the virtual image distance is $S' = -24$ cm, since it is measured against the ongoing light.

Hence, applying the general refraction-at-a-surface formula, with $R = \infty$, we have

$$\frac{1}{S} + \frac{n}{S'} = \frac{1-n}{R}.$$

$$\therefore \quad \frac{1}{18\text{ cm}} - \frac{n}{24\text{ cm}} = \frac{1-n}{\infty} = 0. \quad \therefore \quad n = \frac{24\text{ cm}}{18\text{ cm}} = 1.33.$$

Alternatively, applying the refraction-at-a-plane-surface formula, we have

$$\frac{S'}{S} = -\frac{24\text{ cm}}{18\text{ cm}} = -\frac{n}{1}. \quad \therefore \quad n = 1.33 \quad \text{as before.}$$

PROBLEM 39.5

A cross is made on a piece of paper and a plano-convex lens placed on top of it with its plane side uppermost. The cross is viewed in a microscope through the glass. The lens is turned over and the microscope has to be racked down 0.25 cm to bring the cross into focus again. The refractive index of the glass is 1.5 and the radius of curvature of the convex face is 9 cm. What is the thickness of the lens at its center?

Solution. Since the lens and paper are in contact, the cross is an object on one surface of the lens in each case. The problem resolves itself into solving two simultaneous equations, one derived from refraction at a plane surface and the other from refraction at a curved surface.

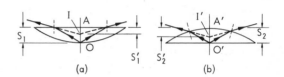

(a) (b)

Treating the first case, we have $S_1'/S_1 = -1/n$.

$$\therefore \quad S_1' = -\frac{S_1}{n} = -\frac{2S_1}{3}.$$

Treating the second case, we have

$$\frac{n}{S_2} + \frac{1}{S_2'} = \frac{1-n}{-R} \quad \text{or} \quad \frac{1}{S_2'} = \frac{n-1}{R} - \frac{n}{S_2}.$$

$$\therefore \quad S_2' = \frac{RS_2}{(n-1)S_2 - nR}.$$

The microscope collects the rays after refraction and thus focuses on the virtual image in each case. It has to be racked down 0.25 cm to focus the second image. But A and A' are at the same height above the cross and S_1' and S_2' are thus measured downward from the same height. Thus

$$S_1' = S_2' = 0.25\text{ cm} = -\frac{2S_1}{3} - \frac{RS_2}{(n-1)S_2 - nR}.$$

But $S_1 = S_2 = S$, the thickness required. Thus

$$-0.25\text{ cm} = \frac{2(n-1)S^2 + R(3-2n)S}{3(n-1)S - 3nR} = \frac{S^2}{1.5S - 40.5}\text{ cm}.$$

$$\therefore \quad 8S^2 + S \times 3\text{ cm} - 81\text{ cm}^2 = 0. \quad \therefore \quad (S - 3\text{ cm})(8S + 27\text{ cm}) = 0.$$

Therefore $S = 3$ cm, since a negative answer for S is clearly inadmissible.

40

Lenses and Optical Instruments

PROBLEM 40.1

A luminous object and a screen are placed at a fixed distance D apart. Show that if a converging lens of focal length f, where $f < D/4$, is inserted between them, it will produce a real image of the object on the screen for two positions separated by a distance $d = \sqrt{D(D - 4f)}$, and that the ratio of the two image sizes for these two positions of the lens is $(D - d)^2/(D + d)^2$.

Solution. In both cases,

$$\frac{1}{s} + \frac{1}{s'} = \frac{1}{f}.$$

$$\therefore \quad \frac{ss'}{s + s'} = f \quad \text{or} \quad \frac{ss'}{D} = f.$$

$$\therefore \quad ss' = fD \tag{1}$$

and

$$s + s' = D. \tag{2}$$

Let $d = s - s'$.

$$\therefore \quad d^2 = (s - s')^2 = (s + s')^2 - 4ss' = D^2 - 4fD.$$

Therefore $d = \sqrt{D(D - 4f)}$. Also, from Eqs. (1) and (2),

$$s + \frac{fD}{s} = D \quad \text{or} \quad s^2 - Ds + fD = 0.$$

$$\therefore \quad s = \frac{D \pm \sqrt{D^2 - 4fD}}{2} = \frac{D \pm d}{2}.$$

$$\therefore \quad s_1 = \tfrac{1}{2}(D - d) \quad \text{and} \quad s_2 = \tfrac{1}{2}(D + d).$$

$$\therefore \quad s_1' = D - s_1 = \tfrac{1}{2}(D + d) \quad \text{and} \quad s_2' = D - s_2 = \tfrac{1}{2}(D - d).$$

Therefore $s_2 - s_1 = d$, and the two positions of the lens are separated by the distance $d = \sqrt{D(D - 4f)}$. Also

$$m_1 = -\frac{s_1'}{s_1} = \frac{y_1}{y} \quad \text{and} \quad m_2 = -\frac{s_2'}{s_2} = \frac{y_2}{y}.$$

$$\therefore \quad \frac{y_2}{y_1} = \frac{m_2}{m_1} = \frac{s_1 s_2'}{s_1' s_2} = \frac{\tfrac{1}{4}(D - d)^2}{\tfrac{1}{4}(D + d)^2} = \frac{(D - d)^2}{(D + d)^2}.$$

This is the basis of Glazebrook's method of determining the apparent slit separation, y, in an interference experiment using a Fresnel biprism. By measuring y_1 and y_2 with a microscope, one can determine y. For, from the above, one has

$$m_1 m_2 = \frac{y_1 y_2}{y^2} = \frac{s_1' s_2'}{s_1 s_2} = \frac{\frac{1}{4}(D-d)(D+d)}{\frac{1}{4}(D-d)(D+d)} = 1.$$

$$\therefore \quad y = \sqrt{y_1 y_2}.$$

Note that this method only works if $f < D/4$; for otherwise d^2 is negative and d is thus imaginary.

PROBLEM 40.2

An elderly landscape artist can see distinctly without eyeglasses only objects between 75 cm and 200 cm from his eyes. What kind of eyeglasses does he require in order to see both distant objects and his canvas at a distance of 25 cm? Which parts of a landscape that he paints while wearing his eyeglasses are likely to be omitted from the picture?

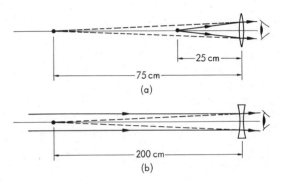

Solution. The artist can only see down to 75 cm. He needs to see down to 25 cm. For this defect of his eyes he requires a lens which, when receiving light from an object 25 cm away, will converge it sufficiently so that to the eye behind the lens it will appear to have come from a point 75 cm away. In other words, with a real object at distance 25 cm, the lens will have a virtual image at distance 75 cm.

Applying the lens formula $(1/s) + (1/s') = 1/f$ to this case, we have

$$\frac{1}{f} = \frac{1}{25 \text{ cm}} - \frac{1}{75 \text{ cm}} = \frac{2}{75 \text{ cm}}. \quad \therefore \quad f = 37.5 \text{ cm}.$$

Let us analyze in a similar fashion the other defect, the inability to see distant objects clearly. The lens required is one which, with an object at infinity, produces a virtual image at 200 cm.

$$\therefore \quad \frac{1}{f'} = \frac{1}{\infty} - \frac{1}{200 \text{ cm}}. \quad \therefore \quad f' = -200 \text{ cm}.$$

The eyeglasses required are therefore bifocals, the top portion of each lens being a diverging lens of focal length -200 cm and the bottom portion being a converging lens of focal length $+37.5$ cm.

When the artist is looking through the diverging portion of his eyeglasses, he can clearly see objects which appear to him to lie between 75 cm and 200 cm, i.e., virtual images of the lens which lie between these distances. A virtual image at 200 cm is produced by objects at infinity. A virtual image at 75 cm is produced by an object at a distance x from the lens, where $(1/x) - (1/75 \text{ cm}) = -1/200 \text{ cm}$.

$$\therefore \quad \frac{1}{x} = \frac{1}{75 \text{ cm}} - \frac{1}{200 \text{ cm}} = \frac{5}{600 \text{ cm}}. \quad \therefore \quad x = 120 \text{ cm}.$$

All objects from infinity down to 120 cm are thus seen clearly by the artist when he is looking through the top portion of his eyeglasses.

Similarly, for the bottom portion of his eyeglasses, he will see clearly through them all objects from 25 cm to a distance y, where the object at y produces a virtual image at 200 cm. Therefore

$$\frac{1}{y} - \frac{1}{200 \text{ cm}} = \frac{2}{75 \text{ cm}}. \quad \therefore \quad \frac{1}{y} = \frac{2}{75 \text{ cm}} + \frac{1}{200 \text{ cm}} = \frac{19}{600 \text{ cm}}. \quad \therefore \quad y = 31.6 \text{ cm}.$$

The artist can thus see clearly all objects from 25 cm up to 31.6 cm when he is looking through the bottom portion of his eyeglasses.

There is a gap in his vision between 31.6 cm and 120 cm and objects in this range may be omitted from his canvas.

PROBLEM 40.3

The simplest method of finding the focal length of a converging lens is to place the lens between a luminous point object and a plane mirror and alter its position until an image is formed at the position of the object. The distance between the object and the vertex of the lens equals the focal length of the lens. Show why this is so.

A student does the experiment and finds to his horror that he can obtain three positions of the lens that give coincidence of the object and its image. How have the spurious images been formed and how can the student tell which is the correct focal length?

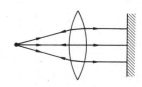

Solution. The first diagram shows how the correct image is formed. If the object is at the focal point of the lens, a beam of rays all parallel to the axis emerges from the other side of the lens. These strike the plane mirror normally and therefore return along their original paths and converge back to the object point to form an image. This can happen only if the object is at the focal point of the lens.

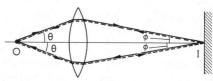

If the distance between the object and the plane mirror is at least four times the focal length of the lens (cf. Problem 40.1), it is also possible to form an image of the object on the plane mirror for two positions of the lens. The second diagram shows one of these. Consider two rays starting from the object at equal angles θ above and below the axis. The upper of these rays is brought to the axis at the position of the plane mirror making an angle ϕ with the axis. The lower ray by symmetry strikes the mirror on the axis at exactly the same angle. But the law of reflection tells us that each of these rays after reflection at the plane mirror makes an angle ϕ with the axis on the opposite side. Thus the upper ray returns through the lens by the path originally traversed by the lower ray, and vice versa. This is true for *any* pair of symmetrical rays, and thus all rays converge to the object position after reflection at the plane mirror. A second image is again formed at the object position.

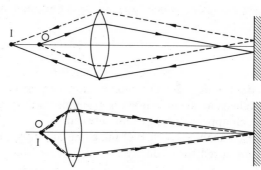

The student may now find which is the correct focal length by moving the plane mirror. The first diagram does not depend on the lens–mirror distance, and the image remains when the plane mirror is moved away from or toward the lens. In the second diagram the position of the plane mirror is critical. If it is moved from the position shown in the second diagram to that shown in the third, symmetrical rays no longer retrace the paths of each other and the image is formed beyond the object.

It should be noted that the image can be returned to its former position by moving the lens closer to this object, as shown in the fourth diagram.

In doing an experiment of this type to find the focal length of a lens, the trouble discussed above can be avoided completely if the lens is placed against the plane mirror and the two are moved as one unit away from the object. The spurious image cannot now be formed.

PROBLEM 40.4

The student of the preceding example, elated at solving the problem for himself and having measured the focal length of the lens to be 45 cm, decides to experiment further. He removes the plane mirror, leaving only the point source of light and the lens, and discovers that, when he moves the lens about, he can obtain a faint image coincident with the object, if the lens is 20 cm from the object. He reverses the lens and finds that coincidence of object and image now occurs when the lens–object distance is

25 cm. Correctly concluding that the image is due to a reflection at the back of the lens, he triumphantly works out the refractive index of the glass. What answer does he obtain?

Solution. Although the problem is concerned with a lens, and we must know and use the lensmaker's formula, it is essentially a problem in reflection and refraction at curved surfaces.

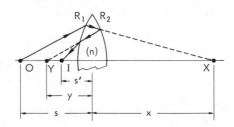

Problems of this type, involving reflection or refraction at several successive surfaces in turn, are best done by quite distinct consideration of each surface, application of the appropriate formula in each case, and a final simultaneous solution of the equations obtained.

Consider the diagram and deal with refraction at the first surface only. Let R_1 and R_2 be the *magnitudes* of the radii of curvature of the two surfaces and n be the refractive index of the glass. The real object for the first surface is at O, which is a distance s from the vertex of the surface. Were no other surface involved, a real image would be formed at X, a distance x from the vertex of the surface.

$$\therefore \quad \frac{1}{s} + \frac{n}{x} = \frac{n-1}{R_1}.$$

The light now falls on the back surface in the medium of refractive index n. Part of the light is transmitted but, as in all cases of light falling on an interface, part is also reflected, and it is only with this light that we are concerned. The back surface is acting, so far as this light is concerned, as a spherical reflector. X is a virtual object for this reflector and, in the absence of any other surface, a real image would be formed at Y, a distance y from the vertex of the back surface. The lens is thin, so that its thickness is neglected.

$$\therefore \quad -\frac{1}{x} + \frac{1}{y} = \frac{2}{R_2}.$$

Refraction at the first surface of light reflected from the back surface now takes place. Y acts as a virtual object for this surface and a final real object is formed at I, a distance s' from the vertex of the front surface.

$$\therefore \quad -\frac{n}{y} + \frac{1}{s'} = \frac{1-n}{-R_1}.$$

Note that in each of the previous two cases the radius of curvature was measured with the ongoing light and was thus positive. Here the radius is measured in a direction opposite to the ongoing light and is thus negative.

The equations obtained (the second now multiplied by n) are

$$\frac{1}{s} + \frac{n}{x} = \frac{n-1}{R_1}, \qquad -\frac{n}{x} + \frac{n}{y} = \frac{2n}{R_2}, \qquad \text{and} \qquad -\frac{n}{y} + \frac{1}{s'} = \frac{n-1}{R_1}.$$

Adding all three equations gives

$$\frac{1}{s} + \frac{1}{s'} = \frac{2(n-1)}{R_1} + \frac{2n}{R_2},$$

or, since in this problem $s' = s$,

$$\frac{2}{s} = \frac{2(n-1)}{R_1} + \frac{2n}{R_2} \qquad \text{or} \qquad \frac{n-1}{R_1} + \frac{n}{R_2} = \frac{1}{20 \text{ cm}}.$$

Reversing the lens alters s to 25 cm and interchanges R_1 and R_2, but does not alter the rest of the analysis.

$$\therefore \quad \frac{n-1}{R_2} + \frac{n}{R_1} = \frac{1}{25 \text{ cm}}.$$

Adding the last two equations, we obtain

$$\frac{2n-1}{R_1} + \frac{2n-1}{R_2} = (2n-1)\left(\frac{1}{R_1} + \frac{1}{R_2}\right) = \frac{1}{20\text{ cm}} + \frac{1}{25\text{ cm}} = \frac{9}{100\text{ cm}}.$$

But, from the lensmaker's formula,

$$\frac{1}{f} = (n-1)\left(\frac{1}{R_1} - \frac{1}{-R_2}\right) = (n-1)\left(\frac{1}{R_1} + \frac{1}{R_2}\right).$$

$$\therefore \quad \frac{2n-1}{(n-1)f} = \frac{9}{100\text{ cm}}. \qquad \therefore \quad \frac{2n-1}{n-1} = \frac{9 \times 45\text{ cm}}{100\text{ cm}} = \frac{81}{20}.$$

$$\therefore \quad 40n - 20 = 81n - 81. \qquad \therefore \quad 41n = 61 \quad \text{or} \quad n = \frac{61}{41} = 1.49.$$

PROBLEM 40.5

The frames in a home movie must be magnified 143 times before the picture formed on a screen 12 ft from the projection lens is large enough to please the family watching. What distance must the film be from the lens and what is the focal length of the lens?

Solution. The magnification produced by the lens is given by

$$m = -\frac{s'}{s} = -\frac{12\text{ ft}}{s} = -143.$$

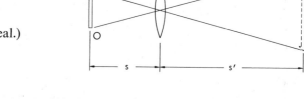

(The image must be inverted since s must be real.)
Thus the film-to-lens distance is

$$s = \frac{12}{143}\text{ ft} = \frac{144}{143}\text{ in.} = 1.007\text{ in.}$$

Applying the lens formula, we can obtain the focal length, since

$$\frac{1}{f} = \frac{1}{s} + \frac{1}{s'} = \frac{143}{12\text{ ft}} + \frac{1}{12\text{ ft}} = \frac{144}{12\text{ ft}}.$$

$$\therefore \quad f = \frac{12}{144}\text{ ft} = 1\text{ in.}$$

PROBLEM 40.6

Part of one end of an aquarium tank is a thin lens so that corals in the tank can be seen magnified. Show that the two focal lengths of the lens are unequal, and prove that the lens formula in this case is $f/s + f'/s' = 1$.

Solution. Consider the refraction at the first surface of radius of curvature $+R_1$, separating the two media, air and glass, of refractive index n. A real image would be formed at X in the absence of any other surface. Thus

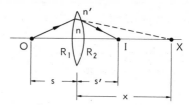

$$\frac{1}{s} + \frac{n}{x} = \frac{n-1}{R_1}.$$

Here X acts as a virtual object for refraction at the second surface of radius of curvature $-R_2$, separating the two media, glass and water of refractive index n'. A final real image is formed at I. Thus

$$-\frac{n}{x} + \frac{n'}{s'} = \frac{n'-n}{-R_2} = \frac{n-n'}{R_2}. \qquad \therefore \quad \frac{1}{s} + \frac{n'}{s'} = \frac{n-1}{R_1} + \frac{n-n'}{R_2}.$$

If O is at infinity, then by definition I coincides with F', the second focal point of the lens.

$$\therefore \quad \frac{1}{\infty} + \frac{n'}{f'} = \frac{n-1}{R_1} + \frac{n-n'}{R_2}. \qquad \therefore \quad \frac{1}{f'} = \frac{1}{n'}\left(\frac{n-1}{R_1} + \frac{n-n'}{R_2}\right).$$

Similarly, if O is at F, the first focal point of the lens, a parallel beam emerges into the water. That is, I is at infinity.

$$\therefore \quad \frac{1}{f} + \frac{n'}{\infty} = \frac{n-1}{R_1} + \frac{n-n'}{R_2}. \qquad \therefore \quad \frac{1}{f} = \frac{n-1}{R_1} + \frac{n-n'}{R_2}.$$

Thus $f/f' = 1/n'$, and the focal lengths are unequal. Further, if

$$\frac{n-1}{R_1} + \frac{n-n'}{R_2} = P,$$

then

$$\frac{1}{s} + \frac{n'}{s'} = P. \qquad \therefore \quad \frac{1}{sP} + \frac{n'}{s'P} = 1.$$

But $1/f = P$ and $n'/f' = P$.

$$\therefore \quad \frac{f}{s} + \frac{f'}{s'} = 1.$$

PROBLEM 40.7

The lens in the aquarium tank of the preceding question has $R_1 = 15$ cm, $R_2 = 10$ cm, and the refractive indexes for glass and water are $\frac{3}{2}$ and $\frac{4}{3}$, respectively. A fish swims right up to the lens and views a man standing 30 cm from the glass. Where is the image the fish sees, and what is the angular magnification which the magnifier has produced?

Solution. Application of the formulas obtained in the preceding question gives us

$$\frac{1}{f'} = \frac{3}{4}\left(\frac{3/2 - 1}{15 \text{ cm}} + \frac{3/2 - 4/3}{10 \text{ cm}}\right) = \frac{3}{4}\left(\frac{1}{30 \text{ cm}} - \frac{1}{60 \text{ cm}}\right) = \frac{1}{80 \text{ cm}}.$$

$$\therefore \quad f' = 80 \text{ cm}.$$

Similarly $f = 60$ cm. Since $(f/s) + (f'/s') = 1$, then

$$\frac{60 \text{ cm}}{30 \text{ cm}} + \frac{80 \text{ cm}}{s'} = 1. \qquad \therefore \quad s' = -80 \text{ cm}.$$

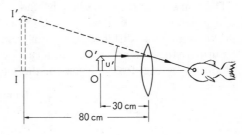

The fish therefore sees the man 80 cm beyond the lens.

Refer again to the preceding question; the magnification produced by the first surface is $m_1 = -x/ns$, and by the second surface $m_2 = +(ns'/n's)$.

Thus the total magnification is $m = m_1 m_2 = -(s'/n's)$.

If the man's height is y, the image's height is $-s'y/n's$. Thus

$$u' = -\frac{s'y}{n's} \times \frac{1}{-s'} = -\frac{y}{n's}.$$

But, by definition, $u = y/25$ cm, and thus the angular magnification is

$$M = \frac{u'}{u} = \frac{25 \text{ cm}}{n's} = \frac{25 \text{ cm}}{\frac{4}{3} \times 30 \text{ cm}} = \frac{5}{8}.$$

PROBLEM 40.8

A box camera has a lens of focal length 11 cm and a fixed aperture of diameter 1 cm. A novice decides to use it in conjunction with an exposure meter of rather more sophisticated design than the camera. He finds that for a particular scene, the exposure meter informs him that he should use an exposure of $\frac{1}{100}$ s at $f/2.8$. How can he work out the correct exposure time for the box camera?

Solution. The f-number is the ratio of the focal length of the lens to the diameter of the aperture. Thus the f-number of the camera lens is $f/11$.

The required exposure is $\frac{1}{100}$ s at $f/2.8$. This is equivalent to time t at $f/11$. But we know that the exposure time multiplied by the area of the aperture is proportional to the intensity of illumination required.

$$\therefore \quad \frac{1 \text{ s}}{100} \times \frac{1}{2.8^2 \text{ cm}^2} = t \times \frac{1}{11^2 \text{ cm}^2} . \qquad \therefore \quad t = \left(\frac{11}{2.8}\right)^2 \times \frac{1}{100} \text{ s} = 0.154 \text{ s}.$$

PROBLEM 40.9

A simple telephoto lens consists of a converging lens of focal length 20 cm followed at a distance of 20 cm by a diverging lens of focal length -10 cm. Where must a film be placed to receive the final image if the object is 100 cm from the first lens?

Suppose that the diverging lens can be swung out and a second diverging lens swung in. Where must this second lens be located and what must be its focal length to produce twice the magnification of the first system?

Solution. If the converging lens were alone, the object at O would produce a real image at X, a distance x from the lens.

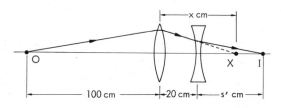

$$\therefore \quad \frac{1}{100 \text{ cm}} + \frac{1}{x} = \frac{1}{20 \text{ cm}} .$$

$$\therefore \quad \frac{1}{x} = \frac{1}{20 \text{ cm}} - \frac{1}{100 \text{ cm}} \quad \text{or} \quad x = 25 \text{ cm}.$$

The rays never reach X because of the presence of the diverging lens. Thus X acts as a virtual object for this lens, producing a final real image at I. The object distance is $(20 - 25) \text{ cm} = -5 \text{ cm}$.

$$\therefore \quad -\frac{1}{5 \text{ cm}} + \frac{1}{s'} = -\frac{1}{10 \text{ cm}} . \qquad \therefore \quad \frac{1}{s'} = \frac{1}{5 \text{ cm}} - \frac{1}{10 \text{ cm}} . \qquad \therefore \quad s' = 10 \text{ cm}.$$

The film should thus be 10 cm behind the diverging lens.

In general, if the distance between the lenses is d and the distance from diverging lens to film is p, we know that the distance from converging lens to film is as before. Therefore $p + d = 30$ cm.

Further, the magnification produced by the converging lens is unchanged. Thus the magnification produced by the diverging lens in the second case is

$$2\left(-\frac{s'}{20 \text{ cm} - x}\right) = 2 \cdot \frac{10 \text{ cm}}{5 \text{ cm}} = 4.$$

$$\therefore \quad \frac{-p}{d - 25 \text{ cm}} = 4. \qquad \therefore \quad -p = 4d - 100 \text{ cm}.$$

That is, $p + 4d = 100$ cm and $p + d = 30$ cm.

$$\therefore \quad 3d = 70 \text{ cm} \quad \text{or} \quad d = \frac{70 \text{ cm}}{3} = 23\tfrac{1}{3} \text{ cm}. \qquad \therefore \quad p = \frac{20 \text{ cm}}{3} = 6\tfrac{2}{3} \text{ cm}.$$

This determines the location of the diverging lens. It is a lens which, with a virtual object $(23\tfrac{1}{3} - 25) \text{ cm} = -1\tfrac{2}{3} \text{ cm}$ from it, produces a real image at a distance of $6\tfrac{2}{3}$ cm from it. Thus, if the focal length of the new lens is f,

$$-\frac{1}{1\tfrac{2}{3} \text{ cm}} + \frac{1}{6\tfrac{2}{3} \text{ cm}} = \frac{1}{f} ;$$

That is,

$$\frac{1}{f} = -\frac{3}{5 \text{ cm}} + \frac{3}{20 \text{ cm}} = -\frac{9}{20 \text{ cm}} . \qquad \therefore \quad f = -\frac{20 \text{ cm}}{9} = -2\tfrac{2}{9} \text{ cm}.$$

PROBLEM 40.10

A compound microscope consists of objective and eye lenses of focal lengths 0.6 cm and 2 cm, respectively. An object is placed $\frac{5}{8}$ cm from the objective and the image is viewed by a scientist at the least distance of distinct vision (25 cm). Find the magnifying power of the system and the distance of separation of the lenses.

Solution. For a simple microscope (or telescope) problem, always apply the lens formula to each of the lenses in turn. The objective has, as shown in the diagram, a real object at O and a real image at X.

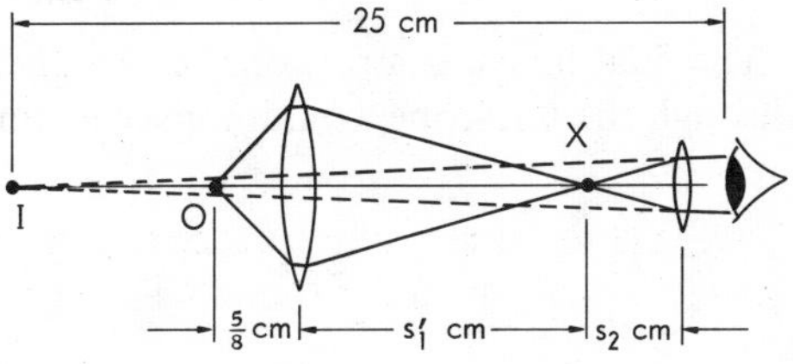

$$\therefore \quad \frac{1}{\frac{5}{8}\,\text{cm}} + \frac{1}{s_1'} = \frac{1}{0.6\,\text{cm}}.$$

$$\therefore \quad \frac{1}{s_1'} = \frac{1}{0.6\,\text{cm}} - \frac{8}{5\,\text{cm}} \quad \text{or} \quad s_1' = 15\,\text{cm}.$$

The eye lens has a real object at X and a virtual image at I. Therefore $(1/s_2) - (1/25\,\text{cm}) = 1/2\,\text{cm}$.

$$\therefore \quad \frac{1}{s_2} = \frac{1}{2\,\text{cm}} + \frac{1}{25\,\text{cm}} \quad \text{or} \quad s_2 = \frac{50\,\text{cm}}{27} = 1.85\,\text{cm}.$$

Thus the separation of the lenses is $s_1' + s_2 = 16.85\,\text{cm}$.
The linear magnification produced by the objective is

$$m_1 = -\frac{s_1'}{s_1} = -\frac{15\,\text{cm}}{\frac{5}{8}\,\text{cm}} = -24.$$

The angular magnification produced by the eye lens is

$$M = \frac{u'}{u} = \frac{y/s_2}{y/25\,\text{cm}} = \frac{25\,\text{cm}}{s_2} = 13\tfrac{1}{2}.$$

The magnifying power of the system is thus $m_1 \times M = -24 \times 13\tfrac{1}{2} = -324$.
Note that the linear magnification produced by the eye lens is

$$m_2 = -\frac{s_2'}{s_2} = -\frac{-25\,\text{cm}}{50\,\text{cm}/27} = +13\tfrac{1}{2} = M.$$

The linear magnification always equals the angular magnification for a simple magnifier if the final image is at the least distance of distinct vision.

PROBLEM 40.11

In one of Edgar Allan Poe's stories, the author describes his terrifying experience of focusing a telescope on a distant hill and observing a "dragon" crawling up it. The punch line comes when he realizes that the dragon is an ant crawling up the windowpane through which he is observing the hill. Although this is a good story, explain why it is bad optics.

Solution. The distant hill is, for all practical purposes, at infinity. The objective lens of the telescope forms an image of it at its second focal point, which is also the first focal point of the eye lens. The final image is being viewed at infinity. Unless the ant is at infinity or at the second focal point of the objective lens, i.e., unless it occupies the same position as the object or the intermediate image, its final image cannot be at infinity also, and thus it will not be viewed at the same position as the image of the hill.

In fact, assuming that the telescope has focal lengths of 100 cm and 10 cm for its objective and eye lenses, respectively, and that the ant is 200 cm from the objective, we can work out where the final image lies.

Treating the objective, we find that

$$\frac{1}{s_1} + \frac{1}{s_1'} = \frac{1}{f_1} \quad \text{or} \quad \frac{1}{200 \text{ cm}} + \frac{1}{s_1'} = \frac{1}{100 \text{ cm}}.$$

$$\therefore \quad s_1' = 200 \text{ cm}.$$

The objective lens and eye lens are 110 cm apart and the image formed by the objective will act as a virtual object for the eye lens. The object distance is $s_2 = (110 - 200) \text{ cm} = -90 \text{ cm}$.

$$\therefore \quad -\frac{1}{90 \text{ cm}} + \frac{1}{s_2'} = \frac{1}{10 \text{ cm}}. \quad \therefore \quad s_2' = 9 \text{ cm}.$$

The final image is a real one on the observer's side of the eye lens and therefore Poe, when he looked through the telescope, could not see an image of the ant.

41

Interference and Diffraction

PROBLEM 41.1

A radio telescope sited on the edge of a cliff overlooking the sea operates on a wavelength of 100 m. A radio star rises above the horizon and is tracked by the telescope. The first minimum of the received signal occurs when the star is 30° above the horizontal. Explain why the minimum occurs and determine the height of the cliff, assuming that radio waves suffer a phase change of π on reflection at a water surface.

Solution. The radio telescope is receiving signals direct from the star and also by reflection in the water surface, which is acting like a plane mirror. The situation is therefore analogous to the Lloyd's-mirror experiment in optics. In this case the source of the radiation is far enough away to be considered at infinity and the rays are

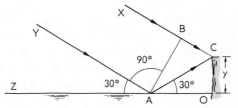

descending on the earth in a parallel beam. When the path difference between rays AC and BC is such that they reach the telescope exactly out of phase, destructive interference occurs and the signal at C will be a minimum. The plane through C perpendicular to the water surface contains an interference pattern due to the combined effect of direct and reflected rays, i.e., due to interference between radiation from the star and radiation which appears to come from its reflection in the water surface.

Consider the diagram. If AB is drawn perpendicular to XC, it will also be perpendicular to YA, and AB is a plane wave front of the incoming beam. Thus the disturbances at A and B have the same phase at all times. A phase change of π occurs at A and this is equivalent to an increase in path of $\lambda/2$. Thus the path difference between the two rays is $\delta = AC + (\lambda/2) - BC$. But by the laws of reflection $\angle YAZ = \angle CAO = 30°$, and therefore $\angle BAC = 180° - 90° - 30° - 30° = 30°$.

$$\therefore \quad \delta = AC + \frac{\lambda}{2} - AC\sin 30° = \frac{\lambda}{2} + AC(1 - \sin 30°) = \frac{\lambda}{2} + \frac{y}{\sin 30°}(1 - \sin 30°) = \frac{\lambda}{2} + y.$$

If $\delta = \lambda/2$, $y = 0$, and this corresponds to the center of the interference pattern being a minimum, as in the Lloyd's-mirror experiment. Since this is the first minimum the telescope receives, C must be at the first minimum above O for the situation shown in the diagram. (Were it a minimum other than the first, a previous minimum must have occurred for an angle lower than 30°.) Therefore δ must be $3\lambda/2$.

$$\therefore \quad \frac{3\lambda}{2} = \frac{\lambda}{2} + y. \quad \therefore \quad y = \lambda = 100 \text{ m}.$$

PROBLEM 41.2

In a Young's double-slit experiment employing light of wavelength 5.50×10^{-7} m, the zero-order bright fringe of the interference pattern is centrally placed on the viewing screen. When a thin film of transparent material of refractive index 1.45 is placed over one of the slits, the central position is now found to be occupied by the fourth-order bright fringe (as checked by the use of white light). What is the thickness of the inserted film?

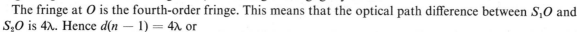

Solution. When both slits are uncovered, the position of the zero-order bright fringe on the screen is at the point O equidistant from S_1 and S_2. At this point waves from S_1 and S_2, having traveled equal distances, are in phase.

When slit S_1 is covered by the transparent film of thickness d and refractive index n, light traversing the film has traveled an optical length (cf. Problem 38.1) of nd. Light from S_2 traversing a corresponding thickness d of air has traveled an optical length of only d (assuming air to have a refractive index of 1). There is therefore an optical path difference between the light from the two slits of $nd - d = d(n - 1)$. The fact that light in traveling from S_1 to O passes through the film at a slight angle to the normal is ignored, as the angle is negligibly small.

The fringe at O is the fourth-order fringe. This means that the optical path difference between S_1O and S_2O is 4λ. Hence $d(n - 1) = 4\lambda$ or

$$d = \frac{4\lambda}{n - 1} = \frac{4 \times 5.50 \times 10^{-7}}{0.45} \text{ m} = 4.89 \times 10^{-6} \text{ m}.$$

PROBLEM 41.3

Show that in a Newton's-rings experiment in which the fringe pattern is viewed in reflected light which has struck the plane surface normally, $r_p^2 - r_q^2 = R(p - q)\lambda$, where λ is the wavelength of the light used, R is the radius of curvature of the bottom face of the lens, and r_p and r_q are the radii of the pth and qth rings of the system.

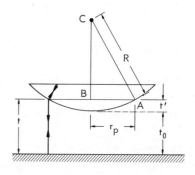

Solution. Interference is occurring between the rays reflected at the bottom face of the lens and those reflected from the plane surface. It should be noted that no phase change occurs on reflection at the bottom lens surface, which is from a more-dense to a less-dense medium, but a phase change of π occurs at the other reflection from air to glass (equivalent to a path increase of $\lambda/2$).

In general, the two surfaces are not in contact and the path difference between the interfering beams is thus $2t + (\lambda/2) = 2t_0 + 2t' + (\lambda/2)$. Now

$$CA^2 = CB^2 + BA^2 \quad \text{or} \quad R^2 = (R - t')^2 + BA^2.$$

$$\therefore \quad BA^2 = 2Rt' - t'^2.$$

But t' is very small, and thus t'^2 is negligible in comparison with $2Rt'$. Therefore $BA^2 = 2Rt'$.

If BA is the radius of the interference fringe, r_p, due to a path difference of $p\lambda$ between the interfering rays, then

$$p\lambda = 2t_0 + 2t' + \frac{\lambda}{2} = 2t_0 + \frac{\lambda}{2} + \frac{r_p^2}{R}.$$

Similarly, we find that

$$q\lambda = 2t_0 + \frac{\lambda}{2} + \frac{r_q^2}{R}.$$

$$\therefore \quad (p - q)\lambda = \frac{1}{R}(r_p^2 - r_q^2).$$

It is always advantageous to use this formula, since one can never guarantee that the lens and plate are in contact. In this formula no such assumption is made, and one has only to measure the differences in order between two rings and not attempt to find the absolute order of a particular ring.

PROBLEM 41.4

A thin lens of long focal length is supported horizontally a short distance above the flat polished end of a steel cylinder. The cylinder is 5 cm high and its lower end is rigidly held. Newton's rings are produced between the lens and the upper end of the cylinder, using normally incident light of wavelength 6000 Å, and viewed from above by means of a microscope. When the temperature of the cylinder is raised 25 C deg, 50 rings move past the cross-wires of the microscope. What is the coefficient of linear expansion of steel?

Solution. Initially the cylinder has a length d, and a gap of length t_0 exists between the top of the cylinder and the bottom surface of the lens in the portion of the air wedge viewed in the microscope at the same position as the cross-wires. Newton's rings are produced in the air wedge, and for a bright fringe to appear at the cross-wires, $2t_0 = (n + \frac{1}{2})\lambda$, where n is an unknown integer.

After one heats the cylinder through a temperature difference T, the length of the cylinder is $d(1 + \alpha T)$, where α is the coefficient of linear expansion of steel, and the gap will have been reduced to t, where $t_0 - t = d\alpha T$.

If a bright fringe is again seen at the position of the cross-wires, then $2t = (m + \frac{1}{2})\lambda$, where m is an integer.

$$\therefore \quad 2(t_0 - t) = 2d\alpha T = (n - m)\lambda.$$

During the heating process, $(n - m)$ bright fringes must have passed over the cross-wires. Thus

$$\alpha = \frac{(n - m)\lambda}{2dT} = \frac{50 \times 6 \times 10^{-5} \text{ cm}}{2 \times 5 \text{ cm} \times 25 \text{ C deg}} = 1.2 \times 10^{-5} \text{ per } °\text{C}.$$

PROBLEM 41.5

A slit of width d is placed in front of a lens of focal length 50 cm and is illuminated normally with light of wavelength 5.89×10^{-5} cm. The first minima on either side of the central maximum of the diffraction pattern observed in the focal plane of the lens are separated by 0.20 cm. What is the value of d?

Solution. The rays diffracted in the direction at which the first minimum occurs above the central maximum will be brought to a focus in the focal plane of the lens. Similarly for the first minimum below the central maximum. Take typical rays AOB and COD from these two beams such that both pass through the center of the lens and are therefore undeviated. The angles between the rays on the two sides of the lens are thus equal.

$$\therefore \quad 2\sin^{-1}\frac{\lambda}{d} = 2\tan^{-1}\frac{DB}{2f} = 2\tan^{-1}\frac{0.20 \text{ cm}}{2 \times 50 \text{ cm}}.$$

$$\therefore \quad \sin^{-1}\frac{\lambda}{d} = \tan^{-1} 0.002.$$

But the angle is small, and thus the sine and tan are almost exactly equal to the angle. Therefore $\lambda/d = 0.002$ or

$$d = \frac{5.89 \times 10^{-5} \text{ cm}}{2 \times 10^{-3}} = 2.945 \times 10^{-2} \text{ cm}.$$

PROBLEM 41.6

The spectrum of a particular light source consists of lines and bands stretching from a wavelength of 5.0×10^{-5} cm to 7.5×10^{-5} cm. When a diffraction grating is illuminated normally with this light it is found that two adjacent spectra formed just overlap, the junction of the two spectra occurring at an angle of 45°. How many lines per centimeter are ruled on the grating?

Solution. At the angle of 45°, we have $d \sin 45° = m \times 7.5 \times 10^{-5}$ cm, and also $d \sin 45° = (m+1) \times 5.0 \times 10^{-5}$ cm.

$$\therefore \quad \frac{m+1}{m} = \frac{7.5 \text{ cm}}{5.0 \text{ cm}} = \frac{3}{2}. \quad \therefore \quad m = 2.$$

The second-order spectrum thus just overlaps with the third. Also

$$d = \frac{2 \times 7.5 \times 10^{-5} \text{ cm}}{\sin 45°} = 2.12 \times 10^{-4} \text{ cm}.$$

This is the separation of the rulings. Hence the number of rulings per centimeter, n, is

$$n = \frac{1}{d} = \frac{10^4}{2.12 \text{ cm}} = 4715 \text{ per cm}.$$

PROBLEM 41.7

Sodium yellow light, which consists of the two wavelengths 5890 Å and 5896 Å, falls normally on a plane diffraction grating with 1500 rulings per centimeter. What is the angular separation of the two lines observed in the first-order spectrum, and under what conditions will they be seen as separated?

Solution. The grating formula, in the usual notation, is $a \sin \theta = m\lambda$. But the number of rulings per unit distance p is equal to $1/a$. Therefore $\sin \theta = m\lambda/a = mp\lambda$. If a small change in wavelength to $\lambda + d\lambda$ produces a change in the angle of diffraction to $\theta + d\theta$, then $\cos \theta \, d\theta = mp \, d\lambda$.

$$\therefore \quad d\theta = \frac{mp \, d\lambda}{\cos \theta} = \frac{mp \, d\lambda}{\sqrt{1 - m^2 p^2 \lambda^2}}.$$

The separation of the sodium lines in the first order is thus

$$d\theta = \frac{1 \times 1500 \text{ cm}^{-1} \times 6 \times 10^{-8} \text{ cm}}{\sqrt{1 - 1^2 \times 1500^2 \text{ cm}^{-2} \times 5893^2 \times 10^{-16} \text{ cm}^2}} = \frac{9 \times 10^{-5}}{0.9961} = 9.04 \times 10^{-5} \text{ rad}.$$

The resolving power of a grating is mn, where n is the total number of lines on the grating. Thus $\lambda/d\lambda = mn$ or $n = \lambda/m \, d\lambda$. For the first-order spectrum of the grating,

$$n = \frac{5893 \times 10^{-8} \text{ cm}}{1 \times 6 \times 10^{-8} \text{ cm}} = 982 \text{ rulings}.$$

As long as the grating is wide enough to contain 982 rulings, the sodium yellow lines will be resolved in the first order.

PROBLEM 41.8

In a detective story an escaped convict, intent on avenging himself against the gang boss who allowed him to take the rap for a murder, drove into an enclosed valley at night and was blown up in a booby trap. One of the inhabitants of the valley, who lived at the other end, 6 miles from the scene of the explosion, stated that he had been sitting on his verandah and had seen the twin headlights of the car come over the ridge at the entrance to the valley just before the explosion took place. The very intelligent detective suspected him of being the gang boss. Why? Where in the valley should the house have been in order to make the statement convincing?

Solution. The diaphragm of the eye limits the amount of the wave front from any illuminated object that can enter the eye and fall on the retina to form an image. The image is thus the diffraction pattern produced by the circular aperture, and instead of seeing a point image of a point object, we actually observe a fringe system. The eye's ability to resolve two close point objects is thus severely limited. Applying Rayleigh's criterion for resolution to the case of diffraction at a circular aperture, we find that two point objects are not distinguishable unless they subtend at the eye an angle greater than $(1.22 \lambda/a)$ rad, where λ is the wavelength of light and a is the diameter of the pupil of the eye.

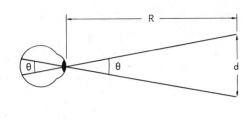

Apply this to the problem. The headlights of a car are separated by a distance no greater than 5 ft. The witness saw the car at a distance of 6 mi. The angle subtended by the headlights at his eyes is thus at most

$$\theta = \frac{5 \text{ ft}}{6 \times 5280 \text{ ft}} = \frac{1}{6336} = 1.58 \times 10^{-4} \text{ rad.}$$

Taking the mean wavelength of the light emitted by the headlights as 5×10^{-5} cm, approximately the wavelength at which the eye is most sensitive, and the diameter of the pupil as 3 mm (though this decreases in adapting to the intensity of the light received by the eye), we find that the maximum angular resolution of the eye is

$$\theta' = \frac{1.22 \times 5 \times 10^{-5} \text{ cm}}{0.3 \text{ cm}} = 2.03 \times 10^{-4} \text{ rad.}$$

The figure normally quoted is in fact a little higher than this.

The witness is thus claiming to have seen as distinct points of light two objects subtending an angle less than that which his eye can resolve. The witness is therefore lying, and there would be no reason to do this unless he had something to hide.

To make his story convincing, the witness would have to live nearer the end of the valley, at a distance no greater than d, where

$$\frac{5 \text{ ft}}{d \times 5280 \text{ ft} \cdot \text{mi}^{-1}} = 2.03 \times 10^{-4}. \qquad \text{That is,} \qquad d = \frac{1 \text{ mi}}{1056 \times 2.03 \times 10^{-4}} = 4.7 \text{ mi.}$$

PROBLEM 41.9

The experimentally minded student of the preceding chapter sets up a Young's experiment using a sodium vapor lamp as a light source and placing his slits 1 m from a screen. He is unsure of the slit separation and, standing beside the slits, he varies the separation and finds that the interference pattern vanishes if the slits are too far apart. If the angular resolution of his eye is 1 minute of arc, how far apart are the slits when he just cannot see the interference fringes?

Solution. The position of the mth bright fringe of the fringe system from the center O is given by

$$y_m = \frac{mR\lambda}{d},$$

where λ is the wavelength used. Similarly, for the $(m + 1)$th fringe,

$$y_{m+1} = \frac{(m + 1)R\lambda}{d}.$$

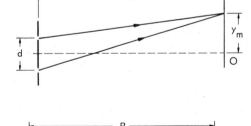

Thus the fringe separation is

$$y_{m+1} - y_m = \frac{R\lambda}{d},$$

a quantity independent of m and thus constant throughout the fringe system.

The angle subtended by this fringe separation at the student's eye is

$$\theta = \frac{R\lambda/d}{R} = \frac{\lambda}{d} \text{ rad.}$$

But the student cannot see the fringes as distinct unless the angle neighboring fringes subtend at his eye ≥ 1 minute of arc $= \pi/(180 \times 60)$ rad.

$$\therefore \quad \theta_{\min} = \frac{\lambda}{d_{\max}} = \frac{\pi}{180 \times 60}.$$

$$\therefore \quad d_{\max} = \frac{180 \times 60 \times 5.89 \times 10^{-5}}{\pi} \text{ cm} = 2.025 \text{ mm}.$$

42

Polarization

PROBLEM 42.1

The captain of a submarine fitted with a directional transmitter finds that he receives bad echoes from the sea bed when he is submerged if the transmission direction makes an angle greater than 45° with the vertical. He wishes to transmit a message to an agent in a foreign country using radiation which is completely horizontally polarized, since all other receivers in the locality use vertical aerial systems. How far from the coast should he surface if his agent owns a house on top of a coastal cliff 500 ft high and he intends to polarize his radiation by reflection on the sea surface? Take the location of the transmitter as 12 ft above the water when the submarine has surfaced.

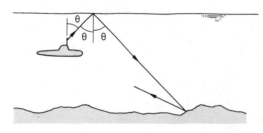

Solution. If the transmission direction makes a small angle with the vertical, most of the radiation passes through the water surface into the air and only a small fraction is reflected back to the ocean bed to produce echoes. The amount reflected increases with the angle until, when the critical angle is reached, reflection is total, and the echo becomes troublesome. It follows that the refractive index of water for the radiation used is

$$n = \frac{1}{\sin 45°} = \sqrt{2} = 1.414.$$

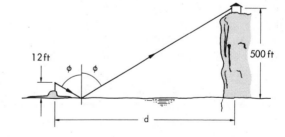

When the submarine has surfaced, it can produce a completely plane-polarized beam by reflection of the radiation at the Brewster angle from the surface of the sea. The angle required is $\tan \phi = n = 1.414$. That is, $\phi = 54.75°$.

Thus the distance of the submarine from the cliff is

$$d = \frac{500 \text{ ft}}{\tan 35.25°} + \frac{12 \text{ ft}}{\tan 35.25°} = \frac{512}{0.707} \text{ ft} = 724 \text{ ft.}$$

PROBLEM 42.2

A polaroid sheet is not a perfect polarizer. When plane-polarized light falls on it, it transmits a substantial fraction α of the incident intensity when the vibration axis of the light is parallel to its transmission axis; but it also transmits a very small fraction β of the incident intensity when the two axes are at right angles to one another.

Suppose that three polaroid sheets are arranged axially, the first and last crossed and the middle one rotated through 45° with respect to the other two. What fraction of the light intensity of an initially unpolarized beam gets through the system? Suppose that the incident light were plane-polarized. Would this alter the analysis of the problem?

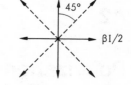

Solution. All the vibrations in the incident unpolarized light can be resolved into components in two directions at right angles, these directions coinciding with the transmission axis of the polaroid and an axis at right angles to this. By symmetry the intensity of vibration in each of these directions will be $I/2$.
After transmission through the first polaroid the intensities in the two directions will be $\alpha I/2$ and $\beta I/2$. Since the incident light was unpolarized, these two beams have no fixed phase relation to one another, may therefore be considered as incoherent, and, even if brought back to vibrating in the same direction, cannot interfere with one another. Under these circumstances the two beams are independent of one another and one may deal with the *intensities* transmitted by each polaroid. As we shall see later, this is not true for beams which are coherent.

Since the amplitude of either of the vibrations emerging from the first polaroid may be split into components vibrating along and at right angles to the transmission direction of the second polaroid, and since the intensity of a vibration is the square of its amplitude, the light striking the second polaroid may be considered as two vibrations of intensities

$$\frac{\alpha I}{2}\cos^2 45° + \frac{\beta I}{2}\sin^2 45°$$

and

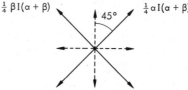

$$\frac{\alpha I}{2}\sin^2 45° + \frac{\beta I}{2}\cos^2 45°,$$

along and at right angles to the transmission direction. Both vibrations thus have intensity $\frac{1}{4}I(\alpha + \beta)$. After transmission through the second polaroid, the intensities will be $\frac{1}{4}\alpha I(\alpha + \beta)$ and $\frac{1}{4}\beta I(\alpha + \beta)$.

By similar reasoning the light falling on the third polaroid may be considered to be two vibrations, each of intensity $\frac{1}{4}\alpha I(\alpha + \beta)\cos^2 45° + \frac{1}{4}\beta I(\alpha + \beta)\sin^2 45° = \frac{1}{8}I(\alpha + \beta)^2$ along and at right angles to the transmission direction. After transmission through the polaroid the intensities will have become $\frac{1}{8}\alpha I(\alpha + \beta)^2$ and $\frac{1}{8}\beta I(\alpha + \beta)^2$. The total intensity after passage through the whole system is thus the sum of these, that is, $\frac{1}{8}I(\alpha + \beta)^3$. The fraction of the light intensity transmitted is thus $\frac{1}{8}(\alpha + \beta)^3$.

If the light incident on the first polaroid of the system is plane polarized at angle θ to the transmission axis, intensities $\alpha I\cos^2 \theta$ and $\beta I\sin^2 \theta$ are transmitted by this polaroid in the two mutually perpendicular directions by the foregoing analysis. But now the two vibrations in the mutually perpendicular directions have a fixed phase relation to one another. Before transmission through the polaroid the vibrations were in phase; after transmission there will be in general a phase difference between them due to the different speeds with which the two beams travel through the polaroid. But this phase difference remains the same at all times.

When the two vibrations of *amplitude* $\sqrt{\alpha I}\cos \theta$ and $\sqrt{\beta I}\sin \theta$ strike the second polaroid, they may each be resolved into their components vibrating along and at right angles to the transmission axis of this polaroid. Since there is a component from each vibration in either direction, and since these components have a fixed phase relation between them, interference takes place between the coherent components in each direction. When one squares the resultant amplitude to find the intensity, one obtains a value different from the previous one. This effect will occur at the third polaroid also.

The analysis is now much more complicated than in the previous case and cannot be carried through without a knowledge of the phase difference introduced between the two beams which are transmitted by any of the polaroids.

PROBLEM 42.3

Show that a particle subjected to two simple harmonic vibrations of the same frequency, at right angles and out of phase, traces an elliptical path which degenerates to two coincident straight lines if the phase difference is π. Indicate the relevance of this to a half-wave plate.

Solution. Let the vibrations be taking place along the x- and y-axes with a phase difference of ϕ between them. Then if $x = a \sin \omega t$, $y = b \sin (\omega t + \phi)$.

$$\therefore \quad \frac{y}{b} = \sin \omega t \cos \phi + \cos \omega t \sin \phi = \frac{x}{a} \cos \phi + \sqrt{1 - \frac{x^2}{a^2}} \cdot \sin \phi.$$

$$\therefore \quad \frac{y^2}{b^2} + \frac{x^2}{a^2} \cos^2 \phi - \frac{2xy}{ab} \cos \phi = \left(1 - \frac{x^2}{a^2}\right) \sin^2 \phi.$$

$$\therefore \quad \frac{x^2}{a^2}(\cos^2 \phi + \sin^2 \phi) + \frac{y^2}{b^2} - \frac{2xy}{ab} \cos \phi = \sin^2 \phi$$

or

$$\frac{x^2}{a^2} + \frac{y^2}{b^2} - \frac{2xy}{ab} \cos \phi = \sin^2 \phi.$$

This is the general equation of an ellipse where the major and minor axes do not coincide with the x- and y-axes. Thus the particle always has x- and y-coordinates such that the point they define lies on an ellipse. The particle thus follows an elliptical path.

If $\phi = \pi/2, 3\pi/2, 5\pi/2, \ldots$, the equation of the path reduces to $(x^2/a^2) + (y^2/b^2) = 1$, which is an ellipse with the major and minor axes coincident with the coordinate axes.

When $\phi = \pi$, the equation of the path becomes

$$\frac{x^2}{a^2} + \frac{y^2}{b^2} + \frac{2xy}{ab} = 0,$$

that is,

$$\left(\frac{x}{a} + \frac{y}{b}\right)^2 = 0.$$

This is the equation of two coincident straight lines $x/a = -y/b$, inclined to the negative x-axis at an angle $\tan^{-1}(b/a)$.

In the case of a half-wave plate, plane-polarized light striking the plate is split up into two components, O and E, plane-polarized at right angles to one another and initially in phase. These pass through the plate at different speeds and the thickness is such that on emergence the two beams are out of phase by π. Any particle affected by the two components will thus be affected by two simple harmonic vibrations at right angles, out of phase by π. As can be seen from the above analysis, the particle would trace a straight-line path. This means that the two components are equivalent to a single vibration at an angle $\tan^{-1}(b/a)$ to the slower component, b/a being the ratio of the amplitudes of the components of the incident light on entering the plate. If the plane-polarized light is striking the plate at an angle of 45° to the two transmission directions, then it is resolved into two equal components so that $b = a$. The emerging light is thus plane-polarized in a direction making an angle of $-45°$ with each of the principal directions in the plate.

PROBLEM 42.4

A quarter-wave plate is to be used with sodium light of mean wavelength 589.3 nm, and is to be constructed from a crystal whose principal refractive indexes for sodium light, n_O and n_E, are 1.5936 and 1.5977. In what direction should it be cut from the crystal to give a minimum thickness of plate? What is this thickness?

Solution. The spherical and ellipsoidal wave fronts in a uniaxial crystal touch along the optic axis. The difference in speed of the O- and E-waves in the crystal is thus a maximum when the light is traveling at right angles to the optic axis. Since light is passed normally through the plate, the thickness of the plate is minimal when the optic axis is at right angles to the thickness, that is, when it lies in the surface.

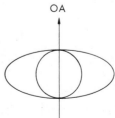

The wavelength of the O-waves in the plate is λ/n_o, and of the E-waves is λ/n_E. If the thickness of the plate is t, the number of wavelengths of each component corresponding to this distance is tn_o/λ and tn_E/λ, respectively. The difference in the number of wavelengths of each component is $(tn_E/\lambda) - (tn_o/\lambda)$, and when this difference is $\frac{1}{4}$, a phase difference of $\pi/2$ exists between them. Thus

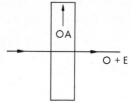

$$\frac{t_{\min}}{\lambda}(n_E - n_o) = \frac{1}{4} \quad \text{or} \quad t_{\min} = \frac{\lambda}{4(n_E - n_o)} = \frac{589.3 \times 10^{-9} \text{ m}}{4 \times 0.0041} = 3.594 \times 10^{-5} \text{ m} = 0.03594 \text{ mm}.$$

43

Quantum Theory of Radiation

PROBLEM 43.1

A camera photographs a 120-W sodium lamp 100 m away, the film being exposed for 1/100 s. The aperture of the camera has a diameter of 4 cm. How many photons enter the camera during the exposure? The wavelength of sodium light is 5893 Å, and all the energy of the lamp is assumed to be emitted as light.

Solution. The energy possessed by one photon of sodium light is

$$hf = h\frac{c}{\lambda} = 6.625 \times 10^{-34}\,\text{J·s} \times \frac{2.998 \times 10^8\,\text{m·s}^{-1}}{5893 \times 10^{-10}\,\text{m}} = 3.37 \times 10^{-19}\,\text{J}.$$

The lamp consumes 120 J of energy per second. Therefore the number of photons emitted per second is

$$n = \frac{120\,\text{J·s}^{-1}}{3.37 \times 10^{-19}\,\text{J}} = 3.55 \times 10^{20}\,\text{s}^{-1}.$$

These photons are emitted in all directions and 100 m from the lamp are distributed evenly over a spherical surface of that radius. The number entering the aperture of the camera per second is thus n multiplied by the fraction of this surface occupied by the aperture. That is,

$$3.55 \times 10^{20}\,\text{s}^{-1} \times \frac{\pi \times (0.02)^2\,\text{m}^2}{4\pi \times (100)^2\,\text{m}^2} = 3.55 \times 10^{12}\,\text{s}^{-1}.$$

Thus in $\frac{1}{100}$ s the number of photons entering the camera is 3.55×10^{10}.

PROBLEM 43.2

Show that Wien's law and the Rayleigh-Jeans law are special cases of the Planck radiation formula.

Solution. The monochromatic energy density within an isothermal blackbody enclosure is given by Planck's relation

$$\Psi_\lambda = \frac{8\pi ch\lambda^{-5}}{\exp(ch/\lambda kT) - 1}.$$

If $ch/\lambda kT$ is very large, i.e., for small λ and/or T, $\exp(ch/\lambda kT) \gg 1$, and the latter may be ignored in comparison with the former. Thus, for this case,

$$\Psi_\lambda = \frac{8\pi ch\lambda^{-5}}{\exp(ch/\lambda kT)},$$

which is Wien's law, with $8\pi ch = c_1$ and $ch/k = c_2$.

On the other hand, if $ch/\lambda kT$ is very small, i.e., for large λ and/or T, $\exp(ch/\lambda kT)$ can be replaced by the first two terms in the expansion of that function in terms of powers of its exponent. Subsequent terms

181

in the expansion will be so small as to be negligible. Hence

$$\exp\left(\frac{ch}{\lambda kT}\right) - 1 = 1 + \frac{ch}{\lambda kT} - 1 = \frac{ch}{\lambda kT}. \qquad \therefore \qquad \Psi_\lambda = 8\pi ch\lambda^{-5} \times \frac{\lambda kT}{ch} = 8\pi kT\lambda^{-4},$$

which is the Rayleigh-Jeans law.

PROBLEM 43.3

Starting from Planck's radiation law, show that one can obtain Wien's displacement law, $\lambda_{max}T = $ constant. It is known that this constant is equal to 2.891×10^6 nm·K deg. Obtain the value of Planck's constant, given that Boltzmann's constant is 1.380×10^{-23} J·K deg^{-1}.

Solution. Planck's radiation law connects the monochromatic energy density in an isothermal blackbody enclosure with the wavelength by the expression

$$\Psi_\lambda = \frac{8\pi ch\lambda^{-5}}{\exp\left(ch/\lambda kT\right) - 1}.$$

Thus

$$\frac{d\Psi_\lambda}{d\lambda} = -\frac{40\pi ch\lambda^{-6}}{\exp\left(ch/\lambda kT\right) - 1} - \frac{8\pi ch\lambda^{-5} \times \left[-(ch/kT\lambda^2)\exp\left(ch/\lambda kT\right)\right]}{\left[\exp\left(ch/\lambda kT\right) - 1\right]^2}$$

$$= \frac{8\pi ch\lambda^{-6}}{\exp\left(ch/\lambda kT\right) - 1}\left[-5 + \frac{(ch/\lambda kT)\exp\left(ch/\lambda kT\right)}{\exp\left(ch/\lambda kT\right) - 1}\right].$$

For maxima or minima of $\Psi_\lambda, d\Psi_\lambda/d\lambda$ must be zero. The term outside the bracket becomes zero for either $\lambda = 0$ or $\lambda = \infty$. Both of these are minima, as can be verified by differentiating again. When the expression inside the bracket becomes zero, we have a maximum, and for this

$$\exp\left(-\frac{ch}{\lambda kT}\right) = 1 - \frac{ch}{5\lambda kT}.$$

Reference to exponential tables shows that

$$\exp\left(-4.965\right) = 0.002 = 1 - \frac{4.965}{5}.$$

Thus for a maximum of the radiation curve,

$$\exp\left(-\frac{ch}{\lambda kT}\right) = 1 - \frac{ch}{5\lambda kT},$$

and this implies that $ch/\lambda kT = 4.965$.

$$\therefore \qquad \lambda_{max}T = \frac{ch}{4.965\,k} = \text{const},$$

which is Wien's displacement law.

Experimentally, $\lambda_{max}T = 2.891 \times 10^6$ nm·K deg $= 2.891 \times 10^{-3}$ m·K deg.

$$\therefore \qquad h = \frac{4.965k \times 2.891 \times 10^{-3}\,\text{m}\cdot\text{K deg}}{c}$$

$$= \frac{4.965 \times 1.380 \times 10^{-23}\,\text{J}\cdot\text{K deg}^{-1} \times 2.891 \times 10^{-3}\,\text{m}\cdot\text{K deg}}{2.998 \times 10^8\,\text{m}\cdot\text{s}^{-1}} = 6.607 \times 10^{-34}\,\text{J}\cdot\text{s}.$$

PROBLEM 43.4

When the wavelength of the incident light exceeds 6500 Å, the emission of photoelectrons from a surface ceases. The surface is irradiated with light of wavelength 3900 Å. What will be the maximum energy, in electron volts, of the electrons emitted from the surface?

Solution. Einstein's photoelectric equation relates the energy of the incident quanta to the maximum energy of the emitted electrons by the relation

$$hf = h\frac{c}{\lambda} = W + W_0 = W + hf_0 = W + h\frac{c}{\lambda_0},$$

where W_0 is the work function of the surface and λ_0 the cut-off wavelength. Hence the maximum energy of the emitted photoelectrons in the problem is

$$W = hc\left(\frac{1}{\lambda} - \frac{1}{\lambda_0}\right) = 6.6 \times 10^{-34}\,\text{J}\cdot\text{s} \times 3.0 \times 10^8\,\text{m}\cdot\text{s}^{-1}\left(\frac{1}{3.9 \times 10^{-7}\,\text{m}} - \frac{1}{6.5 \times 10^{-7}\,\text{m}}\right)$$

$$= 19.8 \times 10^{-19}\left(\frac{1}{3.9} - \frac{1}{6.5}\right)\text{J} = \frac{19.8 \times 10^{-19}}{1.6 \times 10^{-19}} \times \frac{2.6}{3.9 \times 6.5}\,\text{eV} = 1.27\,\text{eV}.$$

44

The Atomic Models of Rutherford and Bohr

PROBLEM 44.1

Doubly charged α-particles of energy 7.33 MeV are emitted from one isotope of thorium. What is the distance of closest approach of such an α-particle to a gold nucleus? The mass of the α-particle is 6.69 $\times$ 10^{-27} kg, and the atomic number of gold is 79.

Solution. The α-particle on emission possesses a kinetic energy of 7.33 MeV $= 7.33 \times 1.602 \times 10^{-13}$ J $= 11.743 \times 10^{-13}$ J. By the time it is at the distance of closest approach to the gold nucleus, d, all this kinetic energy has been transformed into potential energy which it possesses by virtue of its position in the electric field of the nucleus. Thus

$$11.743 \times 10^{-13} \text{ J} = \frac{Zee'}{4\pi\epsilon_0 d},$$

where Ze is the charge on the gold nucleus and e' is the charge carried by the α-particle.

$$\therefore \quad d = \frac{79 \times 1.602 \times 10^{-19} \text{ C} \times 2 \times 1.602 \times 10^{-19} \text{ C}}{4\pi \times 8.85 \times 10^{-12} \text{ C}^2 \cdot \text{N}^{-1} \cdot \text{m}^{-2} \times 11.743 \times 10^{-13} \text{ J}} = 3.103 \times 10^{-14} \text{ m}.$$

PROBLEM 44.2

Electrons of energies 10.20 eV, 12.09 eV, and 13.06 eV can cause radiation to be emitted from hydrogen atoms. Calculate in each case the principal quantum number of the orbit to which the electron in the hydrogen atom is raised and the wavelength of the radiation emitted if it drops back to the ground state.

Solution. Bohr theory relates the wavelength of the radiation emitted by a hydrogen atom to the principal quantum numbers of the energy levels involved by the equation

$$\frac{1}{\lambda} = R\left(\frac{1}{n_1^2} - \frac{1}{n_2^2}\right). \qquad \therefore \quad f = \frac{c}{\lambda} = Rc\left(\frac{1}{n_1^2} - \frac{1}{n_2^2}\right),$$

and the energy of the quantum of radiation emitted is

$$E = hf = Rch\left(\frac{1}{n_1^2} - \frac{1}{n_2^2}\right) = 1.097 \times 10^7 \text{ m}^{-1} \times 2.997 \times 10^8 \text{ m} \cdot \text{s}^{-1} \times 6.625 \times 10^{-34} \text{ J} \cdot \text{s} \times \left(\frac{1}{n_1^2} - \frac{1}{n_2^2}\right)$$

$$= 2.178 \times 10^{-18} \left(\frac{1}{n_1^2} - \frac{1}{n_2^2}\right) \text{J} = \frac{2.178 \times 10^{-18}}{1.602 \times 10^{-19}}\left(\frac{1}{n_1^2} - \frac{1}{n_2^2}\right) \text{eV} = 13.60\left(\frac{1}{n_1^2} - \frac{1}{n_2^2}\right) \text{eV}.$$

This is the energy emitted in the form of a quantum of radiation when the electron drops from the orbit characterized by the quantum number n_2 to that characterized by the quantum number n_1. If the electron is raised from the orbit with quantum number n_1 to the orbit with quantum number n_2, it must absorb an equal amount of energy.

Before being struck by an electron, a hydrogen atom will be in the ground state with $n_1 = 1$. It is in any case obvious that if n_1 had a value higher than 1, then E, the absorbed energy, could not be greater than 3.40 eV, the limiting energy for $n_1 = 2$. Thus if E has the values 10.20 eV, 12.09 eV, and 13.06 eV, the atom absorbing these energies from the incoming electrons,

$$\left(\frac{1}{n_1^2} - \frac{1}{n_2^2}\right) = \left(1 - \frac{1}{n_2^2}\right) = \frac{10.20}{13.60}, \frac{12.09}{13.60}, \text{ and } \frac{13.06}{13.60}, \quad \text{that is,} \quad \frac{3}{4}, \frac{8}{9}, \text{ and } \frac{24}{25}.$$

$$\therefore \quad n_2^2 = 4, 9, \text{ and } 25 \quad \text{or} \quad n_2 = 2, 3, \text{ and } 5.$$

In dropping back to the ground state, the wavelength emitted in the three cases will be given from the original equation quoted. Thus

$$\lambda = \frac{4}{3R}, \frac{9}{8R}, \text{ and } \frac{25}{24R} = \frac{4}{3 \times 1.0968 \times 10^7 \text{m}^{-1}}, \quad \frac{9}{8 \times 1.0968 \times 10^7 \text{m}^{-1}}, \quad \text{and } \frac{25}{24 \times 1.0968 \times 10^7 \text{m}^{-1}}$$

$$= 121.57 \text{ nm}, \quad 102.57 \text{ nm}, \quad \text{and } 94.97 \text{ nm}.$$

PROBLEM 44.3

Show that for large values of the principal quantum number, the frequencies of revolution of an electron in adjacent energy levels of a hydrogen atom and the radiated frequency for a transition between these levels all approach the same value.

Solution. The Bohr condition for the angular momentum of an electron in a permitted orbit of the hydrogen atom is $mvr = nh/2\pi$.

$$\therefore \quad v = \frac{nh}{2\pi mr}.$$

The frequency of revolution of the electron in the orbit is thus

$$\nu = \frac{v}{2\pi r} = \frac{nh}{4\pi^2 mr^2} = \frac{me^4}{4\epsilon_0^2 n^3 h^3}.$$

But the Rydberg constant is given by the equation

$$R = \frac{me^4}{8\epsilon_0^2 ch^3}. \qquad \therefore \quad \nu = \frac{2Rc}{n^3}.$$

Also the expression for the frequency of the radiation emitted in a transition between two permitted energy levels is $f = Rc[(1/p^2) - (1/n^2)]$. In particular, if $p = n - 1$,

$$f = Rc\left[\frac{1}{(n-1)^2} - \frac{1}{n^2}\right] = Rc\frac{2n-1}{n^2(n^2-1)},$$

and, if $n \gg 1$,

$$f \longrightarrow Rc\frac{2n}{n^4} = \frac{2Rc}{n^3}.$$

But $\nu_n = 2Rc/n^3$ and

$$\nu_{n-1} = \frac{2Rc}{(n-1)^3} \approx \frac{2Rc}{n^3}$$

when $n \gg 1$. Thus for large values of n, the magnitudes of f, ν_n, and ν_{n-1} all tend to the same value, $2Rc/n^3$. At large quantum numbers, classical and quantum mechanical results agree. This is an example of Bohr's correspondence principle.

PROBLEM 44.4

The Rydberg constants for hydrogen and singly ionized helium are 10,967,757.6 m^{-1} and 10,972,226.6 m^{-1}, respectively. From the mass spectrograph it is known that the ratio of the mass of a helium nucleus to that of a proton is 3.9726. Calculate the ratio of the mass of the proton to the mass of the electron, and hence find the ratio of the charge to the mass of an electron, given that the faraday has the value 96,522 $C \cdot mole^{-1}$, and that the proton has a mass of 1.00759 amu.

Solution. The Rydberg constant for a single-electron atom is seen by Bohr theory to be given by the equation

$$R = \frac{\mu e^4}{8\epsilon_0^2 ch^3},$$

where μ is the appropriate reduced mass of the electron. Thus

$$\frac{R_H}{R_{He}} = \frac{\mu_H}{\mu_{He}} = \frac{m}{1 + (m/M)} \times \frac{1 + (m/M')}{m} = \frac{1 + y(M/M')}{1 + y},$$

where m, M, and M' are the rest masses of the electron, the hydrogen nucleus, and the helium nucleus, respectively, and y is m/M. Thus

$$y = \frac{R_{He} - R_H}{R_H - (M/M') \times R_{He}} = \frac{4469 \text{ m}^{-1}}{10,967,757.6 \text{ m}^{-1} - (10,972,226.6/3.9726) \text{ m}^{-1}} = \frac{1}{1836.2},$$

which is the ratio of the mass of the electron to the mass of the proton. The reciprocal, 1836.2, is the answer required.

A proton has a mass of 1.00759 amu. A mole of protons has thus a mass of 1.00759 g. But the faraday is the charge carried by a mole of singly charged atoms, and protons are singly charged hydrogen atoms. Thus the ratio of the charge to the mass of the proton is

$$\frac{e}{M} = \frac{96,522 \text{ C} \cdot \text{mole}^{-1}}{1.00759 \text{ g} \cdot \text{mole}^{-1}} = \frac{96,522}{1.00759} \times 10^3 \text{ C} \cdot \text{kg}^{-1}.$$

Thus

$$\frac{e}{M} = \frac{e}{M} \cdot \frac{M}{m} = \frac{96,552}{1.00759} \times 1836.2 \times 10^3 \text{ C} \cdot \text{kg}^{-1} = 1.7590 \times 10^{11} \text{ C} \cdot \text{kg}^{-1}.$$

45

Special Relativity

PROBLEM 45.1

Three inertial systems S, S', and S'' have a common x-axis. With respect to S, S' moves in the direction of the x-axis with a speed v, and S'' accelerates along the x-axis with acceleration a. At time $t = 0$ the origins of all three coordinate systems coincide and S'' has zero velocity with respect to S. At that instant a man starts out running from the origin along the x-axis and an observer in S measures his speed as constant and of magnitude u ($u > v$). How do observers in S' and S'' describe his motion, using Galilean relativity?

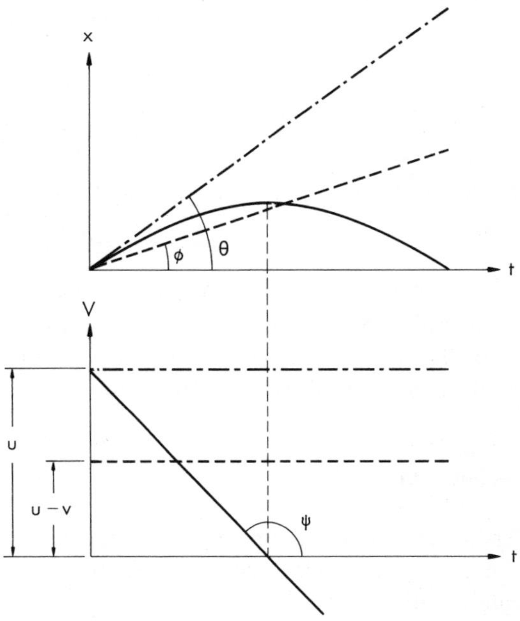

Solution. The observer in S sees the man running along the x-axis with constant speed u. The motion is thus observed as one in which the x-displacement increases linearly with time. On a displacement–time diagram, the motion appears as the dot-dashed straight line at an angle θ to the t-axis, where $\tan \theta = x/t = u$; and on a velocity–time diagram it appears as the dot-dashed straight line parallel to the t-axis.

To an observer in S', the man has only the speed $(u - v)$, the relative speed between the two. But the man is still seen as moving with constant speed and his motion is shown in the diagrams by the dashed straight lines. The angle ϕ is such that $\tan \phi = u - v$.

An observer in S'', who is accelerating along the x-axis with acceleration a relative to S and therefore to the running man, considers himself at rest and therefore attributes to the runner an acceleration of $-a$. The runner appears to start off with velocity u but to decelerate gradually to rest and then go backward. His velocity at any time is seen to be $V = u - at$, and on the velocity–time diagram this is represented by the full line at an angle ψ to the t-axis, where $\tan \psi = -a$. Also his x-displacement relative to the origin of S'' is $x = ut - \frac{1}{2}at^2$, which is represented by a parabola in the displacement–time diagram, tangent to the dot-dashed line at the origin and having its highest point at the time t where the corresponding velocity–time graph cuts the t-axis.

PROBLEM 45.2

Two inertial systems S and S' have a common x-axis and parallel y-axes, and S' moves with a speed of $0.6c$ relative to S in the direction of the x-axis. An observer in S sees a rocket moving with a speed of

0.1c in the positive y-direction. What is the speed and direction of the rocket as seen by an observer in the S'-system?

Solution. By the Lorentz transformation, in the usual notation,

$$x' = \frac{x - vt}{\sqrt{1 - (v^2/c^2)}}, \qquad y' = y, \qquad t' = \frac{t - (vx/c^2)}{\sqrt{1 - (v^2/c^2)}}.$$

It follows that

$$u'_x = \frac{dx'}{dt'} = \frac{(dx/dt') - v(dt/dt')}{\sqrt{1 - (v^2/c^2)}} = \frac{(dx/dt) \times (dt/dt') - v(dt/dt')}{\sqrt{1 - (v^2/c^2)}}.$$

But, from the initial equations, we have

$$t = \sqrt{1 - (v^2/c^2)}\,t' + (vx/c^2).$$

$$\therefore \quad \frac{dt}{dt'} = \sqrt{1 - \frac{v^2}{c^2}} + \frac{v}{c^2}\frac{dx}{dt} \times \frac{dt}{dt'}.$$

$$\therefore \quad \frac{dt}{dt'}\left(1 - \frac{vu_x}{c^2}\right) = \sqrt{1 - \frac{v^2}{c^2}} \quad \text{or} \quad \frac{dt}{dt'} = \frac{\sqrt{1 - (v^2/c^2)}}{1 - (u_x v/c^2)}.$$

$$\therefore \quad u'_x = \frac{[(dx/dt) - v](dt/dt')}{\sqrt{1 - (v^2/c^2)}} = \frac{u_x - v}{\sqrt{1 - (v^2/c^2)}} \times \frac{\sqrt{1 - (v^2/c^2)}}{1 - (u_x v/c^2)} = \frac{u_x - v}{1 - (u_x v/c^2)}.$$

Similarly,

$$u'_y = \frac{dy}{dt} \times \frac{dt}{dt'} = \frac{u_y\sqrt{1 - (v^2/c^2)}}{1 - (u_x v/c^2)}.$$

In this problem $u_x = 0$, $u_y = 0.1c$, and $v = 0.6c$.

$$\therefore \quad u'_x = -0.6c, \qquad u'_y = 0.1c \times \sqrt{1 - 0.6^2} = 0.08c.$$

To an observer in S', therefore, the rocket appears to have components of velocity of $-0.6c$ in the x-direction and of $0.08c$ in the y-direction. It thus appears to have a total velocity of $\sqrt{0.6^2 + 0.08^2}\,c$ $= 0.605c$ in a direction making an angle of $\tan^{-1}(0.08/0.60) = \tan^{-1} 0.133$, that is, an angle of $7°36'$ with the negative direction of the x-axis.

PROBLEM 45.3

The mean proper lifetime of π^+ mesons is 2.5×10^{-8} s. In a beam of π^+ mesons of speed $0.99c$, what is the average distance a meson travels before it decays? What would this value be if the relativistic time dilation did not exist?

Solution. In a coordinate system S' moving with the mesons the average lifetime of the mesons is 2.5×10^{-8} s. A laboratory observer makes his measurements in a system S fixed in the laboratory, with respect to which S' is moving at a speed of $0.99c$. He therefore measures a longer average lifetime. For, according to the time-dilation formula, in the usual notation,

$$T = \frac{T'}{\sqrt{1 - (v^2/c^2)}} = \frac{2.5 \times 10^{-8}}{\sqrt{1 - 0.99^2}}\,\text{s} = \frac{2.5 \times 10^{-8}}{0.141}\,\text{s}.$$

The distance traveled in this time d is $0.99c \times T$.

$$\therefore \quad d = \frac{2.5 \times 10^{-8}}{0.141}\,\text{s} \times 0.99 \times 3.0 \times 10^8\,\text{m}\cdot\text{s}^{-1} = 52.7\,\text{m}.$$

If time dilation did not exist, the distance traveled would be d_0, where

$$d_0 = 2.5 \times 10^{-8}\,\text{s} \times 0.99 \times 3.0 \times 10^8\,\text{m}\cdot\text{s}^{-1} = 7.43\,\text{m}.$$

PROBLEM 45.4

An unaccelerated observer in space sees two spaceships approaching him from opposite directions and measures their speeds as $0.5c$ and $0.7c$, respectively. At what speed does an observer on one spaceship see the other approaching?

Solution. The unaccelerated observer measures in his reference frame S the speeds of the two spaceships along the direction taken as the x-axis and finds one to be $+0.5c$ and the other to be $-0.7c$. An observer in the first of these ships refers everything to his own reference frame S', which is moving along the x-axis relative to S at a speed of $0.5c$. When he measures the speed of the other ship, he does not obtain the value of $1.2c$ which is the relative speed of the two ships in S. Instead he finds a value obtained from the observations in S by the use of the Lorentz transformation. If u' is the speed of the second spaceship along the x-axis as measured by the first, u the corresponding speed measured by an observer in S, and v the velocity of S' relative to S, then application of the Lorentz transformation, as in Problem 45.2, gives

$$u' = \frac{u - v}{1 + (uv/c^2)}.$$

Hence, in this case,

$$u' = \frac{-0.7c - 0.5c}{1 + (0.7c \times 0.5c/c^2)} = -\frac{1.2}{1.35}c = -0.889c.$$

The observer in S' thus sees the other ship approaching at a speed of $0.889c$.

PROBLEM 45.5

With what speed is an electron moving if its kinetic energy is 1% different from the value that would be calculated if relativistic effects were not present? What is the value of the kinetic energy of the electron?

Solution. The relativistic expression for the kinetic energy of a particle of rest mass m_0 and mass m traveling with speed v is

$$E = (m - m_0)c^2 = m_0 c^2 \left(\frac{1}{\sqrt{1 - (v^2/c^2)}} - 1 \right) = m_0 c^2 \left(1 - \frac{v^2}{c^2} \right)^{-1/2} - 1$$

$$= m_0 c^2 \left(\frac{1}{2} \frac{v^2}{c^2} + \frac{3}{8} \frac{v^4}{c^4} + \cdots \right) = \frac{1}{2} m_0 v^2 \left(1 + \frac{3}{4} \frac{v^2}{c^2} \right),$$

when we ignore terms of higher order than those in v^2/c^2.

But $\frac{1}{2} m_0 v^2$ is the nonrelativistic expression for the kinetic energy of the particle, and thus, for the electron in the problem,

$$\frac{1}{2} m_0 v^2 \left(1 + \frac{3}{4} \frac{v^2}{c^2} \right) = \frac{101}{100} \times \frac{1}{2} m_0 v^2 \quad \text{or} \quad v^2 = \frac{4}{300} c^2.$$

$$\therefore \quad v = 0.1155c.$$

$$\therefore \quad E = \frac{101}{100} \times \frac{1}{2} m_0 v^2$$

$$= \frac{101}{100} \times \frac{1}{2} \times 9.108 \times 10^{-31} \, \text{kg} \times \frac{4}{300} \times 2.998^2 \times 10^{16} \, \text{m}^2 \cdot \text{s}^2$$

$$= 5.512 \times 10^{-16} \, \text{J} = 3442 \, \text{eV}.$$

PROBLEM 45.6

An interstellar spaceship takes off from earth and accelerates in a negligible distance to a speed of $0.5c$ in the direction of Proxima Centauri. After it has been traveling at this speed for 10 hr, the captain observes two explosions 10 million miles apart taking place simultaneously on the path he has just traveled.

They appear to him to take place symmetrically about the midpoint of the line joining the ship to earth. How far away do observers on the planet see the explosions? Do the explosions appear to them to be simultaneous?

Solution. In the Brehme diagram the subscript A refers to the earth's system of coordinates and the subscript B to the spaceship's system of coordinates. The relative velocity between the two systems is $\pm 0.5c$. Hence the angle α between corresponding axes is given by

$$\sin \alpha = \frac{v_{BA}}{c} = \frac{1}{2} \quad \text{or} \quad \alpha = 30°.$$

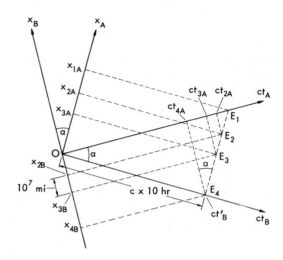

The four events E_1, E_2, E_3, and E_4 specify the positions of the spaceship, the two explosions, and the earth, respectively, at the time the captain of the ship sees the explosion. These events have the same t-coordinate in the B-system but it is apparent that they have different t-coordinates in the A-system. The x-coordinates are shown in both systems, and it is apparent that they are measured differently on the earth and in the ship.

The distance Ox_{4B} has the value

$$Ox_{4B} = -v_{AB} \times t = -0.5 \times 186,000 \text{ mi} \cdot \text{s}^{-1} \times 10 \text{ hr} \times 60 \text{ min} \cdot \text{hr}^{-1} \times 60 \text{ s} \cdot \text{min}^{-1}$$
$$= -3348 \times 10^6 \text{ mi.}$$

It is clear from the diagram that

$$Ox_{1A} = \frac{|Ox_{4B}|}{\cos \alpha} = \frac{2}{\sqrt{3}} \times 3348 \times 10^6 \text{ mi}$$

and

$$x_{2A} - x_{3A} = \frac{|x_{3B} - x_{2B}|}{\cos \alpha} = \frac{2}{\sqrt{3}} \times 10^7 \text{ mi.}$$

Since x_{3B} and x_{2B} are symmetrically placed about the midpoint of Ox_{4B}, it is clear from the diagram that x_{3A} and x_{2A} are similarly placed with regard to Ox_{1A}. Hence the two explosions as seen from the earth occur at positions which are

$$\left(\frac{1}{\sqrt{3}} \times 3348 \times 10^6 \pm \frac{1}{\sqrt{3}} \times 10^7 \right) \text{ mi}$$

from the earth, that is, at positions 1927.2 million miles and 1938.8 million miles from the earth. Also

$$ct_{2A} - ct_{3A} = (x_{2B} - x_{3B}) \tan \alpha.$$

$$\therefore \quad t_{2A} - t_{3A} = \frac{10^7 \text{ mi} \times (1/\sqrt{3})}{186,000 \text{ mi} \cdot \text{s}^{-1}} = 31 \text{ s.}$$

The explosions are thus not viewed from the earth as being simultaneous but as occurring 31 s apart.

Note that the problem can be done without the use of a Brehme diagram by the conversion of all distances, employing the equation

$$x_A = \frac{x_B + v_{BA} t_B}{\sqrt{1 - (v_{BA}^2/c^2)}},$$

and by the conversion of all times, employing the equation

$$ct_A = \frac{ct_B + v_{BA} x_B/c}{\sqrt{1 - (v_{BA}^2/c^2)}}.$$

This leads to the same results, but use of the Brehme diagram shows much more clearly what is happening.

46

X-Rays

PROBLEM 46.1

The radiation from an x-ray tube operated at 50 kV is diffracted by a cubic KCl crystal of molecular mass 74.6 and density 1.99×10^3 kg·m⁻³. Calculate (a) the short-wavelength limit of the spectrum from the tube, and (b) the glancing angle for first-order reflection from the principal planes of the crystal for that wavelength.

Solution. (a) When an electron passes through a potential difference V, it acquires energy eV. If all this energy is used in producing one quantum of x-radiation, then $hf = eV$ or $f = eV/h$.

$$\therefore \quad \lambda = \frac{c}{f} = \frac{ch}{eV}.$$

The electron may have lost some of its acquired energy before producing the quantum of radiation. The f-value calculated above is thus the maximum possible frequency of the x-radiation emitted and λ the corresponding short-wavelength limit of the emitted spectrum. The value is

$$\lambda = \frac{3.0 \times 10^8 \text{ m·s}^{-1} \times 6.6 \times 10^{-34} \text{ J·s}}{1.6 \times 10^{-19} \text{ C} \times 5 \times 10^4 \text{ V}} = 0.248 \text{ Å}.$$

(b) In order to apply Bragg's law, we must find the separation of the principal planes of the KCl crystal. We know that 74.6 g of KCl is one mole. Thus 1 m³ contains $(1.99 \times 10^6)/74.6$ moles. Each mole contains 6.0×10^{23} molecules and each molecule contains one atom each of K and Cl. Thus the total number of atoms in 1 m³ of KCl is

$$n = \frac{1.99 \times 10^6}{74.6} \text{ moles} \times 2 \times 6.0 \times 10^{23} \text{ mole}^{-1},$$

and each atom will occupy a volume of

$$v = \frac{1 \text{ m}^3}{n} = \frac{74.6}{23.88 \times 10^{29}} \text{ m}^3.$$

Thus the linear separation of atoms, i.e., the separation of the principal planes, is

$$d = v^{1/3} = \sqrt[3]{\frac{74.6}{23.88 \times 10^{29}}} \text{ m} = 3.150 \times 10^{-10} \text{ m} = 3.150 \text{ Å}.$$

Bragg's law relates the glancing angle to d by the equation $2d \sin \theta = m\lambda$. Giving λ the value calculated above, we obtain

$$\sin \theta = \frac{m\lambda}{2d} = \frac{0.248 \text{ Å}}{2 \times 3.150 \text{ Å}} = 0.0394. \quad \therefore \quad \theta = 2.25°.$$

PROBLEM 46.2

At a temperature of 18°C a beam of diffracted monochromatic x-rays is observed at an angle of 150.8° to the incident beam after being diffracted by a crystal with cubic structure. At a temperature of 318°C the corresponding beam makes an angle of 141.6° with the incident beam. What is the mean coefficient of linear expansion of the crystal in the given temperature range?

Solution. If a beam of monochromatic x-rays is deviated by an angle ϕ after diffraction from a set of crystal planes, it is obvious from the diagram that, if θ is the glancing angle of the x-rays on this set of planes,

$$2\theta + (180 - \phi) = 180° \quad \text{or} \quad \theta = \frac{\phi}{2}.$$

When the temperature is 18°C, the appropriate interplanar spacing is d, and the glancing angle for diffraction from this set of planes is 150.8°/2 = 75.4°. Thus $2d \sin 75.4° = m\lambda$.

When the temperature is 318°C, the interplanar spacing has increased to d', and the glancing angle has dropped to 141.6°/2 = 70.8°. Thus $2d' \sin 70.8° = m\lambda$, the wavelength and order of diffraction being unchanged.

$$\therefore \quad \frac{d'}{d} = \frac{\sin 75.4°}{\sin 70.8°} = 1.024.$$

But $d' = d(1 + \alpha \times 300\,\text{C deg})$, where α is the mean coefficient of linear expansion at right angles to the set of planes considered. Since the crystal is cubic, the coefficient of linear expansion is the same in all directions.

$$\therefore \quad 1 + 300\,\text{C deg} \times \alpha = 1.024. \qquad \therefore \quad \alpha = \frac{0.024}{300\,\text{C deg}} = 8.3 \times 10^{-5}\,\text{per C deg.}$$

PROBLEM 46.3

The K_α and L_α absorption edges of copper occur at wavelengths of 1.380 Å and 13.288 Å, respectively. Given that the atomic number of copper is 29, calculate a value for the Rydberg constant.

Solution. The absorption of radiation in any substance increases sharply and discontinuously at an absorption edge, because at that wavelength a quantum of the radiation has just sufficient energy to overcome the binding energy of an electron in an atom at that level. Calculation of the quantum energy corresponding to an absorption edge thus gives the binding energy of an electron at the appropriate level. Thus if W_K and W_L denote the binding energy of an electron in the K- and L-levels of copper, respectively, then

$$-W_K = hf_K = h\frac{c}{\lambda_K} = \frac{6.625 \times 10^{-34}\,\text{J·s} \times 2.997 \times 10^8\,\text{m·s}^{-1}}{1.380 \times 10^{-10}\,\text{m}} = 14.388 \times 10^{-16}\,\text{J}$$

and

$$-W_L = hf_L = h\frac{c}{\lambda_L} = \frac{6.625 \times 10^{-34}\,\text{J·s} \times 2.997 \times 10^8\,\text{m·s}^{-1}}{13.288 \times 10^{-10}\,\text{m}} = 1.494 \times 10^{-16}\,\text{J}.$$

Copper emits a quantum of K_α radiation when an electron drops from the L-level to the K-level, the energy of the quantum being the difference between the binding energies of the electron in the two levels. From the calculation above, this is

$$W_L - W_K = (-1.494 + 14.388) \times 10^{-16}\,\text{J} = 12.894 \times 10^{-16}\,\text{J}.$$

The wavelength of the quantum emitted is thus given by the relation $h(c/\lambda) = W_K - W_L$ or

$$\frac{1}{\lambda} = \frac{12.894 \times 10^{-16}\,\text{J}}{6.625 \times 10^{-34}\,\text{J·s} \times 2.997 \times 10^8\,\text{m·s}^{-1}} = 0.6494 \times 10^{10}\,\text{m}^{-1}.$$

But, by Moseley's law,

$$\frac{1}{\lambda} = R(Z-1)^2\left(\frac{1}{1^2} - \frac{1}{2^2}\right).$$

Therefore the Rydberg constant is

$$R = \frac{4}{3\lambda(Z-1)^2} = \frac{4 \times 0.6494 \times 10^{10} \text{ m}^{-1}}{3 \times 28^2} = 1.104 \times 10^7 \text{ m}^{-1}.$$

PROBLEM 46.4

An x-ray tube with a copper target is found to be emitting lines other than those due to copper. The K_α line of copper is known to have a wavelength of 1.5405 Å, and the other two K_α lines observed have wavelengths of 0.7092 Å and 1.6578 Å. Identify the impurities.

Solution. According to Moseley's equation for K_α radiation,

$$\frac{1}{\lambda} = R(Z-1)^2\left(\frac{1}{1^2} - \frac{1}{2^2}\right).$$

Thus, if λ is the wavelength of $\text{Cu}\,K_\alpha$ radiation and λ_1 and λ_2 the wavelengths of the two unknown K_α radiations, then

$$\frac{\lambda_1}{\lambda} = \frac{(Z-1)^2}{(Z_1-1)^2} = \frac{0.7092 \text{ Å}}{1.5405 \text{ Å}}.$$

But for copper $Z = 29$. Therefore

$$Z_1 - 1 = 28\sqrt{1.5405/0.7092} = 41. \qquad \therefore \qquad Z_1 = 42,$$

and we know that the impurity is molybdenum. Similarly,

$$Z_2 - 1 = 28\sqrt{1.5405/1.6578} = 27. \qquad \therefore \qquad Z_2 = 28,$$

and we know that the impurity is nickel.

PROBLEM 46.5

The mass absorption coefficients for the K_α and K_β radiations of silver are 13.6 cm²·g⁻¹ and 58.0 cm²·g⁻¹ when palladium is used as an absorber. What thickness of palladium foil of density 11.4 g·cm⁻³ reduces the intensity of the K_α radiation to one-tenth of its incident value? What is then the percentage reduction in the intensity of the K_β radiation?

Solution. The relation which describes the absorption of x-radiation is, in the usual notation, $I = I_0 e^{-\mu z}$.

$$\therefore \qquad z = \frac{1}{\mu}\ln\frac{I_0}{I} = \frac{1}{\mu_m \rho}\ln\frac{I_0}{I},$$

where μ is the linear absorption coefficient, μ_m the mass absorption coefficient, and ρ the density of the absorber. If the K_α radiation is to be reduced to one-tenth of its incident value, the thickness required is

$$z = \frac{1}{13.6 \text{ cm}^2\cdot\text{g}^{-1} \times 11.4 \text{ g}\cdot\text{cm}^{-3}}\ln 10 = 1.49 \times 10^{-2} \text{ cm}.$$

For the K_β radiation with this thickness of absorber,

$$\frac{I}{I_0} = \exp\left(-58.0 \text{ cm}^2\cdot\text{g}^{-1} \times 11.4 \text{ g}\cdot\text{cm}^{-3} \times 1.49 \times 10^{-2} \text{ cm}\right) = \exp\left(-9.85\right) = 5.28 \times 10^{-5}.$$

$$\therefore \qquad \frac{I_0 - I}{I_0} \times 100 = 99.995\%,$$

which is the percentage reduction in the intensity of the K_β radiation.

PROBLEM 46.6

X-radiation of wavelength 0.8560 Å is scattered from a carbon target. Calculate the change in wavelength produced for radiation scattered at 90°, and the energy and direction of the corresponding recoil electrons.

Solution. In a Compton collision the resulting change in wavelength is given by the formula

$$\lambda' - \lambda = 2\frac{h}{mc}\sin^2\frac{\theta}{2},$$

where θ is the angle of scatter. If θ is 90°,

$$\lambda' - \lambda = \frac{h}{mc} = \frac{6.625 \times 10^{-34}\,\text{J·s}}{9.108 \times 10^{-31}\,\text{kg} \times 2.998 \times 10^8\,\text{m·s}^{-1}} = 0.0242\,\text{Å}.$$

The energy given to the electron is therefore

$$E = h\frac{c}{\lambda} - h\frac{c}{\lambda'} = 6.625 \times 10^{-34}\,\text{J·s} \times 2.998 \times 10^8\,\text{m·s}^{-1} \times \left(\frac{10^{10}}{0.8560\,\text{m}} - \frac{10^{10}}{0.8802\,\text{m}}\right)$$

$$= 6.377 \times 10^{-17}\,\text{J}.$$

In order that momentum may be conserved in the collision, the electron must have a momentum in the initial direction of h/λ and a momentum of h/λ' at right angles to this. The tangent of the angle ϕ at which the electron is scattered is the ratio of the latter momentum to the former, since these momenta are proportional to the components of the electron's velocity in the two mutually perpendicular directions. Hence

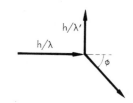

$$\tan\phi = \frac{h/\lambda'}{h/\lambda} = \frac{\lambda}{\lambda'} = \frac{0.8560\,\text{Å}}{0.8802\,\text{Å}} = 0.9725.$$

$$\therefore \quad \phi = 44°12'.$$

PROBLEM 46.7

The maximum permissible dosage for scientific workers using γ-radiation is 6.25 milliroentgens per hour. What is the safe working distance from a 20-Ci* source of cobalt-60 which has a dose rate of 27 roentgens (R) per hour at a distance of 1 m? If the source is used in a lead container which reduces the γ-radiation emitted to 1%, how much closer can the scientists work?

Solution. The radiation from the source is emitted uniformly in all directions. Hence at any distance r the radiation is passing through an area $4\pi r^2$. The intensity of radiation per unit volume thus decreases as r increases according to an inverse-square-power law. The diminution of the intensity of the γ-radiation due to absorption in the air may be neglected in comparison with this inverse-square-law effect. Hence if r is the safe working distance,

$$I_r = 6.25 \times 10^{-3}\,\text{R·hr}^{-1} = \frac{k}{r^2} \quad \text{and} \quad I_0 = 27\,\text{R·hr}^{-1} = \frac{k}{1\,\text{m}^2},$$

where k is a constant depending on the source strength.

$$\therefore \quad \frac{r^2}{1\,\text{m}^2} = \frac{27}{6.25 \times 10^{-3}} \quad \text{or} \quad r = \sqrt{\frac{27 \times 10^3}{6.25}} \times 1\,\text{m} = 65.7\,\text{m}.$$

If the lead container cuts the radiation to 1% of its former value, then by the same arguments, the new safe working distance r_1 is given by

$$r_1 = \sqrt{(0.27 \times 10^3)/6.25} \times 1\,\text{m} = 6.57\,\text{m}.$$

---

*The letters Ci have been adopted by the International Union of Pure and Applied Physics as the abbreviation for curie. The letter R denotes roentgen.

47

Waves and Corpuscles

PROBLEM 47.1

What are the de Broglie wavelengths of (a) a bullet weighing 5 g and having a speed of 500 m·s⁻¹, (b) a proton moving with a speed of 5×10^5 cm·s⁻¹, and (c) an electron having a total energy of 2.5 MeV?

Solution. In the first two cases relativistic effects do not enter and the de Broglie wavelength is given by $h/p = h/mv$. In the third case the electron is moving with a velocity close to that of light and, while $\lambda = h/p$, the value of p is now obtained from the relativistic equation linking energy and momentum, $E^2 = p^2 c^2 + m_0^2 c^4$. Therefore $p = \sqrt{(E^2/c^2) - m_0^2 c^2}$.

(a)
$$\lambda = \frac{h}{mv} = \frac{6.6 \times 10^{-34}\,\text{J·s}}{5 \times 10^{-3}\,\text{kg} \times 500\,\text{m·s}^{-1}} = 2.64 \times 10^{-34}\,\text{m},$$

which is undetectable.

(b)
$$\lambda = \frac{h}{mv} = \frac{6.6 \times 10^{-34}\,\text{J·s}}{1.67 \times 10^{-27}\,\text{kg} \times 5 \times 10^3\,\text{m·s}^{-1}} = 0.791\,\text{Å}.$$

(c)
$$\lambda = \frac{h}{\sqrt{\dfrac{E^2}{c^2} - m_0^2 c^2}} = \frac{6.6 \times 10^{-34}\,\text{J·s}}{\sqrt{\left(\dfrac{2.5 \times 1.6 \times 10^{-13}\,\text{J}}{3.0 \times 10^8\,\text{m·s}^{-1}}\right)^2 - (9.1 \times 10^{-31}\,\text{kg} \times 3.0 \times 10^8\,\text{m·s}^{-1})^2}}$$

$$= \frac{6.6 \times 10^{-34}\,\text{J·s}}{1.33 \times 10^{-21}\,\text{N·s}} = 4.95 \times 10^{-13}\,\text{m} = 0.00495\,\text{Å}.$$

PROBLEM 47.2

A collimated beam of silver atoms emerges from a furnace at 1500°K, passes through a circular hole, and falls on a screen 1 m away. Assume that all the atoms travel with the same speed. What size hole is likely to give the smallest spot size on the screen? The mass of a silver atom is 1.8×10^{-25} kg.

Solution. If the hole has a radius a, the uncertainty in the z-coordinate of an atom passing through the hole is $2a$. Thus
$$\Delta z = 2a.$$

But if p_z is the momentum of the atom in the z-direction, then, at the hole, $\Delta p_z\,\Delta z \approx h$.

$$\therefore \quad m\,\Delta v_z \approx \frac{h}{2a} \quad \text{or} \quad \Delta v_z \approx \frac{h}{2am}.$$

Thus the atoms have an uncertainty in velocity in the

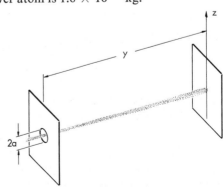

z-direction of the order of $h/2am$. But the velocity in the z-direction is classically zero. So that the atoms by quantum-mechanical arguments have velocities around the value $h/2am$ in the z-direction.

In the y-direction the atoms have a velocity which is assumed for simplicity to be the same for all atoms. The average kinetic energy possessed by an atom at temperature T is $\frac{3}{2}kT$, where k is Boltzmann's constant. Thus the silver atoms of mass m have velocities v_y given by $v_y = \sqrt{3kT/m}$.

They traverse the distance y in time t, given by $t = y/v_y$, and in the same time the maximum distance achieved in the z-direction due to the z-velocity of the atoms is

$$z = \Delta v_z \times t = \frac{y\,\Delta v_z}{v_y} = \frac{hy}{2am}\sqrt{\frac{m}{3kT}} = \frac{6.6 \times 10^{-34}\,\text{J·s} \times 1\,\text{m}}{2a}$$

$$\times \sqrt{\frac{1}{3 \times 1.8 \times 10^{-25}\,\text{kg} \times 1.38 \times 10^{-23}\,\text{J·K deg}^{-1} \times 1500\,\text{K deg}}} = \frac{3.12}{a} \times 10^{-12}\,\text{m}^2.$$

Thus the largest possible distance from the axis at which a silver atom can strike the screen is $r = a + z = a + (3.12/a) \times 10^{-12}\,\text{m}^2.$

$$\therefore \quad \frac{dr}{da} = 1 - \frac{3.12}{a^2} \times 10^{-12}\,\text{m}^2,$$

and for a minimum of r this quantity must be zero. It is clear that it is a minimum, but this can be verified by a second differentiation. Thus the radius of the hole which gives the smallest spot on the screen is that for which

$$\frac{3.12}{a^2} \times 10^{-12}\,\text{m}^2 = 1 \quad \text{or} \quad a = 1.77 \times 10^{-6}\,\text{m}.$$

In classical physics the spot size would be decreased indefinitely by reducing the size of the hole. Because of the wave nature of the electron, quantum mechanics does not supply the same answer. After a certain point, diminishing the size of the hole increases the size of the spot because of diffraction effects produced by the hole on the silver atoms. A minimum size of spot therefore results for a finite hole size.

PROBLEM 47.3

Determine the phase velocity of the de Broglie waves associated with a neutron which has an energy of 25 eV.

Solution. If the neutron has energy $25\,\text{eV} = 25 \times 1.602 \times 10^{-19}\,\text{J} = 4.00 \times 10^{-18}\,\text{J}$, then its speed is given by the relation

$$\frac{1}{2}mv^2 = 4.00 \times 10^{-18}\,\text{J} \quad \text{or} \quad v = \sqrt{\frac{8.00 \times 10^{-18}\,\text{J}}{1.67 \times 10^{-27}\,\text{kg}}} = 6.92 \times 10^4\,\text{m·s}^{-1}.$$

The phase velocity of the associated de Broglie waves is

$$v_p = \frac{c^2}{v} = \frac{(3.00 \times 10^8)^2\,\text{m}^2\cdot\text{s}^{-2}}{6.92 \times 10^4\,\text{m·s}^{-1}} = 1.30 \times 10^{12}\,\text{m·s}^{-1}.$$

48

Radioactivity

PROBLEM 48.1

A solution containing radiophosphorus, P^{32}, which is a β-emitter with a half-life of 14 days, surrounds a Geiger counter which records 10^3 counts per minute. If the same experiment is performed 28 days later, what counting rate will be obtained?

Solution. The number of radioactive atoms still present after time t is

$$N = N_0 e^{-\lambda t} = N_0 \exp\left(-\frac{t \ln 2}{\tau}\right).$$

$$\therefore \quad -\frac{dN}{dt} = \lambda N_0 e^{-\lambda t} = \lambda N_0 \exp\left(-\frac{t \ln 2}{\tau}\right).$$

But $\lambda N_0 = -(dN/dt)_{t=0}$.

$$\therefore \quad -\frac{dN}{dt} = 10^3 \exp\left(-\frac{28}{14} \ln 2\right) \text{ counts/min} = 10^3 \exp\left(-\ln 4\right) \text{ counts/min}$$

$$= \frac{10^3}{4} = 250 \text{ counts/min}.$$

Note that the time involved is two half-lives. Thus the final counting rate will be $(\frac{1}{2})^2 = \frac{1}{4}$ of the initial counting rate.

PROBLEM 48.2

At a particular time, N_0 atoms of a radioactive substance with a disintegration constant λ_1 are separated chemically from all the other members of the radioactive series. At what time thereafter is the number of radioactive atoms of the daughter product with disintegration constant λ_2 a maximum?

Solution. Analysis of the growth and decay of atoms in a radioactive series shows that the number of atoms of the daughter product N_2 present at time t is given by the relation

$$N_2 = \frac{N_0 \lambda_1}{\lambda_2 - \lambda_1}(e^{-\lambda_1 t} - e^{\lambda_2 t}). \qquad \therefore \quad \frac{dN_2}{dt} = \frac{N_0 \lambda_1}{\lambda_2 - \lambda_1}(-\lambda_1 e^{-\lambda_1 t} + \lambda_2 e^{-\lambda_2 t}).$$

At $t = 0$ and $t = \infty$, there are no atoms of N_2 present. Between these two times is one for which N_2 is a maximum, and this occurs for $dN_2/dt = 0$. Thus for a maximum, $\lambda_1 e^{-\lambda_1 t} = \lambda_2 e^{-\lambda_2 t}$.

$$\therefore \quad e^{(\lambda_2 - \lambda_1)t} = \frac{\lambda_2}{\lambda_1} \quad \text{or} \quad t = \frac{1}{\lambda_2 - \lambda_1}\ln\left(\frac{\lambda_2}{\lambda_1}\right).$$

Thus when t has the value given in the last equation the number of atoms of the daughter product is a maximum.

PROBLEM 48.3

A fixed quantity of a radioactive isotope is delivered to a hospital at the same time every week. One day a doctor finds an unopened bottle of the isotope with no label attached. He places it in front of a Geiger counter and records 4200 counts per second. When he substitutes a bottle received that day, the count becomes 47,500 per second. If the isotope has a half-life of 8 days, how long has the unlabeled bottle been in the hospital?

Solution. If the unlabeled bottle has been in the hospital for time t, then the number of counts recorded, λN, must be related to the number which would have been recorded when it arrived, λN_0, by the relation

$$\lambda N = \lambda N_0 \exp(-\lambda t) = \lambda N_0 \exp\left(-\frac{t \ln 2}{\tau}\right),$$

where τ is the half-life of the isotope.

But a fixed quantity is delivered each time. Thus any batch records the same number of counts on arrival.

$$\therefore \quad \frac{\lambda N_0}{\lambda N} = \exp\left(\frac{t \ln 2}{\tau}\right) = 2^{t/\tau}.$$

$$\therefore \quad t = \frac{\tau \log(\lambda N_0/\lambda N)}{\log 2} = \frac{8 \text{ days} \times \log(47,500/4,200)}{\log 2} = \frac{8 \times 1.0535}{0.3010} \text{ days} = 28 \text{ days}.$$

Thus the unlabeled bottle was delivered 4 weeks previously.

PROBLEM 48.4

Three lines in the β-spectrum of radium E have energies of 0.309×10^5, 0.315×10^5, and 0.338×10^5 eV, and the x-ray L absorption edges of the same element correspond to energies of 0.163×10^5, 0.157×10^5, and 0.134×10^5 eV, respectively. Show that the three lines correspond to the same excitation energy of the nucleus and calculate the wavelength of the γ-ray that may be alternatively emitted by the nucleus.

Solution. The line spectra in the β-spectrum of radium E are due to the internal conversion effect. Here the excitation energy of the nucleus is passed on to an extranuclear electron, providing it with sufficient energy to overcome its binding energy to the atom and be emitted with the remainder as kinetic energy.

The binding energies of an electron in the three L-levels of the atom are given. Adding each of these to one of the kinetic energies of the emitted electrons gives 0.472×10^5 eV in each case. Thus the three lines correspond to the case in which the nucleus has an excitation energy of 0.472×10^5 eV, this energy being used in each case to free an electron from the L-level of the atom and then emit the electron with a kinetic energy equal to the excitation energy remaining.

Alternatively, the nucleus may get rid of its excitation energy by emitting a γ-ray of energy 0.472×10^5 eV. Thus the wavelength of the γ-ray will be obtained from the equation

$$hf = h\frac{c}{\lambda} = 0.472 \times 10^5 \text{ eV} = 0.472 \times 10^5 \times 1.602 \times 10^{-19} \text{ J}.$$

$$\therefore \quad \lambda = \frac{6.625 \times 10^{-34} \text{ J·s} \times 2.998 \times 10^8 \text{ m·s}^{-1}}{0.472 \times 1.602 \times 10^{-14} \text{ J}} = 2.627 \times 10^{11} \text{ m} = 0.2627 \text{ Å}.$$

PROBLEM 48.5

A curie was originally defined as the activity of the amount of radon in equilibrium with 1 g of radium. How many disintegrations per second does this represent if the atomic mass of radium is 226 amu and its half-life is 1620 yr?

Solution. Since the two radioelements are in equilibrium, their activities are equal. Hence the number of disintegrations of the radon is the same as the number of disintegrations of 1 g of radium. But 1 g of radium is $\frac{1}{226}$ mole of radium, and this quantity contains $(6.025 \times 10^{23})/226$ atoms, 6.025×10^{23} atoms per mole being Avogadro's number. Thus the activity of 1 g of radium is

$$A = \lambda N = \lambda \times \frac{6.025 \times 10^{23}}{226} = \frac{\ln 2}{\tau} \times \frac{6.025 \times 10^{23}}{226},$$

where λ and τ are the disintegration constant and half-life of radium. Hence

$$A = \frac{0.6932}{1620 \times 365 \times 24 \times 60 \times 60 \text{ s}} \times \frac{6.025 \times 10^{23}}{226} = 3.627 \times 10^{10} \text{ dis} \cdot \text{s}^{-1}.$$

The curie is now internationally defined as an activity of 3.7000×10^{10} dis·s^{-1}.

PROBLEM 48.6

A radon seed is prepared to give a required therapeutic dose in 5 days if inserted at a prearranged time. The implant is delayed 24 hr due to unforeseen circumstances. How long must the seed now be left in position to give the required dose? The decay constant of radon is 2.10×10^{-6} s^{-1}.

Solution. If the seed had been implanted at the correct time, after 5 days the number of atoms present would have been

$$N_1 = N_0 \exp(-\lambda t_1) = N_0 \exp(-2.10 \times 10^{-6} \text{ s}^{-1} \times 60 \times 60 \times 24 \times 5 \text{ s}) = N_0 \exp(-0.9075).$$

The number of disintegrations that would have taken place, i.e., the dose given, would have been

$$N_0 - N_1 = N_0[1 - \exp(-0.9075)].$$

After the 24-hr delay, the number of atoms present is N_2, where

$$N_2 = N_0 \exp(-2.10 \times 10^{-6} \text{ s}^{-1} \times 60 \times 60 \times 24 \text{ s}) = N_0 \exp(-0.1815).$$

After the required therapeutic dose has been given in time t seconds, the number of atoms left is N, where $N = N_2 \exp(-\lambda t)$, and the number of disintegrations taking place is $N_2 - N = N_2[1 - \exp(-\lambda t)]$.
But this is the same dose as before. Thus $N_0 - N_1 = N_2 - N$.

$$\therefore \quad N_0[1 - \exp(-0.9075)] = N_2[1 - \exp(-\lambda t)] = N_0 \exp(-0.1815)[1 - \exp(-\lambda t)].$$

$$\therefore \quad \exp(-\lambda t) = 1 - \frac{1 - \exp(-0.9075)}{\exp(-0.1815)} = 1 - \frac{1 - 0.406}{0.835} = 0.289.$$

$$\therefore \quad \lambda t = 1.250.$$

$$\therefore \quad t = \frac{1.250}{2.10 \times 10^{-6}} \text{ s} = \frac{1.250}{2.10 \times 10^{-6} \times 60 \times 60 \times 24} \text{ days} = 6.89 \text{ days}.$$

PROBLEM 48.7

A hospital receives and puts into storage a batch of 100 mCi* of radioiodine which has a half-life of 8 days. For how long can the batch be kept in storage and still provide a therapeutic dose of 12 mCi·hr?

Solution. The activity diminishes according to the formula, in the usual notation, $I = I_0 e^{-\lambda t}$, and a dose administered from time t to time t' has the value

$$D = I_0 \int_t^{t'} e^{-\lambda t} \, dt.$$

If the radioelement may be left in an implant for a long period, t' can be made to tend to infinity. Thus

$$D = I_0 \left[-\frac{1}{\lambda} e^{-\lambda t} \right]_t^\infty = \frac{I_0}{\lambda} e^{-\lambda t} = \frac{I_0 \tau}{\ln 2} e^{-\lambda t},$$

---

*The letters mCi have been adopted by the International Union of Pure and Applied Physics as the symbol for millicurie.

where τ is the half-life of radioiodine. Thus

$$12 \text{ mCi} \cdot \text{hr} = \frac{100 \text{ mCi} \times 8 \times 24 \text{ hr}}{0.6932} e^{-\lambda t}.$$

$$e^{-\lambda t} = 4.327 \times 10^{-4}, \quad \text{or} \quad \exp\left\{-\frac{t \ln 2}{\tau}\right\} = 4.327 \times 10^{-4}.$$

$$\therefore \quad t = \frac{\tau \log\left[1/(4.327 \times 10^{-4})\right]}{\log 2} = \frac{8 \times 3.3638}{0.3010} \text{ days} = 89.4 \text{ days}.$$

The batch may thus be used for 89.4 days.

PROBLEM 48.8

A sample of gold is exposed to a beam of neutrons, and the reaction $Au^{197}(n,\gamma)$ Au^{198} absorbs 10^6 neutrons per second. Au^{198} emits β-particles and has a half-life of 2.70 days. How many atoms of Au^{198} are present after 2 days of continuous irradiation?

Solution. At any instant during the irradiation, the increase in the number of Au^{198} atoms in unit time will be the number being produced less the number disintegrating. Thus, in the usual notation,

$$dN/dt = 10^6 \text{ s}^{-1} - \lambda N.$$

$$\therefore \quad \frac{dN}{10^6 \text{ s}^{-1} - \lambda N} = dt. \quad \therefore \quad \int_0^N \frac{dN}{10^6 \text{ s}^{-1} - \lambda N} = \int_0^t dt,$$

there being no atoms of Au^{198} present at time $t = 0$ when the irradiation starts.

$$\therefore \quad -\frac{1}{\lambda} \log\left(\frac{10^6 \text{ s}^{-1} - \lambda N}{10^6 \text{ s}^{-1}}\right) = t. \quad \therefore \quad 1 - \frac{\lambda N}{10^6 \text{ s}^{-1}} = \exp\left(-\lambda t\right).$$

$$\therefore \quad N = \frac{10^6 \text{ s}^{-1}}{\lambda}\left[1 - \exp\left(-\lambda t\right)\right] = \frac{10^6 \text{ s}^{-1} \tau}{\ln 2}\left[1 - \exp\left(-\frac{t \ln 2}{\tau}\right)\right],$$

where τ is the half-life period of the β-activity. After 2 days,

$$N = \frac{10^6 \text{ s}^{-1} \times 2.7 \times 24 \times 60 \times 60 \text{ s}}{0.6932}\left[1 - \exp\left(-\frac{2 \ln 2}{2.7}\right)\right] = \frac{10^6 \times 2.7 \times 24 \times 60 \times 60}{0.6932} \times 0.402$$

$$= 1.35 \times 10^{11} \text{ atoms}.$$

49

Nuclear Reactions

PROBLEM 49.1

Calculate the mass of the light isotope of helium from the following reaction, which has a Q-value of 3.945 MeV:

$$_3Li^6 + {}_1H^1 = {}_2He^4 + {}_2He^3.$$

The masses in amu of $_1H^1$, $_2He^4$, and $_3Li^6$ are 1.00813, 4.00386, and 6.01692, respectively.

Solution. In the reaction 3.945 MeV of energy is released. This is equivalent to a diminution of the mass present of $(3.945/931)$ amu $= 0.00424$ amu. The sum of the masses of the initial particles is

$$1.00813 + 6.01692 = 7.02505 \text{ amu.}$$

From this is to be subtracted the mass of the α-particle, 4.00386 amu, and the mass equivalent of the energy released, 0.00424 amu. The mass left, 3.01695 amu, must be the mass of an atom of the light isotope of helium.

PROBLEM 49.2

In the reaction $_5B^{11} + {}_2He^4 \rightarrow {}_7N^{14} + {}_0n^1$, the masses of the boron and nitrogen atoms and the α-particle are 11.01280 amu, 14.00752 amu, and 4.00387 amu, respectively. If the incident α-particle had 5.250 MeV of kinetic energy and the resultant neutron and nitrogen atom had energies of 3.260 MeV and 2.139 MeV, respectively, what is the mass of the neutron?

Solution. The Q-value of the reaction is

$$(3.260 + 2.139 - 5.250) \text{ MeV} = +0.149 \text{ MeV.}$$

This is equivalent to a decrease in mass of $0.149/931 = 0.00016$ amu. The combined mass of the initial particles is 15.01667 amu. Thus the combined mass of the final particles is $15.01667 - 0.00016 = 15.01651$ amu. But the mass of the nitrogen atom is 14.00752 amu. The mass of the neutron is thus $15.01651 - 14.00752 = 1.00899$ amu.

PROBLEM 49.3

When lithium is bombarded by 10-MeV deuterons, neutrons are observed to emerge at right angles to the direction of the incident beam. Calculate the energy of these neutrons and the energy and angle of recoil of the associated beryllium atom. Relevant masses in amu are: $_0n^1 = 1.00893$, $_3Li^7 = 7.01784$, $_1H^2 = 2.01472$, and $_4Be^8 = 8.00776$.

Solution. The equation governing the reaction is

$$_3\text{Li}^7 + {}_1\text{H}^2 = {}_0\text{n}^1 + {}_4\text{Be}^8.$$

The sum of the masses of the initial atoms is 9.03256 amu, and of the final atoms 9.01669 amu. The difference in mass, 0.01587 amu, appears as 0.01587×931 MeV $= 14.77$ MeV of kinetic energy. Since total energy is conserved in the reaction, the final products have a combined kinetic energy of

$$(10 + 14.77)\ \text{MeV} = 24.77\ \text{MeV}.$$

When we remember that the momentum of a particle p is related to its kinetic energy E by the relation $p = \sqrt{2mE}$, then the principle of conservation of momentum, applied in the initial direction and at right angles to it, gives the following equations, in self-explanatory notation:

$$\sqrt{2m_D E_D} = \sqrt{2m_B E_B}\ \cos\theta$$

and

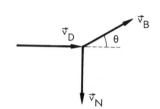

$$\sqrt{2m_N E_N} = \sqrt{2m_B E_B}\ \sin\theta.$$

$$\therefore \quad 2m_D E_D + 2m_N E_N = 2m_B E_B.$$

It was also shown above that

$$E_N + E_B = 24.77\ \text{MeV}.$$

Solving these last two equations simultaneously gives

$$E_N = 19.76\ \text{MeV}, \qquad E_B = 5.01\ \text{MeV}.$$

Further, we obtain for the angle of recoil

$$\tan\theta = \sqrt{\frac{m_N E_N}{m_D E_D}} = 0.9897. \qquad \therefore \qquad \theta = 44°42'.$$

PROBLEM 49.4

In a cloud-chamber photograph a proton is seen to have undergone an elastic collision, its track being deviated by 60°. The struck particle makes a track at an angle of 30° with the incident proton direction. What mass does this particle possess?

Solution. Let the incident proton have mass m and velocity **u**, the velocity becoming **v** after scatter. Let the struck particle of mass M acquire velocity **V** after the collision. Then, by the principle of conservation of energy, $\frac{1}{2}mu^2 = \frac{1}{2}mv^2 + \frac{1}{2}MV^2$, and by the principle of conservation of momentum, $mu = mv\cos 60° + MV\cos 30°$ and $mv\sin 60° = MV\sin 30°$. Thus

$$V = \frac{m}{M}v\frac{\sin 60°}{\sin 30°} = \sqrt{3}\,\frac{m}{M}v.$$

Substituting into the other two equations gives

$$\frac{1}{2}mu^2 = \frac{1}{2}mv^2 + \frac{3}{2}\frac{m^2}{M}v^2 \qquad \text{and} \qquad mu = \frac{1}{2}mv + \frac{3}{2}mv.$$

$$\therefore \quad \left(1 + 3\frac{m}{M}\right) = \frac{u^2}{v^2} = \left(\frac{1}{2} + \frac{3}{2}\right)^2 = 4. \qquad \therefore \quad \frac{m}{M} = 1,$$

and the struck particle must have been a hydrogen nucleus.

PROBLEM 49.5

What is the total binding energy and the binding energy per nucleon of the nucleus of $_{24}\text{Cr}^{52}$ which has a mass of 51.95699 amu?

Solution. The nucleus of $_{24}Cr^{52}$ is made up of 24 protons and $52 - 24 = 28$ neutrons. The combined mass of the particles making up the Cr nucleus is thus

$$\Sigma m = 24 \times 1.00819 + 28 \times 1.00893 = 52.44600 \text{ amu.}$$

The mass defect is $52.44660 - 51.95699 = 0.48961$ amu, and the binding energy is

$$0.48961 \times 931 \text{ MeV} = 455.83 \text{ MeV.}$$

The binding energy per nucleon is thus $455.83/52 = 8.77$ MeV.

50

Nuclear Energy

PROBLEM 50.1

A railway engine develops an average power of 1200 kW during a 10-hr run from New York to Cleveland. If the engine were driven by an atomic power plant of 20% efficiency, how much U^{235} would be consumed on the run?

Solution. The energy consumed during the run is

$$E = 1.2 \times 10^6 \text{ W} \times 10 \times 60 \times 60 \text{ s} = 4.32 \times 10^{10} \text{ J}.$$

If an atomic power plant were used, y grams of U^{235} would be consumed. This quantity is $y/235$ moles and thus contains $(y \times 6.02 \times 10^{23})/235$ atoms, 6.02×10^{23} being Avogadro's number. Each atom releases 180 MeV $= 180 \times 1.60 \times 10^{-13}$ J $= 2.88 \times 10^{-11}$ J on fission. Thus the total energy released by y grams of U^{235} is

$$E' = \frac{6.02 \times 10^{23}\, y}{235} \times 2.88 \times 10^{-11} \text{ J}.$$

But $E' = 5E$, since the system is 20% efficient. Thus

$$\frac{6.02 \times 10^{23}\, y}{235} \times 2.88 \times 10^{-11} \text{ J} = 5 \times 4.32 \times 10^{10} \text{ J}.$$

$$\therefore \quad y = \frac{5 \times 4.32 \times 235 \times 10^{10}}{6.02 \times 10^{23} \times 288 \times 10^{-11}} = 2.93.$$

Thus 2.93 g of U^{235} would be consumed on the run.

PROBLEM 50.2

The masses of $_1\text{H}^1$ and $_2\text{He}^4$ atoms are 1.00813 amu and 4.00386 amu, respectively. How much hydrogen must be converted to helium in the sun per second if the solar constant is 1.35 kW·m^{-2} and the earth is 1.5×10^8 km from the sun?

Solution. The energy falling on a 1-m^2 area at the distance of the sun from the earth is 1.35×10^3 J·s^{-1}. The total energy radiated from the sun is thus

$$E = 1.35 \times 10^3 \text{ J·s}^{-1}\text{·m}^{-2} \times 4\pi \times 1.5^2 \times 10^{22} \text{ m}^2 = 3.82 \times 10^{26} \text{ J·s}^{-1}.$$

If four atoms of hydrogen combine to give one atom of helium, the energy released is

$$E' = (4 \times 1.00813 - 4.00386) \times 931 \text{ MeV} = 0.02866 \times 931 \times 1.6 \times 10^{-13} \text{ J} = 4.27 \times 10^{-12} \text{ J}.$$

204

The number of hydrogen atoms converted per second to produce the energy radiated by the sun is thus $n = 4 \times (E/E')$, and the number of moles this represents is

$$M = \frac{n}{N_0} = \frac{4E}{N_0 E'},$$

where N_0 is Avogadro's number. But 1 mole of hydrogen has a mass of 1.00813 g. Thus the mass of hydrogen converted per second is

$$\frac{1.00813 \text{ g} \cdot \text{mole}^{-1} \times 4 \times 3.82 \times 10^{26} \text{ J} \cdot \text{s}^{-1}}{6.02 \times 10^{23} \text{ mole}^{-1} \times 4.27 \times 10^{-12} \text{ J}} = 5.99 \times 10^{14} \text{ g} \cdot \text{s}^{-1}.$$

PROBLEM 50.3

A thickness of 48 cm of Al^{27} reduces the intensity of γ-rays from ThC'' to 1% of its original value. The density of aluminum is 2.65 g·cm^{-3}. What is the mass absorption coefficient involved and the atomic cross section for this process?

Solution. The relation involving intensity and linear absorption coefficient is $I = I_0 e^{-\mu x}$.

$$\therefore \qquad \mu = \frac{1}{x} \ln \frac{I_0}{I} = \frac{4.605}{48 \text{ cm}} = 0.0959 \text{ cm}^{-1}.$$

But, if μ_m is the mass absorption coefficient and ρ the density, then $\mu = \mu_m \rho$ or

$$\mu_m = \frac{\mu}{\rho} = \frac{0.0959 \text{ cm}^{-1}}{2.65 \text{ g} \cdot \text{cm}^{-3}} = 0.0362 \text{ cm}^2 \cdot \text{g}^{-1}.$$

A volume of aluminum obtained by taking 1 cm^2 of the surface area and a length of 48 cm perpendicular to this removes 99% of the photons from a γ-ray beam incident at right angles on the surface area. This volume is 48 cm^3 and has a mass of 2.65 g·cm^{-3} × 48 cm^3. The number of moles in this mass is thus $(2.65 \times 48 \text{ g})/27 \text{ g} \cdot \text{mole}^{-1}$, and thus contains $[(2.65 \times 48)/27 \text{ mole} \times 6.02 \times 10^{23} \text{ mole}^{-1}]$ atoms, bringing in Avogadro's number.

If each atom for this purpose has an effective area σ, σ is the atomic cross section for the process, and the projected area of all atoms on the surface must make up 99% of the surface area.

$$\therefore \qquad \frac{2.65 \times 48 \times 6.02 \times 10^{23}}{27} \sigma = \frac{99}{100} \times 1 \text{ cm}^2.$$

$$\therefore \qquad \sigma = \frac{27 \times 99}{2.65 \times 48 \times 6.02 \times 10^{25}} \text{ cm}^2 = 0.349 \times 10^{24} \text{ cm}^2 = 0.349 \text{ barn}.$$

SECTION II

In this section are to be found problems intended as exercises for the student who has read up to this point and wishes to test the knowledge he has gained. The solutions are grouped at the end of the section.

Additional Problems

1. A circular table of mass 1.5 slugs is 6 ft in diameter and stands on four legs placed symmetrically at right angles to the table top at distances of 3 ft from the center. A mass of 2 slugs rests on the table midway between adjacent legs. How much of the weight is carried by each leg?

2. A simple uniform farm gate, 6 ft long and weighing 100 lb, is attached to a post by two rudimentary hinges, one 18 in. vertically above the other. The lower hinge takes all the weight. What force is exerted by the upper hinge when a boy weighing 120 lb swings on the other end?

3. A domestic stepladder is kept upright by a strut one end of which is hinged to the top of the ladder, the other end resting on the ground. The ladder is 5 ft long, weighs 100 lb, and is inclined at 60° to the horizontal when in use; the strut weighs 25 lb and is inclined to the horizontal at 75° when in use.

What are the reactions on the ground and at the hinge when a householder weighing 160 lb is standing centrally three-quarters of the way up the ladder?

4. A train takes 6 min on the journey between two stations 4 mi apart. It accelerates uniformly from rest in the first half-mile, maintaining a uniform speed thereafter until it decelerates to a stop in the last quarter-mile. What is the value of the uniform speed?

5. A uniformly accelerating train passes successive milestones with speeds of 15 mph and 25 mph, respectively. What will its speed be at the next milestone and how long did it take to cover these 2 mi?

6. A train 200 yd long and traveling at 60 mph takes 10 s to pass another train moving in the opposite direction on a parallel track at 30 mph. What is the length of the second train?

7. At what time between 6 o'clock and 7 o'clock is the minute hand of a watch directly over the hour hand?

The hour, minute, and second hands are all coincident at midnight. Are they so again before noon?

8. A ship is steaming east at 8 mph and a passenger on it sees a second ship 10 mi due south. The second vessel is moving in a northeasterly direction at 14 mph. What is the shortest distance between the ships and how long does it take them to reach that position?

9. A book lies on the table in a train which is traveling at 60 mph. If the coefficient of friction between the book and the table is 0.4, what is the shortest distance in which the train can come to a full stop without causing the book to slip?

10. An electric train weighing 500 tons is traveling at 60 mph on a level track. The engineer, by cutting off the electric current to the motors, reduces its speed from 60 mph to 45 mph in 88 s. Assuming that the frictional retarding force is uniform, and neglecting air resistance, find the frictional retarding force.

Suppose that the slowing-down had occurred on a rising gradient of 1 in 100. Assuming the frictional retarding force to be the same in both cases, what would be the speed after the train had traveled a distance of 2972 ft?

11. A long light cord which hangs over a smooth peg carries at its ends masses of 20 g and 40 g. The peg is moved upward in such a way that the 40-g mass remains stationary. What is the acceleration of the other mass and the tension in the cord?

When the speed of the peg is 16 ft·s^{-1}, it is suddenly brought to rest. What is the speed of the 20-g mass at that time and for how long does the cord stay slack?

12. A particle of mass m projected vertically upward with velocity v_0 in a gas experiences a resistance to motion of kv^2 when its velocity is v (k being a constant). Find the height reached by the particle and its velocity when it returns to its starting point.

13. Our helpful physics student observes a man attempting to push a crate over a level sheet of ice. The man is exerting a force horizontally, but every time the crate is about to move, his feet slip from under him. Why does the student advise the man to exert his force at an angle upward from the horizontal? What would happen if the man pushed in a downward direction?

14. Two spheres of lead, each of mass 10^3 kg and placed 1 m apart, attract one another with a force of 6.67×10^{-5} N. The radius of the earth is 6.4×10^6 m. What is the mass of the earth?

15. The angles of inclination to the horizontal at which two cubes, one of wood and the other of metal, and each of mass 20 g, slide with uniform speed down a rough plane are 35° and 31°, respectively. The cubes are then connected by a string and sent down the plane, which is fixed at an angle of inclination of 45°, the metal cube leading. What will be the tension in the string and the acceleration of the system?

16. A particular type of shell exploding on a level surface scatters debris over an area of radius $2a$. Show that a soldier who dives under cover when a shell lands a distance a away must stay there for a time of $2.73\sqrt{a/g}$ before emerging.

17. Some children playing baseball on a vacant lot watch with horror as the ball soars from the bat to shatter a window at a point 6 ft higher than the batter's hands and 343 ft away. The ball left the bat at an angle of 30° to the horizontal. What was the speed of projection?

18. The radius of a railway curve is 1254 yd and a train is to travel round it at a speed of 45 mph. By how much should the outer rail be raised to reduce to a minimum the outward pressure on it? The distance between the rails is 57 in.

19. The mean distance between Mars and its satellite Phobos is 9500 km. What is the period of Phobos? The diameter of Mars is 6800 km and its mean density is 4120 kg·m^{-3}.

20. In a space-medicine research establishment, two astronauts are put into cages mounted at opposite ends of a 20-m arm, and the apparatus is rotated at uniform speed in a vertical circle about the midpoint of the arm. What speed of rotation is required to produce weightlessness at the top of the circle and what weight is then experienced at the bottom?

21. A boy's slingshot is made by joining to a forked stick two rubber bands each 12 cm long and connected by a leather pouch. When a stone of mass 100 g hangs in the pouch, each of the bands stretches by 1 cm. If a pebble of mass 20 g is put in the pouch and the bands are stretched downward to double their length, how high will the pebble rise when the pouch is released?

22. An aircraft in flight experiences a retarding force due to air friction proportional to the square of its velocity. When the engines are switched off, a particular airplane which weighs 112,000 lb can glide down at an angle of 5° to the horizontal with a speed of 60 mph. What will be its speed in level flight when the engines are producing 10,000 hp?

23. A fire engine discharges 2 slugs of water every second with a velocity of 60 mph. One-fifth of the work done is used in overcoming frictional forces. What is the horsepower of the fire engine?

24. A spring of negligible weight is extended by 10 cm when a mass of 1 kg is hung from it. Suppose the spring stands vertically on a table and the mass is dropped onto it from a height of 1 m. How far will the spring be compressed?

25. A rifle bullet of mass 20 g is fired at a speed of 1000 m·s^{-1} at the bob of a simple pendulum of mass 10 kg hanging 2 m below the point of support. The bullet embeds itself to a depth of 5 cm in the bob. What is the retarding force, assumed to be constant, and the time required to bring the bullet to rest? Through what angle does the pendulum swing?

26. A ball weighing $\frac{1}{4}$ lb is balanced in the air by the impact on it of a jet of water issuing vertically at a speed of 20 ft·s^{-1} from a nozzle of cross-sectional area 0.1 in^2. One cubic foot of water weighs 62.5 lb. Find the height of the ball above the nozzle.

27. The final stage of a rocket consists of a 600-kg motor assembly and a 10-kg nose cone. It is orbiting the earth with a velocity of 7 km·s⁻¹ when a signal is sent from the earth which sets off a small explosive charge to detach the nose cone. The velocity of the nose cone becomes 7.5 km·s⁻¹. What is the velocity of the motor assembly?

28. A student who weighs 150 lb is standing in a stationary punt of weight 450 lb when his girl friend, who cannot swim, topples off the end into the water. The student runs 8 ft along the punt to the end. How far will he be from the drowning girl when he gets there?

29. A horizontal disk is rotating freely about a vertical axis through its center at a speed of 72 rev·min⁻¹. A piece of putty of mass 5 g drops onto and sticks to the disk 4 cm from the center. The speed reduces to 60 rev·min⁻¹. What is the moment of inertia of the disk?

30. A uniform circular disk of mass 250 kg and diameter 1 m is rotating at an angular speed of 2500 rev·min⁻¹. Find the constant tangential force which, acting on the rim, will bring it to rest in 3 min.

31. A mass of 10 kg hangs from a light spring which stretches 2 cm for every kilogram of load. The spring and mass are moving upward in relative equilibrium with a uniform velocity of 50 cm·s⁻¹ when the upper end of the spring is suddenly brought to rest. Find the amplitude of vibration of the mass.

32. An internal combustion engine has pistons each weighing 0.75 kg and a stroke of 10 cm. The motion of the pistons is assumed simple harmonic and the engine is running at 3000 rpm. What is the velocity of a piston at the midpoint of its stroke and the force that must be exerted on the piston at the end of the stroke?

33. Assume that the mean densities of the earth and the moon are equal. Determine the length of a simple pendulum which has a period of 2 s at the moon's surface. Radius of the moon/radius of the earth $= 0.273$ and $g = \pi^2$ m·s⁻².

34. A pendulum consists of a light rod, to the lower end of which is attached a brass disk with its plane vertical and in the plane of oscillation of the pendulum. The disk is 20 cm in diameter and has its center of gravity 1 m from the point of suspension of the pendulum. Find the error in the periodic time calculated for this pendulum, if the moment of inertia of the disk about its center is neglected. Take g as π^2 m·s⁻².

35. When equal masses of two substances are mixed, the resultant density is 2.5 g·cm⁻³. When equal volumes are mixed, the resultant density is 4.5 g·cm⁻³. What are the densities of the two substances?

36. A vertical U-tube of cross-sectional area 1.25 cm² contains 10 cm³ of mercury. The mercury on one side is forced down and then released. What is the period of the resulting oscillation? Assume that g is π^2 m·s⁻².

37. A parallel-sided plank of wood of thickness 10 in. and density 0.85 g·cm⁻³ floats in water. A boy gently pours oil of density 0.80 g·cm⁻³ into a knothole which extends right through the plank. What is the depth of oil when the hole is filled?

38. Consider that whipped cream is a mass of touching bubbles of air of diameter 8×10^{-3} cm, in cream of surface tension 30 dynes·cm⁻¹. How much work must be expended in whipping 1 liter of cream?

39. A vertical glass tube is drawn into a long capillary of diameter 0.02 cm at the bottom. Then mercury is poured in. How high must the mercury column be before it pours from the foot of the capillary? Mercury has a surface tension of 465 dynes·cm⁻¹, a density of 13.6 g·cm⁻³, and an angle of contact with glass of 130°.

40. A drop of oil of density 0.9013 g·cm⁻³ falls through air of density 1.300 g·liter⁻¹ and viscosity 1.800×10^{-4} poise, and attains a terminal velocity of 10.00 cm·s⁻¹. What is the radius of the drop?

41. A tank with vertical sides contains water to a depth of 4 ft. A small hole of cross-sectional area 10^{-4} of that of the horizontal section of the tank is punched through the bottom. How long does it take the tank to empty?

42. A clinical thermometer has a tube diameter of 0.02 mm and a bulb of volume 0.04 cm³. What is the length separating Fahrenheit degrees on the thermometer? The coefficients of cubical expansion of glass and mercury are 13×10^{-6} per F deg and 101×10^{-6} per F deg, respectively.

43. A steel container has a net volume independent of temperature because it contains a brass block. The steel container has a gross volume of 2×10^{-1} m^3 at 0°C. Find the volume of the brass block at that temperature. The coefficients of linear expansion of brass and steel are 20×10^{-6} and 12×10^{-6} C deg^{-1}, respectively.

44. The compressibility of alcohol is 77×10^{-5} atm^{-1} and its coefficient of cubical expansion is 1.1×10^{-3} C deg^{-1}. Alcohol at 20°C is placed in a sealed vessel made of material of negligible coefficient of expansion. The vessel can withstand pressures up to 120 atm only. To what temperature must the vessel be raised in order to burst it?

45. An iron rod 2 m long and 2 cm^2 in cross-sectional area is heated to 175°C, and its ends are then clamped rigidly. Find the tension in the rod when it has cooled to 25°C. The coefficient of linear expansion of iron is 1.1×10^{-5} C deg^{-1} and Young's modulus for iron is 2.0×10^{12} dynes·cm^{-2}.

46. A manufacturer's catalog states that their 500-W immersion heater will boil one pint of water in 6 min and will boil 25 pints of water for 1 kWh* of electricity. Show that with a normal starting temperature for the water of 20°C, neither claim is true. One pint of water has a mass of 567 g.

47. A copper calorimeter of mass 50 g and specific heat capacity 0.09 cal·g^{-1}·C deg^{-1} contains a mixture of 200 g of ice and water. Twenty grams of steam are passed into the calorimeter and condense there, the final equilibrium temperature being recorded as 50°C. How much ice was originally present?

48. Ten grams of water are carefully supercooled to -3°C before freezing sets in. How much ice is then formed?

49. An iron hot-water tank kept at 122°F is 2.5 cm thick and the heat passing through the tank walls keeps the outer surface at a temperature of 77°F. How much heat is given off from each square meter of the surface per hour? The thermal conductivity of iron is 0.11 cal·cm^{-1}·s^{-1}·C deg^{-1}.

50. The thermal conductivity of a glass disk of area 100 cm^2 and thickness 0.5 cm is measured by clamping it between two brass disks of the same diameter and each of mass 250 g. When one disk is maintained at 100°C the other settles in equilibrium at a temperature of 90.5°C. The rate of cooling of the latter disk at 90.5°C is 10 C deg per minute. What is the thermal conductivity of brass? The specific heat capacity of brass is 0.38 J·g^{-1}·C deg^{-1}.

51. A diving bell is lowered into a fresh-water lake on a day when the atmospheric pressure is 760 mm of mercury, air being pumped in to keep the water level in the bell constant. Find the ratio of the masses of air in the bell when the water level in the bell is 15 m and 25 m below the surface.

52. A bubble of air of volume 1 cm^3 escapes up the tube of a perfect mercury barometer which is standing at a height of 75 cm. The barometer tube has a cross-sectional area of 1 cm^2 and a length of vacuum of 10 cm. By how much does the mercury level descend?

53. A mass of air which extends to a height of 500 m over an area of countryside of 10^4 m^2 has a dew-point of 15°C, its temperature being 20°C. How many centimeters of rain will fall if the temperature of the air drops to 10°C? The saturated aqueous vapor pressures at 15°C and 10°C are 12.8 mm of mercury and 9.2 mm of mercury, respectively.

54. What is the rate of working of a heart which beats 70 times per minute and pumps 72 cm^3 of blood at each beat against a pressure of 12 cm of mercury?

55. When one gram of water of volume 1 cm^3 is boiled at a pressure of 10^6 dynes·cm^{-2}, 1670 cm^3 of steam are produced. What work is done against the external pressure and what is the increase in internal energy?

56. Calculate the work done when a gas obeying Berthelot's equation of state,

$$\left(p + \frac{a}{TV^2}\right)(V - b) = RT,$$

expands isothermally from volume V_1 to V_2.

---

*The letters kWh have been adopted by the International Union of Pure and Applied Physics to denote kilowatt-hour.

57. Air at 1030 mbars* pressure and a temperature of 17°C is sucked into a coal mine and undergoes adiabatic compression as it descends the shaft. The pressure at the bottom of the shaft is 1000 mbars. What is the temperature of the air when it reaches the bottom? For air, $\gamma = 1.40$.

58. A hot spring produces water at a temperature of 56°C. The water flows into a large lake, with a mean temperature of 14°C, at a rate of 0.1 m³ of water per minute. What is the rate of working of an ideal heat engine which uses all the available energy?

59. A child's popgun consists of a tube 15 cm long. A cork is inserted at one end and a tightly fitting piston is pushed rapidly in at the other end. When the pressure in the tube reaches 1.25 atm the cork is ejected. What is likely to be the frequency of the pop?
   What difference does it make if the piston is pushed in slowly?

60. A brass wire of density 8.5 g·cm⁻³ and radius 0.01 cm is stretched between two points 100 cm apart and subjected to an extension of 0.05 cm. Find the frequency of the fundamental transverse vibration. Young's modulus for brass is 9.6×10^{11} dynes·cm⁻².

61. A tuning fork makes 5 beats per second with a stretched wire of length 112 cm. It also gives 5 beats per second when sounded with a length of the same wire of 116 cm under the same tension. What is the frequency of the tuning fork?

62. How fast must an observer travel between two stationary sources emitting sound of the same frequency so that they may appear to him to have frequencies in the ratio 9:8? The speed of sound in air is 340 m·s⁻¹.

63. Calculate the work that must be expended to bring a charge of 10 pC† from a position 1 m from a charge of 50 μC to a position 1 cm from it.

64. A hollow cylinder made of insulating material is closed at one end by a fixed metal plate and at the other by a well-fitting metal piston. The cylinder contains air at a pressure of 50 N·m⁻² and the distance between plate and piston is 15 cm. A potential difference is applied between piston and plate, and the distance between them decreases by 0.2 mm. What is the value of the applied potential difference?

65. The experimental value of the electric dipole moment of the water molecule is 6.1×10^{-30} C·m. What separation of two particles with $\pm$ the electronic charge would produce such a dipole moment? What would be the electric intensity at a distance of 10 cm along the perpendicular bisector of the dipole?

66. Two insulated spherical conductors, each of radius 3 cm and situated a considerable distance apart, are connected by a wire and charged to a potential of 50 V. A spherical conducting shell of radius 4 cm divided into hemispheres is fitted concentrically around one of the spheres and grounded, thus forming a spherical capacitor; the wire joining the spheres passes through a small hole in the shell. Calculate the final potential of the two conductors.

67. A capacitor of capacitance 5×10^{-3} μF is connected to an electrometer and the combination charged to 80 V. If the electrometer is disconnected, discharged, and reconnected, the potential is found to be 75 V. A second capacitor connected in parallel with the first makes the potential fall further to 40 V. Find the capacitance of the electrometer and the second capacitor.

68. An electric radiator has a resistance of $(50 + \alpha T^2)$ Ω at temperature T °K and emits βT^4 W, α and β being constants. Its resistance is 125 Ω when a potential difference of 50 V is connected across it. What current must be passed through the radiator in order that it will emit 980 W?

69. A film projector manufactured in the United States to run from 115 V and to dissipate 500 W is used by a serviceman who is stationed in Britain, where the supply voltage is 230 V. What resistance must he place in series with the projector before he uses it? What energy is dissipated in the added resistor?

70. A current of 2 A is passed through a heater of resistance 8.4 Ω immersed in 400 g of a liquid contained in a calorimeter and the temperature rises 10 C deg in 3 min. When 560 g of the liquid are used

---

*The abbreviation mbars denotes millibars.
†One pC = 1 picocoulomb = 10^{-12} coulomb.

in the same calorimeter and the same current is passed, the temperature rises 10 C deg in 4 min. Neglecting any heat loss or any change in the resistance of the heater, calculate the heat capacity of the calorimeter and the specific heat capacity of the liquid.

71. The resistance of a resistor is measured by using a voltmeter and ammeter. When the voltmeter is connected directly across the resistor, the readings obtained are 50 V and 0.55 A. When the voltmeter is connected across both the ammeter and resistor, the readings are 54.3 V and 0.54 A. The resistance of the voltmeter is 1000 Ω. Find the resistance of the resistor and of the ammeter.

72. A circuit is connected as in the diagram. The power dissipation in any branch must not exceed 1 W. What is the maximum value of the emf of the battery?

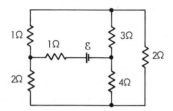

73. A galvanometer whose resistance is 9.9 Ω is fitted with a shunt of resistance 0.1 Ω when it is used as an ammeter with full-scale deflection of 5 A. What current is the galvanometer carrying at maximum deflection? What resistance should be used and how should it be fitted if the galvanometer is to be used as a voltmeter with full-scale deflection of 50 V?

74. Positive, singly charged ions are accelerated through a potential difference and enter a uniform magnetic field normal to their line of motion. If a potential difference of 1000 volts brings Li^6 to the detector, what potential difference would cause Li^7 ions to traverse the same path?

75. A galvanometer coil has 500 turns of wire wound round a frame 2 cm long and 1 cm wide. The coil turns in a magnetic field of 0.05 Wb·m^{-2}, always parallel to its plane and perpendicular to its length. What torque acts on the coil when it carries a current of 10^{-8} A?

76. A student at M.I.T., where the horizontal component of the earth's magnetic field is 1.7×10^{-5} Wb·m^{-2}, is performing an experiment using a compass needle in a laboratory which also contains an experiment involving a long vertical wire carrying a current of 50 A. By what distance should the experiments be separated in order that the compass needle will be negligibly affected by the field of the current-carrying wire?

77. Given a length of current-carrying wire, will a greater value of magnetic induction be produced at the center by bending the wire into a circle or a square?

78. Two students are performing electrical experiments in the same laboratory, one sending alternating current of maximum value 1 A through a long straight wire, the other using a flat rectangular coil of 50 turns of mean area 0.25 m^2. How far apart should they be if the frequency of the alternating current is 1000 cycles·s^{-1} and the second student's results will be affected if an emf of greater than 1 mV is induced in his coil?

79. A 1-H inductor with a resistance of 50 Ω is connected to a potential difference of 25 V. At what rate is the current increasing when it has achieved a magnitude of half its final value, and how long does it take to reach 90% of its final value? How much energy is finally stored in the inductor?

80. The lamp in an ophthalmoscope is rated at 24 V, 36 W, and is to be used from 220-V ac mains. What resistance is required in series with the lamp? What would be a less wasteful method of using the lamp from the mains?

81. When a coil of resistance 26.4 Ω is supplied with alternating current from a 100-V, 50-cycle·s^{-1} supply, it takes 2.5 A. The emf induced in an identical coil nearby is 50 V on open circuit. Calculate the self-inductance of each coil and the mutual inductance between them.

82. One standard method of determining the refractive index of water uses a narrow cell made up of parallel-sided slabs of glass formed into a rectangular box which contains air. The cell is immersed in water and a horizontal beam of light is directed normally onto one face of the box. The cell is rotated about a vertical axis until the light beam emerging from the other side of the box is cut off. The angle through which the cell has been rotated is the critical angle for a water–air interface.

It is not immediately clear that the glass walls of the cell have no disturbing influence on this result. Demonstrate that this is in fact correct.

83. A cube of size 1 in. of a transparent precious stone is found to have a small flaw right at the center. The jeweler who owns it is unwilling to split it, since value drops drastically with size. What fraction of the surface must he cover with the setting if the flaw is not to be seen by the purchaser? The stone has a refractive index of 1.60.

84. The driver of a car has a rear-view mirror 3 ft in front of him which should allow him to see the full width of a 30-ft road at a distance of 40 yd behind him. Calculate the width of the mirror that the manufacturer should supply.

85. Our inquiring student takes two concave mirrors of focal lengths 12 cm and 14 cm and places them facing each other. He places a point source of light at 15 cm from the first mirror and adjusts the position of the second mirror until a single real image is produced coincident with the object. At that position, what is the distance between the mirrors?

86. A biconvex lens of central thickness 3 cm, refractive index 1.50, and radii of curvature 10 cm and 15 cm, is viewed first from one side and then from the other. What is the difference in apparent thickness?

87. A skin diver takes two watch glasses each of radius of curvature 10 cm and joins them together with their vertexes touching in such a way that air is trapped between them. He uses the air lens so formed under water. What is its focal length and how far from a coral does he need to hold it in order that he may see the image, vertical and erect, magnified four times?

88. A surveyor uses a telescope which has an objective of focal length 25 cm and a graticule consisting of two horizontal lines 3.0 mm apart in the first focal plane of the eyepiece. The surveyor sights along a rod held by his assistant 10 m from the objective. What length of the rod is apparently between the graticule lines?

89. The student whose career we have been following with interest sets up a Young's slits experiment in which the slits are 1 mm apart, and illuminates it with light containing two wavelengths of 567 nm and 486 nm. At what distance from the central bright fringe on a screen 150 cm from the slits will a bright fringe from one interference pattern first coincide with a bright fringe from the other?

90. If the student in the preceding problem had used a diffraction grating with 2000 lines to the centimeter instead of slits, at what angle would coincidence of principal maxima due to the two wavelengths have occurred (the grating being illuminated normally)?

91. Radiation of wavelength 1.60×10^{-7} m ejects photoelectrons from a plate of potassium whose work function is 2 V. A magnetic field of 5×10^{-5} Wb·m^{-2} is applied parallel to the plate. Find the radius of the orbits of electrons projected normally from the plate with maximum energy.

92. Calculate the short-wavelength limits of the Lyman, Balmer, Paschen, Brackett, and Pfund series.

93. A cubic rock-salt crystal has a density of 2164 kg·m^{-3} and a molar mass of 58.45 g. At what glancing angle to the principal planes of the crystal will incident Cu K$_\alpha$ x-radiation of wavelength 1.5405 Å produce first-order Bragg reflection?

94. At what glancing angle do 500-eV electrons suffer a second-order Bragg reflection from the principal planes of a cubic crystal whose spacing is 2.86 Å?

95. The mass absorption coefficient of 2.5-MeV x-rays in lead is 0.0042 m^2·kg^{-1}. Find the thickness of lead of density 11,300 kg·m^{-3} which will reduce the intensity of the radiation by a factor of 10.

96. Suppose that a peace commission were able to obtain international agreement to stop the mining of radioactive ore for 1000 years. At the end of that time, would there be more or less radium-226 in the earth's crust?

97. A sample of 1.00×10^{-10} g of Bi^{210} is freshly separated at a time taken as the zero of the measuring scale. The sample decays by emitting a β-particle to Po^{210} with a half-life of 5 days, and Po^{210} further decays to Pb²⁰⁶ by α-emission with a half-life of 140 days. Calculate the maximum mass of Po²¹⁰ present at any time and the activity it then possesses.

98. When nitrogen, whose atoms have a mass of 14.00752 amu, is bombarded with thermal neutrons of negligible energy, the carbon atom and proton produced in any disintegration always have a combined energy of 0.55 MeV. If the masses of proton and neutron are 1.00819 and 1.00899 amu, respectively, what is the mass of the carbon isotope produced?

99. A space rocket weighing 5×10^4 kg and powered by atomic energy can reach escape velocity from the earth in 3 min under constant acceleration. Neglecting air resistance and the change in gravitational potential energy during acceleration, calculate how much uranium-235 is used up by the rocket in escaping from the earth, if the heat converter has an efficiency of 5%. The escape velocity from the earth is 11.3×10^3 m·s⁻¹.

100. On the assumption that the fusion of deuterons gives rise to α-particles, find the energy which would be released by the fusion of 1 g of deuterium. The masses of the deuteron and the α-particle are 2.0147 amu and 4.0039 amu, respectively.

101. Two inertial systems S and S' have a common x-axis, and S' is moving along the x-axis with a speed of 0.95c relative to S. An observer in S holds a rod of length 10 cm at an angle of 30° to the x-axis. What is the length and angle of the rod as measured by an observer in S'?

Solutions to Additional Problems

1. The table is uniform and circular and the line of action of its weight therefore acts through the center of the table top. The floor exerts on each leg a normal force which is vertical. By the symmetry of the system it is obvious that the normal forces on the legs nearest the added mass must be equal, and similarly the normal forces acting on the other two legs must also be equal. If the normal force on each of the nearer legs is R_1 and on each of the two farther legs is R_2, the pair of forces R_1 have a resultant $2R_1$ midway between them, and the pair of forces R_2 have a resultant $2R_2$ midway between them. The system is thus reduced to four parallel forces acting through points lying on a straight line, as shown in the second diagram, where $AB = BC$.

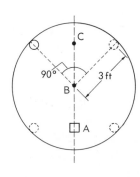

Since the forces are in equilibrium,

$$2(R_1 + R_2) = (2 + 1.5)32 \text{ lb},$$

and, taking moments about A, we have

$$2R_2 \times AC = 4R_2 \times AB = (1.5 \times 32) \text{ lb} \times AB.$$

$$\therefore \quad R_2 = 12 \text{ lb} \quad \text{and} \quad R_1 = (56 - 12) \text{ lb} = 44 \text{ lb}.$$

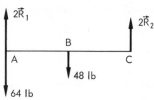

The weight carried by one leg must equal the normal force exerted by the floor on it to preserve equilibrium. Thus the two legs nearest to the added mass each carry a weight of 44 lb and the other two legs each carry a weight of 12 lb.

2. The weight of the gate must act through the geometrical center, since the gate is uniform. Since the lower hinge carries all the weight, it has a vertical and a horizontal force acting on it, while the upper hinge has only a horizontal force acting on it. The gate therefore has five forces acting on it, as shown in the diagram. Since the gate is in equilibrium under the action of these forces,

$$F_1 = 220 \text{ lb} \quad \text{and} \quad R = F_2.$$

Further, taking moments about the lower hinge, we have

$$R \times 1\tfrac{1}{2} \text{ ft} = 100 \text{ lb} \times 3 \text{ ft} + 120 \text{ lb} \times 6 \text{ ft}.$$

$$\therefore \quad R = \frac{1020 \text{ ft} \cdot \text{lb}}{\tfrac{3}{2} \text{ ft}} = 680 \text{ lb}.$$

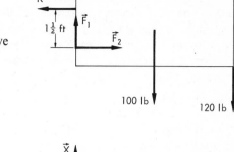

3. Consider the ladder and the strut separately. The forces acting on the ladder are its weight $\mathbf{W}_0$ vertically down through the center, the weight of the householder $\mathbf{W}$ acting vertically downward three-quarters of the way up the ladder, vertical and horizontal forces $\mathbf{X}$ and $\mathbf{Y}$ acting at the hinge, and forces at the ground which may be compounded into a single vertical force $\mathbf{Q}$ and a single horizontal force $\mathbf{P}$ acting in the same plane as the others.

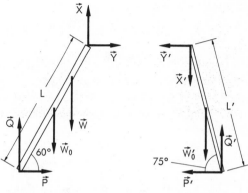

By similar reasoning the forces on the strut are its weight $\mathbf{W}_0'$, vertical and horizontal forces $\mathbf{Q}'$ and $\mathbf{P}'$ at the ground and vertical and horizontal forces $\mathbf{X}'$ and $\mathbf{Y}'$ at the hinge. $\mathbf{X}'$ and $\mathbf{Y}'$ must be equal but opposite to the forces acting on the ladder at the hinge since, by Newton's third law, action and reaction are equal and opposite.

Both the ladder and the strut are in equilibrium. Thus

$$W + W_0 - Q - X = 0, \qquad P + Y = 0,$$

$$W_0' + X - Q' = 0 \quad \text{and} \quad P' + Y = 0.$$

Taking moments about the hinge in each case, we have

$$PL \sin 60^\circ + W_0 \frac{L}{2} \cos 60^\circ + W \frac{L}{4} \cos 60^\circ = QL \cos 60^\circ,$$

and

$$Q'L' \cos 75^\circ = W_0' \frac{L'}{2} \cos 75^\circ + P'L' \sin 75^\circ.$$

Eliminating X and Y, inserting the values for W, W_0, and W_0', and canceling out L and L' throughout gives

$$Q + Q' = 285 \text{ lb}, \qquad P = P',$$

$$P \tan 60^\circ + 90 \text{ lb} = Q, \qquad \text{and} \qquad Q' = 12.5 \text{ lb} + P' \tan 75^\circ.$$

Eliminating P' and Q' gives

$$P \tan 60^\circ + 90 \text{ lb} = Q \qquad \text{and} \qquad 285 \text{ lb} - Q = 12.5 \text{ lb} + P \tan 75^\circ.$$

$$\therefore \quad P = \frac{182.5 \text{ lb}}{\tan 60^\circ + \tan 75^\circ} = 33.4 \text{ lb}.$$

$$\therefore \quad Q = 147.8 \text{ lb}. \quad \therefore \quad P' = 33.4 \text{ lb} \quad \text{and} \quad Q' = 137.2 \text{ lb}.$$

Substitution back in the original equations gives

$$X = 112.2 \text{ lb} \quad \text{and} \quad Y = -33.4 \text{ lb}.$$

The two forces $\mathbf{Y}$ and $\mathbf{Y}'$ are thus in the opposite directions to those shown in the diagram.

4. Construct a velocity–time diagram. The first part of the motion is at uniform acceleration and is thus represented by a straight line passing through the origin and the point with coordinates (t_1, v_0). The second part of the motion takes place at constant speed and is thus a straight line parallel to the

t-axis starting at the point (t_1, v_0) and ending at the point $(t_1 + t_2, v_0)$. The third part of the motion is at uniform deceleration and is thus given by a straight line extending from the point $(t_1 + t_2, v_0)$ to the point $(t_1 + t_2 + t_3, 0)$.

The distance traveled in each part of the motion is known and can also be calculated from the area under each part of the curve. Thus

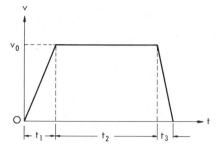

$$\frac{1}{2}\,\text{mi} = \frac{1}{2}v_0 t_1, \quad \left(4 - \frac{1}{2} - \frac{1}{4}\right)\text{mi} = v_0 t_2, \quad \frac{1}{4}\,\text{mi} = \frac{1}{2}v_0 t_3.$$

Multiplying the first and third equations by 2 and adding all the equations, we obtain

$$\left(1 + 3\frac{1}{4} + \frac{1}{2}\right)\text{mi} = v_0(t_1 + t_2 + t_3).$$

But $(t_1 + t_2 + t_3)$ is the whole time of the motion $= \frac{1}{10}$ hr.

$$\therefore \quad v_0 = \frac{4\frac{3}{4}\,\text{mi}}{\frac{1}{10}\,\text{hr}} = \frac{190}{4}\,\text{mph} = 47.5\,\text{mph}.$$

5. Applying the equation of uniformly accelerated motion, $v^2 = v_0^2 + 2as$, to the information given, we have

$$15^2\,(\text{mph})^2 = v_0^2 + 2as \quad\text{and}\quad 25^2\,(\text{mph})^2 = v_0^2 + 2a(s + 1\,\text{mi}).$$

$$\therefore \quad (25^2 - 15^2)\,(\text{mph})^2 = 2a \times 1\,\text{mi} \quad\text{or}\quad a = 200\,\text{mi} \cdot \text{hr}^{-2}.$$

If the speed at the next milestone is u, then $u^2 = v_0^2 + 2a(s + 2\,\text{mi})$.

$$\therefore \quad u^2 - 15^2\,(\text{mph})^2 = 4a\,\text{mi} = 800\,(\text{mph})^2. \quad \therefore \quad u^2 = 1025\,(\text{mph})^2 \quad\text{or}\quad u = 32.02\,\text{mph}.$$

Applying now the equation $u = v + at$, we have

$$t = \frac{u - v}{a} = \frac{(32.02 - 15)\,\text{mph}}{200\,\text{mi} \cdot \text{hr}^{-2}} = 0.085\,\text{hr} = 5.1\,\text{min}.$$

6. If the guard of one train considers the situation relative to himself, then so far as he is concerned, the other train has a speed of $60\,\text{mph} - (-30)\,\text{mph} = 90\,\text{mph}$ relative to him. The length the other train has to travel between the times that the engines are abreast and the time the cabooses are abreast is $(200 + y)$ yd, where y yd is the length of the second train. This process takes $10\,\text{s} = \frac{1}{360}$ hr at constant speed. Thus, converting the length to miles, we obtain

$$\frac{200 + y}{1760}\,\text{mi} = 90\,\text{mph} \times \frac{1}{360}\,\text{hr}. \quad \therefore \quad 200 + y = 440 \quad\text{or}\quad y = 240.$$

The length of the second train is 240 yd.

7. The hour hand travels at an angular speed of $(2\pi/12)\,\text{rad} \cdot \text{hr}^{-1}$ and the minute hand at an angular speed of $2\pi\,\text{rad} \cdot \text{hr}^{-1}$. The relative speed at which the minute hand moves toward the hour hand is thus $[2\pi - (2\pi/12)] = \frac{11}{6}\pi\,\text{rad} \cdot \text{hr}^{-1}$. The two start at 6 o'clock an angular distance of π rad apart. If the minute hand catches up with the hour hand in time t, then

$$\pi\,\text{rad} = \frac{11}{6}\pi\,\text{rad} \cdot \text{hr}^{-1} \times t,$$

since π rad is the relative angular distance traveled at a speed of $\frac{11}{6}\pi\,\text{rad} \cdot \text{hr}^{-1}$. Therefore $t = \frac{6}{11}$ hr. Thus the two are coincident at $\frac{6}{11}$ hr $= \frac{360}{11}$ min after 6 o'clock; that is, at $6.32\frac{8}{11}$ o'clock.

It was shown above that the relative angular velocity of the minute hand with respect to the hour hand was $\frac{11}{6}\pi\,\text{rad} \cdot \text{hr}^{-1}$. Similarly, since the angular velocity of the second hand is $2\pi\,\text{rad} \cdot \text{min}^{-1} = 120\pi\,\text{rad} \cdot \text{hr}^{-1}$, the relative angular velocity of the second hand with respect to the minute hand is $(120\pi - 2\pi) = 118\pi\,\text{rad} \cdot \text{hr}^{-1}$. In either case the two hands involved will coincide only if the faster hand performs an exact number of complete revolutions relative to the other. Thus coincidence occurs for hour and minute hands at times t given by the formula

$$n \times 2\pi\,\text{rad} = \frac{11}{6}\pi\,\text{rad} \cdot \text{hr}^{-1} \times t,$$

where n is an integer, i.e., at times given by $t = \frac{12}{11}n$ hr. Similarly, the minute and second hands coincide at times t' given by the formula

$$m \times 2\pi \text{ rad} = 118\,\pi \text{ rad}\cdot\text{hr}^{-1} \times t',$$

where m is an integer, i.e., at times t' given by $t' = \frac{1}{59}m$ hr. Coincidence of all three hands occurs whenever $t = t'$; that is, when

$$\frac{12}{11}n = \frac{1}{59}m \qquad \text{or} \qquad \frac{m}{n} = \frac{708}{11}.$$

The number 708 is not divisible by 11. Thus coincidence occurs only when $n = 11$, $m = 708$, or $n = 22$, $m = 1416$, etc. But, when $n = 11$, $t = 12$ hr. Thus the three hands coincide only at noon and midnight and at no point in between.

8. To the passenger who considers everything relative to himself, the second vessel has two velocities, the one relative to the water and the other the velocity of the water relative to the passenger's ship. Thus the second vessel has a velocity of 14 mph in a northeasterly direction and one of 8 mph due west, according to the passenger. The addition of these two velocities is done vectorially on the diagram.

$$AC^2 = 14^2 + 8^2 - 2 \times 8 \times 14 \times \cos 45° = 101.63.$$

$$\therefore \qquad AC = 10.08.$$

Also

$$\sin \alpha = \frac{8}{AC}\sin \theta = 0.5612.$$

$$\therefore \qquad \alpha = 34°8'.$$

The velocity of the second ship relative to the first is thus 10.08 mph at an angle of

$$90° - 45° - 34°8' = 10°52'$$

east of the line joining them.

If A and D represent the positions of the two ships at the moment of sighting, then AC is the path of the second ship relative to the first. The closest distance of approach is the perpendicular distance of AC from D, that is, DE. But $DE = AD \sin 10°52'$.

$$\therefore \qquad DE = 10 \text{ mi} \times 0.1886 = 1.886 \text{ mi}.$$

The time taken to reach this position is given by

$$t = \frac{AE}{10.08 \text{ mph}} = \frac{AD \cos 10°52'}{10.08 \text{ mph}} = \frac{10 \text{ mi} \times 0.9825}{10.08 \text{ mph}} = 0.975 \text{ hr} = 58.5 \text{ min}.$$

9. There are three forces acting on the book, its weight **W** acting vertically downward, the normal force **N** exerted by the table acting vertically upward, and a frictional force **F** acting horizontally exerted by the table on the book. Since the table is decelerating with the train, the frictional force **F** is against the direction of motion and is the force producing deceleration on the book. The train will come to a full stop in the shortest distance when F has its maximum value. But this is known to be μN, where μ is the coefficient of static friction involved.

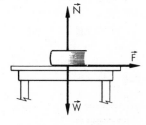

When the train is decelerating as quickly as possible, there is no tendency for the book to rise from the table and thus $N = W = mg$. From the above argument, we obtain $F = \mu N = \mu mg$. But by Newton's second law, we know that $F = ma$. Thus the deceleration $a = \mu g$. Employing the equation $v^2 = v_0^2 - 2as$ enables us to calculate the shortest distance of stopping, s. Here v is zero, v_0 is 60 mph $= 88 \text{ ft}\cdot\text{s}^{-1}$, and a is $0.4g$.

$$\therefore \qquad 0 = 88^2 \text{ ft}^2\cdot\text{s}^{-2} - 2 \times 0.4 \times 32 \text{ ft}\cdot\text{s}^{-2} \times s \qquad \text{or} \qquad s = \frac{88 \times 88}{0.8 \times 32} \text{ ft} = 302.5 \text{ ft}.$$

10. The train reduces speed from 60 mph = 88 ft·s⁻¹ to 45 mph = 66 ft·s⁻¹ in 88 s. Applying the first equation of uniformly accelerated motion $v = v_0 + at$ gives

$$66 \text{ ft·s}^{-1} = 88 \text{ ft·s}^{-1} + a \times 88 \text{ s}. \qquad \therefore \qquad a = -\frac{1}{4} \text{ ft·s}^{-2}.$$

The force producing this deceleration is given by Newton's second law as

$$F = ma = -\frac{500 \text{ tons}}{32 \text{ ft·s}^{-2}} \times \frac{1}{4} \text{ ft·s}^{-2} = -3.9 \text{ ton}.$$

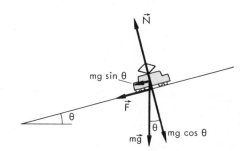

If the slowing-down takes place on a rising gradient, the forces acting are as shown in the diagram. The component of the weight perpendicular to the incline is balanced by the normal force, and the other component of the weight and the frictional force both act against the motion to produce the slowing-down. Thus the total retarding force is

$$F' = F + mg \sin \theta = 3.9 \text{ tons} + \frac{500}{100} \text{ tons} = 8.9 \text{ tons}.$$

The deceleration α is thus

$$\alpha = \frac{F'}{m} = \frac{8.9 \text{ tons}}{500 \text{ tons}} \times 32 \text{ ft·s}^{-2} = 0.57 \text{ ft·s}^{-2}.$$

Applying the equation $v^2 = v_0^2 - 2\alpha s$ gives

$$v^2 = 88^2 \text{ ft}^2\text{·s}^{-2} - 2 \times 0.57 \text{ ft·s}^{-2} \times 2972 \text{ ft} = (7744 - 3388) \text{ ft}^2\text{·s}^{-2} = 4356 \text{ ft}^2\text{·s}^{-2}$$

$$\therefore \qquad v = 66 \text{ ft·s}^{-1} = 45 \text{ mph}.$$

11. When the peg is moving upward, the forces acting are as shown in the first diagram. The 40-g mass is not moving and thus

$$0.40 \text{ kg} \times g = T \qquad \text{or} \qquad T = 3.92 \text{ N}.$$

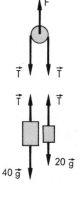

Since the peg is smooth, the same tension acts on the smaller mass, which moves with acceleration a. Thus

$$T - 0.20 \text{ kg} \times g = 0.20 \text{ kg} \times a$$

or

$$0.40 \text{ kg} \times g - 0.20 \text{ kg} \times g = 0.20 \text{ kg} \times a. \qquad \therefore \qquad a = g.$$

The 40-g mass is stationary. The 20-g mass moves upward with increasing speed. At any given instant, in a short time interval dt, the 20-g mass moves upward a distance dy. If the peg moves upward a distance dZ in the same time interval, a length of cord dZ must pass over the peg to keep the 40-g mass at the same level, and a length of cord dZ must also rise on the side of the 20-g mass to keep the cord continuous. If the cord is to remain taut and not break, the amount the end of the cord is raised by the motion of the 20-g mass must equal the length of cord needed to allow the upward motion of the peg. Hence $dy = 2dZ$. Thus in equal times the peg always moves half the distance of the smaller mass, and thus the velocity of the smaller mass is always double that of the peg. Thus at the instant when the peg is stopped the velocity of the smaller mass is 32 ft·s⁻¹.

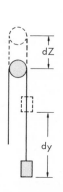

When the peg is brought to rest, the larger mass has no velocity, but the smaller mass is moving upward with a speed of 32 ft·s⁻¹. The latter therefore rises faster than the former can drop and the cord becomes slack. Since there is no tension in the cord the larger mass drops with acceleration g, the only force acting on it being its weight, and likewise the smaller mass, though continuing to rise, slows down under a deceleration of g. At the start of the process the two masses were separated in a path around the peg by a distance equal to the length of the cord. They will again be separated by the length of the cord, and thus the cord will be under tension once more, when each mass has traveled the same distance. This assumes that the length of cord on the side of the smaller mass is great enough for the cord to become taut before the smaller mass goes over the peg. Applying the equation of uniformly accelerated motion, $s = v_0 t + \frac{1}{2}at^2$, to each mass gives

$$s = \frac{1}{2}gt^2 \quad \text{and} \quad s' = 32 \text{ ft·s}^{-1} \times t - \frac{1}{2}gt^2.$$

When $s = s'$, the cord becomes taut again, i.e., when

$$\frac{1}{2}gt^2 = 32 \text{ ft·s}^{-1} \times t - \frac{1}{2}gt^2.$$

$$\therefore \quad t = 0 \text{ or } \frac{32 \text{ ft·s}^{-1}}{g} = 0 \text{ or } 1 \text{ s}.$$

The first answer represents the start of the motion when the cord just stops being taut. It thus remains slack for 1 s.

12. When the particle is moving upward with velocity v it has two forces acting on it, its weight mg downward and the resistive force kv^2, also acting downward. Therefore, applying Newton's second law, we have

$$F = -mg - kv^2 = ma = +mv\frac{dv}{dy},$$

the minus signs arising since, although the y-direction is positive upward, the two forces are directed downward, and are therefore negative.

$$\therefore \quad dy = -\frac{mv\,dv}{mg + kv^2} \quad \text{or} \quad \int_0^h dy = \int_{v_0}^0 -\frac{mv\,dv}{mg + kv^2}.$$

$$\therefore \quad h = \left[-\frac{m}{2k}\ln(mg + kv^2)\right]_{v_0}^0 = \frac{m}{2k}[\ln(mg + kv_0^2) - \ln mg] = \frac{m}{2k}\ln\left(1 + \frac{kv_0^2}{mg}\right).$$

When the particle has reached its peak height and is falling downward, mg is still acting downward, but kv^2 is still opposing the motion and so acts upward. Thus, measuring everything in the downward direction, we have

$$mg - kv^2 = ma' = mv\frac{dv}{dy}. \quad \therefore \quad \int_0^h dy = \int_0^v \frac{mv\,dv}{mg - kv^2}.$$

$$\therefore \quad h = \left[-\frac{m}{2k}\ln(mg - kv^2)\right]_0^v = -\frac{m}{2k}\ln\left(1 - \frac{kv^2}{mg}\right).$$

$$\therefore \quad 1 - \frac{kv^2}{mg} = \exp\left(-\frac{2k}{m}h\right).$$

$$\therefore \quad v^2 = \frac{mg}{k}\left[1 - \exp\left(-\frac{2k}{m}h\right)\right] \quad \text{or} \quad v = \sqrt{\frac{mg}{k}\left[1 - \exp\left(-\frac{2k}{m}h\right)\right]}.$$

Alternatively, to obtain a solution not involving h, consider the equation obtained from analysis of the upward motion,

$$h = \frac{m}{2k}\ln\left(1 + \frac{kv_0^2}{mg}\right),$$

and the equation obtained from analysis of the downward motion,

$$h = -\frac{m}{2k}\ln\left(1 - \frac{kv^2}{mg}\right).$$

$$\therefore \quad \frac{m}{2k}\ln\left(1 + \frac{kv_0^2}{mg}\right) = -\frac{m}{2k}\ln\left(1 - \frac{kv^2}{mg}\right).$$

$$\therefore \quad 1 - \frac{kv^2}{mg} = \frac{1}{1 + (kv_0^2/mg)} \quad \text{or} \quad \frac{kv^2}{mg} = \frac{kv_0^2/mg}{1 + (kv_0^2/mg)}.$$

$$\therefore \quad v = \frac{v_0}{\sqrt{1 + (kv_0^2/mg)}}.$$

13. When the man exerts a force **P** on the box at a general angle θ to the horizontal, the box exerts an equal and opposite force **P** on him. The forces acting on the crate and the man are then as shown in the diagram. Thus, before motion takes place,

$$N = W - P \sin \theta \quad \text{and} \quad F = P \cos \theta.$$
$$N' = W' + P \sin \theta \quad \text{and} \quad F' = P \cos \theta.$$

The frictional forces are related to the normal reactions by the equation $F = \mu N$, where, in the limit, μ will be the coefficient of static friction, μ_s.

$$\therefore \quad F = \mu N = \mu(W - P \sin \theta)$$

and

$$F' = \mu'N' = \mu'(W' + P \sin \theta).$$

$$\therefore \quad \mu = \frac{P \cos \theta}{W - P \sin \theta} \quad \text{and} \quad \mu' = \frac{P \cos \theta}{W' + P \sin \theta}.$$

If P is large enough and θ is positive, θ can be increased until $(W - P \sin \theta)$ is so small that μ exceeds the limiting value μ_s, while $(W' + P \sin \theta)$ is large enough to keep μ' below its limiting value μ'_s. Under these circumstances the crate moves without the man moving.

Since the man slips when $\theta = 0$, this situation gives $\mu' = P/W' > \mu'_s$. With θ negative, $(W' + P \sin \theta)$ decreases faster than $P \cos \theta$, and thus μ' is always greater than μ'_s. The man continues to slip before the crate can be got moving, and the situation is only made worse. The advice from the physics student is thus excellent.

14. The gravitational force between the two lead spheres is given by the relation $F = G(M_1 M_2/R^2)$. In this case, therefore,

$$G = \frac{FR^2}{M_1 M_2} = \frac{6.67 \times 10^{-5} \,\text{N} \times 1 \,\text{m}^2}{10^6 \,\text{kg}^2} = 6.67 \times 10^{-11} \,\text{N} \cdot \text{m}^2 \cdot \text{kg}^{-2}.$$

Further, $g = GM_E/R_E^2$, where M_E and R_E are the mass and radius of the earth, respectively. Thus

$$M_E = \frac{gR_E^2}{G} = \frac{9.8 \,\text{m} \cdot \text{s}^{-2} \times 6.4^2 \times 10^{12} \,\text{m}^2}{6.67 \times 10^{-11} \,\text{N} \cdot \text{m}^2 \cdot \text{kg}^{-2}} = 6.05 \times 10^{24} \,\text{kg}.$$

15. When a block moves down an inclined plane at constant speed, the forces acting on it are those shown in the first diagram, where F, the magnitude of the frictional force, is equal to μN, μ being the coefficient of kinetic friction. The block is in equilibrium and thus

$$N = mg \cos \theta$$

and

$$F = \mu N = \mu mg \cos \theta = mg \sin \theta.$$

$$\therefore \quad \mu = \tan \theta.$$

Thus the coefficients of sliding friction between plane and metal, μ, and between plane and wood, μ', are

$$\tan 31° = 0.60 \quad \text{and} \quad \tan 35° = 0.70,$$

respectively. When the blocks are connected, the forces acting on each block are as shown in the second diagram. There is no movement at right angles to the plane. Hence

$$N = mg \cos 45°$$

and

$$N' = mg \cos 45° = N.$$

Both blocks must move with the same acceleration a.

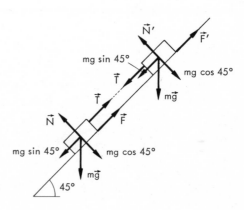

Thus we obtain the following:

$$mg \sin 45° - F - T = ma \qquad \text{and} \qquad T + mg \sin 45° - F' = ma.$$

$$\therefore \quad 2ma = 2mg \sin 45° - (F + F') = 2mg \sin 45° - mg \cos 45°(\mu + \mu').$$

$$\therefore \quad a = g \sin 45° - \frac{g}{2} \cos 45° (\mu + \mu') = \frac{9.80 \text{ m} \cdot \text{s}^{-2}}{\sqrt{2}} \left(1 - \frac{0.6 + 0.7}{2}\right) = 2.43 \text{ m} \cdot \text{s}^{-2}.$$

$$T = mg \sin 45° - F - ma$$

$$= mg \sin 45° - \mu mg \cos 45° - m\left[g \sin 45° - \frac{g}{2} \cos 45°(\mu + \mu')\right]$$

$$= \frac{mg}{2} \cos 45°(\mu' - \mu) = \frac{0.020 \text{ kg} \times 9.8 \text{ m} \cdot \text{s}^{-2}}{2\sqrt{2}}(0.7 - 0.6) = 6.93 \times 10^{-3} \text{ N}.$$

16. The range of a projectile fired with velocity v_0 at an angle of θ_0 to the horizontal is

$$R = \frac{v_0^2 \sin 2\theta_0}{g},$$

and the maximum range occurs when $\sin 2\theta_0 = 1$. Thus if the maximum range of the debris from the shell explosion is $2a$, then $v_0^2 = 2ga$ gives the maximum velocity acquired by the debris at the moment of explosion.

For debris that has a maximum range of a, a similar argument shows that its initial velocity is given by $(v_0')^2 = ga$. Thus debris landing at the position of the soldier must have started with a velocity within the range from $\sqrt{ga}$ to $\sqrt{2ga}$. Debris fired with a velocity $\sqrt{ga}$ has maximum range at a distance a and was thus fired at an angle of 45°. Since the horizontal distance traveled is given by the equation $x = v_0 \cos \theta_0 \times t'$, the time of travel of the debris is

$$t' = \frac{a}{\sqrt{ga} \times (1/\sqrt{2})} = \sqrt{\frac{2a}{g}}.$$

The debris which started off with velocity $\sqrt{2ga}$ and landed a distance a from the explosion must have been fired at an angle θ_0, where

$$0 = v_0 \sin \theta_0 t - \frac{1}{2} gt^2 \qquad \text{and} \qquad a = v_0 \cos \theta_0 t.$$

$$\therefore \quad \sin \theta_0 = \frac{gt}{2v_0} \qquad \text{and} \qquad \cos \theta_0 = \frac{a}{v_0 t}.$$

$$\therefore \quad 1 = \sin^2 \theta_0 + \cos^2 \theta_0 = \frac{g^2 t^2}{4v_0^2} + \frac{a^2}{v_0^2 t^2} = \frac{gt^2}{8a} + \frac{a}{2gt^2}.$$

$$\therefore \quad g^2 t^4 - 8agt^2 + 4a^2 = 0 \qquad \text{or} \qquad t^2 = \frac{8ag \pm \sqrt{64a^2g^2 - 16a^2g^2}}{2g^2} = \frac{a}{g}(4 \pm 2\sqrt{3}).$$

Here t must be positive, and one of the solutions gives a value for t less than t' and one a value greater than t'. Taking the larger value, one obtains

$$t^2 = \frac{a}{g}(4 + 2\sqrt{3}) = 7.464 \frac{a}{g}. \qquad \therefore \qquad t = 2.73\sqrt{\frac{a}{g}}.$$

Debris which starts off with a velocity of $\sqrt{ga}$ arrives at the soldier's position a time $\sqrt{2a/g}$ after the explosion. Debris with higher initial velocity than this arrives earlier or later according as $\theta_0 <$ or $> 45°$. The departure from $\sqrt{2a/g}$ in arrival time increases as the initial velocity increases (this can be checked by taking intermediate values of the initial velocity) until it reaches a maximum of $2.73\sqrt{a/g}$. The soldier must therefore stay under cover for at least a time of $2.73\sqrt{a/g}$ s.

17. Let us take the origin of coordinates at the batter; the ball travels in such a way that

$$x = 343 \text{ ft} \qquad \text{and} \qquad y = 6 \text{ ft}$$

simultaneously a time t after the ball leaves the bat.

Employing the usual notation, we have $x = v_0 \cos \theta_0 t$ and $y = v_0 \sin \theta_0 t - \frac{1}{2} gt^2$.

$$\therefore \quad y = v_0 \sin \theta_0 \cdot \frac{x}{v_0 \cos \theta_0} - \frac{g}{2} \frac{x^2}{v_0^2 \cos \theta_0^2}$$

or

$$v_0^2 = \frac{gx^2}{2 \cos \theta_0^2 (x \tan \theta_0 - y)} = \frac{32 \text{ ft} \cdot \text{s}^{-2} \times 343^2 \text{ ft}^2}{2 \times \frac{3}{4}[(343/\sqrt{3}) \text{ ft} - 6 \text{ ft}]} = \frac{32 \times 343^2}{\frac{3}{2} \times 192} \text{ ft}^2 \cdot \text{s}^{-2} = \frac{343^2}{9} \text{ ft}^2 \cdot \text{s}^{-2}.$$

$$\therefore \quad v_0 = \frac{343}{3} \text{ ft} \cdot \text{s}^{-1} = 78 \text{ mph}.$$

Note that the height of the window above the batter is not a critical factor, since y can vary by quite a large amount without appreciably altering the final value of v_0.

18. The two forces acting on the train are the weight $m\mathbf{g}$ acting downward and the normal force exerted by the rails acting at an angle to the vertical. If the outer rail is raised by an amount d, then $\tan \theta = d/57$ in. Split **N** into its horizontal and vertical components.

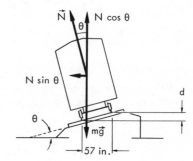

Since there is equilibrium in the vertical direction, $N \cos \theta = mg$.

Further, the horizontal component must supply the centripetal force necessary to keep the train in a circle, since it is desired to have no pressure exerted by the rails for this purpose. Thus

$$N \sin \theta = \frac{mv^2}{r},$$

where v is the train's speed of 45 mph = 66 ft·s^{-1} and r is the radius of the curve it is traveling.

$$\therefore \quad \tan \theta = \frac{v^2}{rg}. \qquad \therefore \quad \frac{d}{57 \text{ in.}} = \frac{66^2 \text{ ft}^2 \cdot \text{s}^{-2}}{3 \times 1254 \text{ ft} \times 32 \text{ ft} \cdot \text{s}^{-2}}.$$

$$\therefore \quad d = \frac{66^2 \times 57}{3 \times 1254 \times 32} \text{ in.} = \frac{33}{16} \text{ in.} = 2\frac{1}{16} \text{ in.}$$

19. The gravitational attraction exerted by Mars on Phobos provides the centripetal force necessary to keep it moving in a circle. Hence, in the usual notation,

$$\frac{mv^2}{r} = \frac{GMm}{r^2} = \frac{Gm \times \frac{4}{3}\pi R^3 \rho}{r^2},$$

where R and ρ are the radius and density of Mars.

$$\therefore \quad v = \sqrt{\frac{\frac{4}{3}\pi G \rho R^3}{r}}$$

or

$$T = \frac{2\pi r}{v} = 2\pi \sqrt{\frac{r^3}{\frac{4}{3}\pi G \rho R^3}} = \sqrt{\frac{3\pi r^3}{G \rho R^3}}$$

$$= \sqrt{\frac{3 \times \pi \times 9.5^3 \times 10^{18} \text{ m}^3}{6.67 \times 10^{-11} \text{ N} \cdot \text{m}^2 \cdot \text{kg}^{-2} \times 4.120 \times 10^3 \text{ kg} \cdot \text{m}^{-3} \times 3.4^3 \times 10^{18} \text{ m}^3}}$$

$$= 2.735 \times 10^4 \text{ s} = 7.6 \text{ hr}.$$

20. The forces acting on the astronaut who is at the top of the circle are his weight $m\mathbf{g}$ acting downward and the normal force **R** exerted by the cage on him. These together provide the centripetal force necessary to keep the astronaut moving in the circle. Weightlessness occurs when $R = 0$, and under these circumstances the weight alone is used to provide the necessary centripetal force.

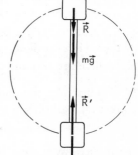

$$\therefore \quad mr\omega^2 = mg$$

or

$$\omega = \sqrt{\frac{g}{r}} = \sqrt{\frac{9.8 \text{ m} \cdot \text{s}^{-2}}{10 \text{ m}}} = 0.99 \text{ rad} \cdot \text{s}^{-1}.$$

The normal force at the bottom of the circle both balances the weight of the astronaut and provides the centripetal force, as will be obvious from the diagram. Thus

$$R' - mg = mr\omega^2 = mg. \qquad \therefore \qquad R' = 2\,mg.$$

Hence the astronaut at the bottom of the circle experiences twice his normal weight.

21. When the stone is placed on the pouch, each of the bands bears half of the weight. Hence, if k is the force constant of either elastic band, then

$$0.05\text{ kg} \times 9.8\text{ m}\cdot\text{s}^{-2} = k \times 0.01\text{ m}. \qquad \therefore \qquad k = 49\text{ N}\cdot\text{m}^{-1}.$$

When the catapult is stretched to twice its natural length, the energy stored in the two stretched elastic bands is

$$E = 2 \times \frac{1}{2}kx^2 = 49\text{ N}\cdot\text{m}^{-2} \times (0.12)^2\text{ m}^2 = 0.7056\text{ J}.$$

This energy, when the catapult is released, is given to the stone as kinetic energy. As the stone rises, the kinetic energy is gradually changed to potential energy and, when the the stone has risen to its maximum height h, the energy possessed by the stone is wholly potential. At that point, since energy is conserved,

$$mgh = 0.7056\text{ J}. \qquad \therefore \qquad h = \frac{0.7056\text{ J}}{20 \times 10^{-3}\text{ kg} \times 9.8\text{ m}\cdot\text{s}^{-2}} = 3.6\text{ m}.$$

22. When the aircraft is gliding down at a constant speed of 60 mph = 88 ft·s^{-1} with the engines switched off, the component of its weight in the forward direction just balances the retarding force due to air friction. Thus, if the retarding force is kv^2, then

$$112{,}000\text{ lb} \times \sin 5° = k \times 88^2\text{ ft}^2\cdot\text{s}^{-2}. \qquad \therefore \qquad k = \frac{112{,}000 \times 0.0872}{88^2}\text{lb}\cdot\text{s}^2\cdot\text{ft}^{-2}.$$

In level flight with the engines on, the speed increases to a value u, where the forward force F is just balanced by the retarding force ku^2. Hence $F = ku^2$. But the rate of working of the engines is

$$\mathbf{F}\cdot\mathbf{u} = Fu = ku^3 = 10^4\text{ hp}.$$

$$\therefore \qquad u^3 = \frac{10^4 \times 550\text{ ft}\cdot\text{lb}\cdot\text{s}^{-1}}{k}$$

or

$$u = \sqrt[3]{\frac{550 \times 10^4\text{ ft}\cdot\text{lb}\cdot\text{s}^{-1} \times 88^2}{112{,}000 \times 0.0872\text{ lb}\cdot\text{s}^2\cdot\text{ft}^{-2}}} = 163.4\text{ ft}\cdot\text{s}^{-1} = 111.4\text{ mph}.$$

23. The fire engine gives kinetic energy to the water of amount

$$E = \frac{1}{2}mv^2 = \frac{1}{2} \times 2\text{ slugs}\cdot\text{s}^{-1} \times 88^2\text{ ft}^2\cdot\text{s}^{-2}.$$

In addition, one-fifth of the work done is used up in overcoming friction. Thus the work done by the engine is

$$E_0 = \frac{5}{4}E = \frac{5}{4} \times 88^2\text{ ft}\cdot\text{lb}\cdot\text{s}^{-1}.$$

But 1 hp is a rate of working of 550 ft·lb·s^{-1}.

$$\therefore \qquad E_0 = \frac{5}{4} \times \frac{88^2\text{ ft}\cdot\text{lb}\cdot\text{s}^{-1}}{550\text{ ft}\cdot\text{lb}\cdot\text{s}^{-1}\cdot\text{hp}^{-1}} = 17.6\text{ hp}.$$

24. Since the spring is extended by 10 cm when a mass of 1 kg is hung from it, the force constant of the spring may be obtained. For

$$1\text{ kg} \times 9.8\text{ m}\cdot\text{s}^{-2} = k \times 0.10\text{ m}. \qquad \therefore \qquad k = 98\text{ N}\cdot\text{m}^{-1}.$$

When the mass is dropped on the spring, the latter compresses by an amount y and the potential energy possessed by the spring is $\frac{1}{2}ky^2$. By the conservation of energy, this must be exactly equal to the potential energy lost by the falling mass, $mg(h + y)$, in dropping through the height $h + y$.

$$\therefore \qquad \frac{1}{2}ky^2 = mg(h + y). \qquad \therefore \qquad y^2 - \frac{2mg}{k}y - \frac{2mgh}{k} = 0.$$

Therefore the amount by which the spring will be compressed is

$$y = \frac{mg}{k} \pm \sqrt{\frac{m^2 g^2}{k^2} + 2\frac{mgh}{k}}$$

$$= \frac{1 \text{ kg} \times 9.8 \text{ m} \cdot \text{s}^{-2}}{98 \text{ N} \cdot \text{m}^{-1}} \pm \sqrt{\frac{1^2 \text{ kg}^2 \times 9.8^2 \text{ m}^2 \cdot \text{s}^{-4}}{98^2 \text{ N}^2 \cdot \text{m}^{-2}} + \frac{2 \times 1 \text{ kg} \times 9.8 \text{ m} \cdot \text{s}^{-1} \times 1 \text{ m}}{98 \text{ N} \cdot \text{m}^{-1}}}$$

$$= 0.1 \text{ m} \pm \sqrt{0.21 \text{ m}^2} = (0.1 \pm 0.458) \text{ m} = 55.8 \text{ cm},$$

since only the positive solution is admissible.

25. The bullet is brought from a speed of 10^3 m·s^{-1} to zero in 5 cm under a retardation a. Thus

$$v^2 = v_0^2 - 2as \quad \text{or} \quad a = \frac{v_0^2 - v^2}{2s} = \frac{(10^6 - 0) \text{ m}^2 \cdot \text{s}^{-2}}{2 \times 5 \times 10^{-2} \text{ m}} = 10^7 \text{ m} \cdot \text{s}^{-2}.$$

The retarding force is thus

$$F = ma = 20 \times 10^{-3} \text{ kg} \times 10^7 \text{ m} \cdot \text{s}^{-2} = 2 \times 10^5 \text{ N}.$$

The time taken is obtained from the equation

$$v = v_0 - at \quad \text{or} \quad t = \frac{v_0 - v}{a} = \frac{(10^3 - 0) \text{ m} \cdot \text{s}^{-1}}{10^7 \text{ m} \cdot \text{s}^{-2}} = 10^{-4} \text{ s}.$$

The collision between bullet and pendulum is inelastic and momentum is conserved. Hence $mv_0 = (m + M)V$, where M is the mass of the pendulum and V the velocity acquired by the system after collision. Hence

$$V = \frac{20 \times 10^{-3} \text{ kg} \times 10^3 \text{ m} \cdot \text{s}^{-1}}{(10 + 20 \times 10^{-3}) \text{ kg}} = 1.996 \text{ m} \cdot \text{s}^{-1}.$$

The pendulum swings until the kinetic energy of the bob is transformed into potential energy. If the angle swung through is θ,

$$\frac{1}{2}(M + m)V^2 = (M + m)gh = (M + m)gl(1 - \cos\theta).$$

$$\therefore \quad 1 - \cos\theta = \frac{V^2}{2gl}$$

or

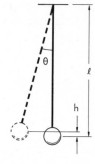

$$\cos\theta = 1 - \frac{V^2}{2gl} = 1 - \frac{(1.996)^2 \text{m}^2 \cdot \text{s}^{-2}}{2 \times 9.8 \text{ m} \cdot \text{s}^{-2} \times 2 \text{ m}} = 0.8984.$$

$$\therefore \quad \theta = 26°3'.$$

26. When the water strikes the ball, it is brought to rest, and therefore, by Newton's second law, the ball is exerting on the water a force equal to the momentum destroyed per second. By Newton's third law the water must exert an equal and opposite force on the ball. At the point at which the ball stays balanced this force must just be equal to the weight of the ball. Thus, if v is the speed of the water when it strikes the ball,

$$F = \frac{mv}{t} = m_0 g,$$

where m_0 is the mass of the ball and m/t is the mass of water striking the ball per second. But 20 ft of water of cross-sectional area 0.1 in^2 issues from the nozzle per second. Thus

$$\frac{m}{t} = 20 \text{ ft} \cdot \text{s}^{-1} \times \frac{0.1}{144} \text{ ft}^2 \times \frac{62.5 \text{ lb} \cdot \text{ft}^{-3}}{32 \text{ ft} \cdot \text{s}^{-2}} = 2.71 \times 10^{-2} \text{ slugs} \cdot \text{s}^{-1}.$$

$$\therefore \quad v = \frac{m_0 g}{m/t} = \frac{\frac{1}{4} \text{ lb}}{2.71 \times 10^{-2} \text{ slugs} \cdot \text{s}^{-1}} = 9.22 \text{ ft} \cdot \text{s}^{-1}.$$

The water leaves the nozzle with a speed of 20 ft·s^{-1} and is decelerated by the gravitational force on it as it rises. After it has risen a height s its speed has dropped to 9.22 ft·s^{-1}, where

$$v^2 = v_0^2 - 2gs \quad \text{or} \quad s = \frac{v_0^2 - v^2}{2g} = \frac{(400 - 9.22^2) \text{ ft}^2 \cdot \text{s}^{-2}}{2 \times 32 \text{ ft} \cdot \text{s}^{-2}} = 4.92 \text{ ft}.$$

27. At the instant of the explosion the assembly is moving tangential to the orbit and motion along this straight line is considered.

Momentum must be conserved in the explosion, since the latter produces only internal forces. Given that the new velocity of the motor assembly is v, then

$$10 \text{ kg} \times 7 \text{ km} \cdot \text{s}^{-1} + 600 \text{ kg} \times 7 \text{ km} \cdot \text{s}^{-1} = 10 \text{ kg} \times 7.5 \text{ km} \cdot \text{s}^{-1} + 600 \text{ kg} \times v.$$

$$\therefore \quad v = \frac{4270 - 75}{600} \text{ km} \cdot \text{s}^{-1} = 6.99 \text{ km} \cdot \text{s}^{-1}.$$

28. The student runs along the punt with velocity v relative to the punt. Therefore, by the principle of conservation of momentum, the punt must move in the opposite direction with velocity V. Relative to the water the punt has thus a velocity V, and relative to the water the student has velocity $v - V$. Hence

$$\frac{150}{32} \text{ slugs} \times (v - V) = \frac{450}{32} \text{ slugs} \times V \quad \text{or} \quad V = \frac{150}{600} v = \frac{v}{4}.$$

In the time it takes the student to run 8 ft along the punt with velocity v, the punt therefore moves $\frac{8}{4}$ ft = 2 ft relative to the water. Hence the student finds, when he reaches the end of the punt, that the girl is 2 ft away from him.

Note that the answer will obviously be the same whether the student moves with constant velocity or not. It is, however, mathematically easier to treat the problem if we assume uniform velocity.

The problem may alternatively, and more easily, be solved if we consider that the center of mass of the system cannot change its position since no external force is acting on it. Thus, when we take moments about the position of the girl, who is at the end of the punt before the student moves and distance y from the end of the punt when the student arrives there,

150 lb × 8 ft + 450 lb × z

$$= 150 \text{ lb} \times y + 450 \text{ lb} \times (z + y). \,.$$

$$\therefore \quad 600 \text{ lb} \times y = 1200 \text{ ft} \cdot \text{lb.} \quad \therefore \quad y = 2 \text{ ft.}$$

29. Initially the disk of moment of inertia I about the vertical axis has a rotational speed ω_0. After the putty of mass m has dropped onto the disk a distance r from the axis, the moment of inertia of the system is $(I + mr^2)$, and the rotational speed has dropped to ω. The angular momentum must stay the same since no external torque is acting. Hence $I\omega_0 = (I + mr^2)\omega$.

$$\therefore \quad I = \frac{\omega}{\omega_0 - \omega} \times mr^2 = \frac{60 \text{ rev} \cdot \text{min}^{-1}}{12 \text{ rev} \cdot \text{min}^{-1}} \times 5 \text{ g} \times 16 \text{ cm}^2 = 400 \text{ g} \cdot \text{cm}^2.$$

30. Employing the equation of uniformly accelerated motion, $\omega = \omega_0 + \alpha t$, to this case where ω is zero and

$$\omega_0 = \frac{2\pi \times 2500}{60} \text{ rad} \cdot \text{s}^{-1},$$

we have

$$0 = \frac{2\pi \times 2500}{60} \text{ rad} \cdot \text{s}^{-1} + \alpha \times 3 \times 60 \text{ s}.$$

$$\therefore \quad \alpha = -\frac{2\pi \times 2500}{3 \times 60 \times 60} \text{ rad} \cdot \text{s}^{-2} = -1.454 \text{ rad} \cdot \text{s}^{-2}.$$

The moment of inertia of the disk is

$$I = \frac{1}{2} Mr^2 = \frac{1}{2} \times 250 \text{ kg} \times \frac{1}{4} \text{ m}^2 = 31 \cdot 25 \text{ kg} \cdot \text{m}^2.$$

Thus the torque necessary to produce the deceleration is

$$\Gamma = I|\alpha| = 31 \cdot 25 \text{ kg} \cdot \text{m}^2 \times 1.454 \text{ rad} \cdot \text{s}^{-2} = 45.45 \text{ N} \cdot \text{m}.$$

But this torque is applied by a tangential force F at a distance of $\frac{1}{2}$ m from the center. Thus

$$F = \frac{\Gamma}{\frac{1}{2} \text{ m}} = 90.9 \text{ N}.$$

Alternatively the problem may be solved by considering that the impulse of the torque must be equal to the change in angular momentum. Thus $\Gamma t = F \times \frac{1}{2} \text{ m} \times t = I\omega_0$.

$$\therefore \quad F = \frac{2I\omega_0 \text{ m}^{-1}}{t} = \frac{2 \text{ m}^{-1} \times 31.25 \text{ kg} \cdot \text{m}^2}{3 \times 60 \text{ s}} \times \frac{2\pi \times 2500}{60} \text{ s}^{-1} = 90.9 \text{ N}.$$

31. For a spring the restoring force is directly proportional to the stretching, or $\mathbf{F} = -k\mathbf{x}$, where k is the force constant of the spring. If the spring stretches 2 cm when carrying 1 kg at its end, the force produced in the spring must be equal and opposite to the weight of 1 kg. Hence

$$1 \text{ kg} \times g = 0.02 \text{ m} \times k \qquad \text{or} \qquad k = 490 \text{ N} \cdot \text{m}^{-1}.$$

If the spring and mass are moving upward in equilibrium without accelerating, the spring will be extended by an amount x, where $kx = mg$, m being the mass carried. The energy possessed by the system when the spring is brought to rest is $\frac{1}{2}mv^2$ due to the motion and $\frac{1}{2}kx^2$ due to the extension of the spring. When the mass has been brought to rest, it will have traveled upward a distance A, losing its kinetic energy completely and gaining mgA of potential energy; the system will now possess $\frac{1}{2}k(x - A)^2$ of elastic energy. By the principle of conservation of energy,

$$\frac{1}{2}mv^2 + \frac{1}{2}kx^2 = \frac{1}{2}k(x - A)^2 + mgA. \qquad \therefore \qquad A^2 - 2A\left(x - \frac{mg}{k}\right) = \frac{m}{k}v^2.$$

But

$$kx = mg. \qquad \therefore \qquad A^2 = \frac{m}{k}v^2$$

or

$$A = \sqrt{\frac{m}{k}}v = \sqrt{\frac{10 \text{ kg}}{490 \text{ N} \cdot \text{m}^{-1}}} \times 0.5 \text{ m} \cdot \text{s}^{-1} = \frac{0.50}{7} \text{ m} = 7.1 \text{ cm}.$$

The mass must oscillate about its equilibrium position and thus A is the amplitude of the subsequent simple harmonic motion.

Note that

$$A^2 = \frac{m}{k}v^2 \qquad \text{or} \qquad \frac{1}{2}kA^2 = \frac{1}{2}mv^2.$$

The kinetic energy initially possessed by the mass is thus equal to the elastic energy stored when the spring is compressed by a distance A. This would have been the equation used to express the conservation of energy if the motion of the spring and mass had not involved gravity; i.e., if the spring and mass had been moving on a smooth horizontal table. It is now clear that the gravitational effects, the initial extension of the spring and the gain in potential energy of the mass, can be ignored in any case, since the effects cancel out and the final equation obtained is effectively gravity-free. This is a very helpful result which can be applied in all elastic problems.

32. If the time $t = 0$ is taken as the moment when the piston is passing through the midpoint of the motion, then, in the usual notation,

$$x = A \sin \omega t \qquad \text{and} \qquad v = A\omega \cos \omega t,$$

where A, the amplitude of the motion, is half the stroke. Thus, when $t = 0$,

$$v = A\omega = 0.05 \text{ m} \times 2\pi \times \frac{3000}{60} \text{ rad} \cdot \text{s}^{-1} = 5\pi \text{ m} \cdot \text{s}^{-1} = 15.7 \text{ m} \cdot \text{s}^{-1}.$$

Further, $a = -A\omega^2 \sin \omega t = -\omega^2 x$. When $x = A$, then $a = -\omega^2 A$, and the force on the piston will be toward the midpoint, and of magnitude

$$F = m|a| = m\omega^2 A = 0.75 \text{ kg} \times \left(2\pi \times \frac{3000}{60}\right)^2 \text{ rad}^2 \cdot \text{s}^{-2} \times 0.05 \text{ m} = 375 \pi^2 \text{ N} = 3700 \text{ N}.$$

33. Given that the acceleration due to gravity on the earth's surface is g, then for any mass m,

$$mg = \frac{GMm}{R^2} = \frac{\frac{4}{3}\pi\rho R^3 Gm}{R^2},$$

where M, ρ, and R are the mass, density, and radius of the earth, respectively. Thus $g = \frac{4}{3}\pi\rho GR$. Similarly, for the moon, $g' = \frac{4}{3}\pi\rho GR'$.

Thus $g/g' = R/R'$. The simple pendulum of length l' on the moon has a period given by $T = 2\pi\sqrt{l'/g'}$.

$$\therefore \quad l' = \frac{g'T^2}{4\pi^2} = \frac{gR'T^2}{4\pi^2 R} = \frac{\pi^2 \text{ m·s}^{-2} \times 0.273 \times 4 \text{ s}^2}{4\pi^2} = 0.273 \text{ m} = 27.3 \text{ cm}.$$

34. If the moment of inertia of the disk of mass m about its center is ignored, the pendulum is assumed to be a simple pendulum of length h; its period is given by the formula $T_0 = 2\pi\sqrt{h/g}$.

If the moment of inertia is not ignored, then $T' = 2\pi\sqrt{I/mgh}$, where I is the moment of inertia of the disk about the point of suspension. The moment of inertia of the disk about an axis through its center and perpendicular to its plane is $\frac{1}{2}mR^2$, where R is the radius of the disk. By the parallel-axes theorem (cf. Problem 9.2), the moment of inertia about a parallel axis through the point of suspension is $I = \frac{1}{2}mR^2 + mh^2$.

$$\therefore \quad T = 2\pi\sqrt{\frac{\frac{1}{2}R^2 + h^3}{gh}} = 2\sqrt{\frac{0.005 \text{ m}^2 + 1 \text{ m}^2}{\pi^2 \text{ m·s}^{-2} \times 1 \text{ m}}} = 2.005 \text{ s},$$

and $T_0 = 2\pi\sqrt{1 \text{ m}/\pi^2 \text{ m·s}^{-2}} = 2$ s. Thus the error in the periodic time is 0.005 s.

35. Let ρ_1 and ρ_2 be the unknown densities, and let the equal masses be m. The volumes of the two substances are thus m/ρ_1 and m/ρ_2. Hence, when the two are mixed, the resultant mass is $2m$ and the volume occupied is $m(1/\rho_1 + 1/\rho_2)$. Thus

$$2.5 \text{ g·cm}^{-3} = 2m/m\left(\frac{1}{\rho_1} + \frac{1}{\rho_2}\right) \quad \text{or} \quad \rho_1\rho_2 = 1.25(\rho_1 + \rho_2) \text{ g·cm}^{-3}.$$

Let the equal volumes be V. The corresponding masses are $\rho_1 V$ and $\rho_2 V$. Hence the mass of the mixture is $V(\rho_1 + \rho_2)$, which occupies a volume $2V$. Thus

$$4.5 \text{ g·cm}^{-3} = V(\rho_1 + \rho_2)/2V \quad \text{or} \quad \rho_1 + \rho_2 = 9 \text{ g·cm}^{-3}.$$

$$\therefore \quad \rho_1\rho_2 = 1.25 \times 9 \text{ g}^2\text{·cm}^{-6} = 11.25 \text{ g}^2\text{·cm}^{-6}.$$

$$\therefore \quad \rho_1 + \frac{11.25 \text{ g}^2\text{·cm}^{-6}}{\rho_1} = 9 \text{ g·cm}^{-3} \quad \text{or} \quad 4\rho_1^2 - 36\rho_1 \text{ g·cm}^{-3} + 45 \text{ g}^2\text{·cm}^{-6} = 0.$$

$$\therefore \quad (2\rho_1 - 15 \text{ g·cm}^{-3})(2\rho_1 - 3 \text{ g·cm}^{-3}) = 0.$$

Thus the densities of the two substances are 7.5 g·cm⁻³ and 1.5 g·cm⁻³, these being the only two possible solutions for both ρ_1 and ρ_2.

36. If the mercury is forced down a distance y in one limb of the U-tube, it will be forced up a distance y in the other limb. The pressure difference between the two sides is thus $P = 2y\rho g$, where ρ is the density of mercury.

The restoring force is therefore $F = -PA = -2y\rho gA$, where A is the cross-sectional area of the tube. If V is the total volume of mercury, the mass on which this force acts is $V\rho$. Thus $F = \rho Va = -2y\rho gA$.

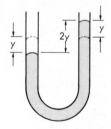

$$\therefore \quad a = -\frac{2gA}{V}y.$$

This is the requisite relation between a and y for simple harmonic motion to result. Hence the period of the vibration is

$$T = \frac{2\pi}{\omega} = 2\pi\sqrt{\frac{V}{2gA}} = 2\pi\sqrt{\frac{10^{-5} \text{ m}^3}{2\pi^2 \text{ m·s}^{-2} \times 1.25 \times 10^{-4} \text{ m}^2}} = \frac{2}{5} \text{ s} = 0.4 \text{ s}.$$

37. If the wood floats, then its weight must be balanced by the upthrust on it due to the water. Thus, if its volume is V, and V_0 is the volume immersed, $0.85 \text{ g·cm}^{-3} \times V = 1 \text{ g·cm}^{-3} \times V_0$.

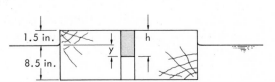

$$\therefore \quad V_0 = 0.85 \, V.$$

Since the wood is in the shape of a plank of thickness 10 in., water thus rises 8.5 in. up the plank.

The level of the water in the knothole will be depressed when oil is poured in up to the top of the plank by an amount y. The pressure acting at the water–oil interface due to the oil is

$$P = \rho gh + P_0 = g\rho(1.5 \text{ in.} + y) + P_0,$$

where ρ is the density of the oil and h its height, and P_0 is the atmospheric pressure. But at this level outside the plank in the water, the pressure is $P' = g \times \rho_0 \times y + P_0$, where ρ_0 is the density of water. The pressure at the same level in a connected liquid is the same. Thus $P = P'$ or $gy\rho_0 = g\rho(1.5 \text{ in.} + y)$.

$$\therefore \quad y = \frac{1.5\rho \text{ in.}}{\rho_0 - \rho} = \frac{1.5 \text{ in.} \times 0.8 \text{ g}\cdot\text{cm}^{-3}}{0.2 \text{ g}\cdot\text{cm}^{-3}} = 6 \text{ in.}$$

Thus the oil depth is $(6 + 1.5) = 7.5$ in.

38. Since the bubbles are touching and each has a diameter of 8×10^{-3} cm, each volume of the whipped cream of size $(8 \times 10^{-3})^3$ cm³ contains one bubble. The number of bubbles in 1 liter of whipped cream is thus

$$n = \frac{10^3 \text{ cm}^3}{512 \times 10^{-9} \text{ cm}^3} = \frac{10^{12}}{512}.$$

The excess pressure inside a bubble is $P = 2\gamma/r$ where γ is the surface tension of cream and r is the radius of the bubble. The total force acting on the surface of the bubble is thus

$$F = PA = \frac{2\gamma}{r} \times 4\pi r^2 = 8\pi\gamma r.$$

If the bubble expands its radius by an amount dr, the work done is $dW = F \, dr = 8\pi\gamma r \, dr$. The total work done in forming the bubble is thus

$$W = \int dW = \int_0^r 8\pi\gamma r \, dr = 4\pi\gamma r^2.$$

The work done in whipping the cream is thus

$$nW = 4\pi n\gamma r^2 = 4\pi \times \frac{10^{12}}{512} \times 30 \text{ dynes}\cdot\text{cm}^{-1} \times (4 \times 10^{-3} \text{ cm})^2 = \frac{3\pi}{8} \times 10^7 \text{ ergs} = 1.178 \text{ J.}$$

39. When the capillary contains mercury, the forces acting on the mercury pellet will be as shown in the diagram. At the top mercury surface the surface-tension forces are acting downward at an angle of 50° to the vertical. The weight of the mercury is also acting downward. At the foot of the capillary the surface-tension forces are acting upward. When there is a negligible amount of mercury in the tube, the angle the surface-tension forces at the foot of the column make with the upward vertical will be very nearly 50° also. But as the amount of mercury in the tube increases, the bottom surface becomes more and more nearly a hemisphere and the surface-tension forces make a smaller and smaller angle with the upward vertical. The greatest upward force on the mercury 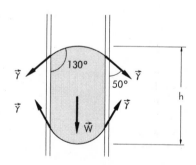 results when the surface-tension forces at the foot the mercury column are vertical, and the greatest length of mercury is then being supported. If this length is h_0, equilibrium is still being maintained and $2\pi r\gamma \cos 50° + \pi r^2 h_0\rho g = 2\pi r\gamma$.

$$\therefore \quad h_0 = \frac{2\gamma(1 - \cos 50°)}{r\rho g} = \frac{2 \times 465 \text{ dynes}\cdot\text{cm}^{-1}(1 - 0.6428)}{0.01 \text{ cm} \times 13.6 \text{ g}\cdot\text{cm}^{-3} \times 981 \text{ cm}\cdot\text{s}^{-2}} = 2.49 \text{ cm.}$$

If the height is increased beyond this value, the upward forces can no longer balance the downward forces and the mercury runs from the tube.

40. The drop has three forces acting on it, its weight acting downward and the viscous force and the buoyant force acting upward. When the terminal velocity is reached, these forces are in equilibrium. Thus, in the usual notation,

$$\tfrac{4}{3}\pi r^3\rho g = 6\pi\eta r v_T + \tfrac{4}{3}\pi r^3 \rho' g.$$

Therefore we obtain, for the radius of the oil drop,

$$r = \sqrt{\frac{6\eta v_T}{\frac{4}{3}g(\rho - \rho')}} = \sqrt{\frac{9 \times 1.8 \times 10^{-4}\,P \times 10\,cm \cdot s^{-1}}{2 \times 981\,cm \cdot s^{-2}\,(0.9013 - 0.0013)\,g \cdot cm^{-3}}} = 3.029 \times 10^{-3}\,cm.$$

41. Since the cross-sectional area of the tank is large in comparison with that of the hole, the water in the tank can be considered as having zero velocity. Further, the air above the tank and outside the hole is in both cases at atmospheric pressure. Applying Bernoulli's theorem, we have

$$p_a + g\rho h + 0 = p_a + \frac{1}{2}\rho v^2,$$

where v is the velocity of efflux of the water through the hole. Thus $v = \sqrt{2gh}$.

In time dt, if a is the area of the hole and A that of the tank, the quantity of water flowing out is $av\,dt = -A\,dh$, where dh is the corresponding increase in height of the water in the tank. If T is the time it takes the tank to empty, then

$$\int_0^T a\,dt = -A\int_4^0 \frac{dh}{v} = -\frac{A}{\sqrt{2g}}\int_4^0 \frac{dh}{h^{1/2}}.$$

$$\therefore \quad T = \frac{2A}{a\sqrt{2g}}\left[h^{1/2}\right]_0^4 = \frac{2 \times 10^4 \times 2\,ft^{1/2}}{\sqrt{2} \times 32\,ft \cdot s^{-2}} = \frac{10^4}{2 \times 60 \times 60}\,hr = 1.39\,hr.$$

42. The area of the tube is $(\pi \times 4 \times 10^{-6}\,cm^2)/4 = \pi \times 10^{-6}\,cm^2$. Even with an appreciable length, the volume of mercury in the tube is negligible in comparison with the volume of mercury in the bulb. Its expansion may therefore be neglected to a first approximation in comparison with the expansion of the bulb.

The glass of the bulb expands, thus increasing the volume to be occupied by the mercury. The mercury expands even more and overflows the bulb. The apparent expansion of the mercury is thus the difference in expansion of mercury and glass. Thus

$$dV = V(\beta_M - \beta_G)dt_F = 4 \times 10^{-2}\,cm^3(101 \times 10^{-6} - 13 \times 10^{-6})\,F\,deg^{-1} \times 1\,F\,deg = 3.52 \times 10^{-6}\,cm^3.$$

This excess volume flows into the tube, the area of which has expanded negligibly. The length of mercury in the tube thus increases by dl, where

$$dl = \frac{dV}{A} = \frac{3.52 \times 10^{-6}\,cm^3}{\pi \times 10^{-6}\,cm^2} = 1.12\,cm.$$

The degree marks are thus separated by a distance of 1.12 cm.

43. Assuming that at 0°C the volume of the brass block is V_0 and the volume of the steel container with the brass block removed is V, then the volume of the container when the block is inserted is $V - V_0$.

If the temperature is raised to t, then the volume of the container becomes $V(1 + 3\alpha_1 t)$ and of the block becomes $V_0(1 + 3\alpha_2 t)$, where α_1 and α_2 are the appropriate coefficients of linear expansion. Hence the net volume is

$$V(1 + 3\alpha_1 t) - V_0(1 + 3\alpha_2 t).$$

But the net volume is to remain independent of temperature, and thus

$$V(1 + 3\alpha_1 t) - V_0(1 + 3\alpha_2 t) = V - V_0. \quad \therefore \quad 3V\alpha_1 t = 3V_0\alpha_2 t.$$

or

$$V_0 = \frac{\alpha_1}{\alpha_2}V = \frac{12 \times 10^{-6}\,C\,deg^{-1}}{20 \times 10^{-6}\,C\,deg^{-1}} \times 2 \times 10^{-4}\,m^3 = 1.2 \times 10^{-4}\,m^3.$$

44. In the usual notation the compressibility is given by the formula $k = (1/p)(dV/V_0)$.

If the container can withstand only a pressure p_0, the maximum change in volume that can be produced on the alcohol without the container bursting is $dV_{max} = kp_0 V_0$.

If the temperature of the container is raised, it expands negligibly, but the contained alcohol would expand if free. If the temperature rise is t, the increase in volume of the alcohol would be $V_0\beta t$, where β is the coefficient of cubical expansion of alcohol. Because the container does not expand, the alcohol cannot do so either, and it is effectively decreased in volume by an amount $V_0\beta t$. The pressure builds up in consequence until bursting occurs. At that time $V_0\beta t = dV_{max} = kp_0 V_0$.

Therefore the rise in temperature is

$$t = \frac{kp_0}{\beta} = \frac{77 \times 10^{-5}\,\text{atm}^{-1} \times 120\,\text{atm}}{1.1 \times 10^{-3}\,\text{C deg}^{-1}} = 84\,\text{C deg.}$$

The vessel therefore bursts when the temperature reaches 104°C.

45. The contraction that would normally take place in the rod on cooling 150°C is

$$\Delta l = l_0 \alpha t = 200\,\text{cm} \times 1.1 \times 10^{-5}\,\text{C deg}^{-1} \times 150\,\text{C deg} = 0.33\,\text{cm.}$$

This contraction is prevented. Therefore, at 25°C, the rod is in a state of tensile stress due to being stretched 0.33 cm. The formula for Young's modulus is

$$Y = \frac{F_n/A}{\Delta l/l_0}.$$

$$\therefore \quad F_n = \frac{AY\,\Delta l}{l_0} = \frac{2\,\text{cm}^2 \times 2.0 \times 10^{12}\,\text{dynes} \cdot \text{cm}^{-2} \times 0.33\,\text{cm}}{200\,\text{cm}} = 6.6 \times 10^9\,\text{dynes.}$$

46. The maximum possible results are obtained if all the available energy is used in either case to increase the temperature of the water. The first claim states that 1 pint = 567 g of water can be boiled in 6 min. The energy necessary is given by the formula $Q = cmt$. Thus

$$Q = 567\,\text{g} \times 80\,\text{C deg} \times 4.186\,\text{J} \cdot \text{g}^{-1} \cdot \text{C deg}^{-1} = 1.90 \times 10^5\,\text{J.}$$

The energy supplied by the immersion heater in 6 min is

$$Q' = 500\,\text{W} \times 60 \times 6\,\text{s} = 1.80 \times 10^5\,\text{J.}$$

Even if all the available energy is used in heating the water (and there must always be a slight heat loss), it is insufficient to raise it to the boiling point.

The second claim refers to the quantity of electricity used to boil 25 pints of water. The energy required to boil one pint of water was 1.90×10^5 J. Hence the energy required to boil 25 pints of water is $1.90 \times 25 \times 10^5$ J $= 4.75 \times 10^6$ J. But 1 kWh of electricity is only 3.60×10^6 J. The second claim is thus also unjustified.

47. The heat lost by the condensing steam and cooling water must equal the heat gained by the calorimeter and contents. Thus if a mass y of ice were originally present, then

20 g × 539 cal·g^{-1} + 20 g × (100 − 50) C deg × 1 cal·g^{-1}·C deg^{-1}

$$= 50\,\text{g} \times 0.09\,\text{cal} \cdot \text{g}^{-1} \cdot \text{C deg}^{-1} \times 50\,\text{C deg} + y \times 80\,\text{cal} \cdot \text{g}^{-1}$$

$$+ y \times 1\,\text{cal} \cdot \text{g}^{-1} \cdot \text{C deg}^{-1} \times 50\,\text{C deg} + (200 - y) \times 1\,\text{cal} \cdot \text{g}^{-1} \cdot \text{C deg}^{-1} \times 50\,\text{C deg.}$$

$$\therefore \quad 80y = 1555\,\text{g.} \qquad \therefore \quad y = 19.44\,\text{g.}$$

48. Let y be the mass of ice formed. The heat given out by the formation of the ice will raise the temperature of the water, and ice will continue to form until ice and water are all at 0°C. The heat given out in the formation of a mass y of ice is thus equivalent to the heat required to raise 10 g of water to 0°C. Thus (L being the latent heat of fusion of ice)

$$yL = 10\,\text{g} \times 1\,\text{cal} \cdot \text{g}^{-1}\,\text{C deg}^{-1} \times 3\,\text{C deg.} \qquad \therefore \quad y = \frac{30\,\text{cal}}{79.7\,\text{cal} \cdot \text{g}^{-1}} = 0.376\,\text{g.}$$

49. To convert degrees Fahrenheit to degrees celsius, we proceed as follows:

$$y°\text{F} = \frac{(y - 32)5}{9}\,°\text{C.}$$

Therefore 122°F = 50°C and 77°F = 25°C. Further, 1 m² = 10⁴ cm². Using the appropriate equation, where all symbols have their usual significance, the heat passing in one hour through 1 m² of the tank walls (and thus the heat given off, since the system is in equilibrium) is

$$Q = KA\frac{(t_2 - t_1)}{L}\tau = 11 \times 10^{-2}\,\text{cal} \cdot \text{cm}^{-1} \cdot \text{s}^{-1} \cdot \text{C deg}^{-1} \times 10^4\,\text{cm}^2 \times \frac{(50 - 25)\,\text{C deg}}{2.5\,\text{cm}} \times 60 \times 60\,\text{s}$$

$$= 3.96 \times 10^7\,\text{cal.}$$

The householder would save a lot of money by insulating the tank!

50. At 90.5°C, the disk drops in temperature by 10°C per minute $= \frac{1}{6}$°C per second. The heat emitted per second is thus

$$Q = cm\, dt = 0.38\ \text{J} \cdot \text{g}^{-1} \cdot \text{C deg}^{-1} \times 250\ \text{g} \times \frac{1}{6}\ \text{C deg} \cdot \text{s}^{-1}.$$

But this lost heat in the main experiment is replaced by the heat flow through the glass from the hotter disk. Hence, in the usual notation,

$$0.38 \times 250 \times \frac{1}{6}\ \text{J} \cdot \text{s}^{-1} = KA\frac{t_2 - t_1}{L}.$$

$$\therefore\quad K = \frac{0.38 \times 250\ \text{J} \cdot \text{s}^{-1} \times 0.5\ \text{cm}}{6 \times 100\ \text{cm}^2 (100 - 90.5)\ \text{C deg}} = \frac{0.38 \times 250 \times 0.5}{6 \times 100 \times 9.5}\ \text{J} \cdot \text{s}^{-1} \cdot \text{cm}^{-1} \cdot \text{C deg}^{-1}$$

$$= 8.33 \times 10^{-3}\ \text{J} \cdot \text{s}^{-1} \cdot \text{cm}^{-1} \cdot \text{C deg}^{-1}.$$

51. When the bell is submerged to a depth of h cm, the pressure on the air in it is atmospheric pressure $+h$ cm of water pressure. But the pressure of h cm of water is equivalent to the pressure of $h/13.6$ cm of mercury. Thus the pressures at 15 m and at 25 m depth are $[76 + (1500/13.6)]$ cm of mercury and $[76 + (2500/13.6)]$ cm of mercury.

Let us say that the volume of the mass of air M_0 in the diving bell at the lesser depth is V_0. This will be compressed into a volume V at the greater depth by the increase of pressure. Applying Boyle's law, since the temperature is unchanged throughout, we have

$$\left(76 + \frac{1500}{13.6}\right)\text{cm} \times V_0 = \left(76 + \frac{2500}{13.6}\right)\text{cm} \times V.$$

$$\therefore\quad V = \frac{76 + (1500/13.6)}{76 + (2500/13.6)} V_0 = 0.717\ V_0.$$

To fill up the extra $0.293\ V_0$ with air at that pressure, it is necessary to pump in a further mass of gas, M. The mass M_0 occupies $0.717\ V_0$ at that depth, and $M + M_0$ occupies V_0. The density of the air pumped in is the same in both cases. Hence the ratio required is

$$\frac{M_0}{M + M_0} = \frac{0.717\ V_0}{V_0} = 0.717.$$

52. The bubble has a volume of 1 cm³ at the atmospheric pressure of 75 cm of mercury. The pressure 75 cm up the tube in the vacuum is zero, and if, once the air is introduced, the mercury level drops y cm, the pressure on the air must be y cm of mercury, according to the laws of hydrostatic pressure. Further, the volume of the air is $[1 \times (10 + y)]$ cm³. Hence, using Boyle's law, we have

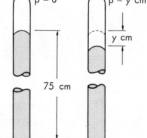

$$1\ \text{cm}^3 \times 75\ \text{cm} = (10 + y)y\ \text{cm}^4.$$

$$\therefore\quad y^2 + 10y - 75 = 0.$$

$$\therefore\quad (y + 15)(y - 5) = 0.$$

$$\therefore\quad y = -15 \quad \text{or} \quad +5.$$

The negative answer is clearly inadmissible. Thus the mercury drops by 5 cm when the air is introduced.

53. The saturated vapor pressure can be expressed as $(12.8/760)$ atm and $(9.2/760)$ atm. Using the gas law, one finds that the number of moles of water vapor present (a) originally and (b) after the drop in temperature are

(a)

$$n_1 = \frac{p_1 V_1}{RT_1} = \frac{(12.8/760)\ \text{atm} \times 5 \times 10^9\ \text{liters}}{0.082\ \text{liter} \cdot \text{atm} \cdot \text{mole}^{-1} \cdot \text{K deg}^{-1} \times 293\ \text{K deg}}$$

and

(b)

$$n_2 = \frac{p_2 V_2}{RT_2} = \frac{(9.2/760)\ \text{atm} \times 5 \times 10^9\ \text{liters}}{0.082\ \text{liter} \cdot \text{atm} \cdot \text{mole}^{-1} \cdot \text{K deg}^{-1} \times 283\ \text{K deg}}$$

expressing the volume in liters and the temperatures in °K. Hence

$$n_1 - n_2 = \frac{5 \times 10^9}{760 \times 0.082}\left(\frac{12.8}{293} - \frac{9.2}{283}\right)\text{mole} = 8.97 \times 10^5 \text{ mole} = 8.97 \times 28.9 \times 10^5 \text{ g} = 2.59 \times 10^7 \text{ g}.$$

This falls as $2.59 \times 10^7 \text{ cm}^3$ of water over an area of $10^4 \text{ m}^2 = 10^8 \text{ cm}^2$ of countryside. The number of centimeters of rain falling on any part of the countryside is thus

$$\frac{2.59 \times 10^7 \text{ cm}^3}{10^8 \text{ cm}^2} = 0.26 \text{ cm of rain}.$$

54. At each beat the work done by the heart is $pV = h\rho gV$. Thus

$$pV = 12 \text{ cm} \times 13.6 \text{ g} \cdot \text{cm}^{-3} \times 981 \text{ cm} \cdot \text{s}^{-2} \times 72 \text{ cm}^3.$$

The work done per second is $12 \times 13.6 \times 981 \times 72 \text{ ergs} \times \frac{70}{60} \text{ s}^{-1} = 1.345 \times 10^7 \text{ ergs} \cdot \text{s}^{-1} = 1.345 \text{ W}$.

55. The work done is the pressure times the change in volume. Thus

$$W = p(V_2 - V_1) = 10^6 \text{ dynes} \cdot \text{cm}^{-2} \times (1670 - 1) \text{ cm}^3 = 1.669 \times 10^9 \text{ ergs} = \frac{1.669}{4.186} \times 10^2 \text{ cal} = 39.9 \text{ cal}.$$

The heat of vaporization is $540 \text{ cal} \cdot \text{g}^{-1}$. Hence the increase in the internal energy of the 1 g of water is

$$\Delta U = (540 - 39.9) \text{ cal} = 500.1 \text{ cal}.$$

56. The work done is

$$W = \int_{V_1}^{V_2} p\, dV = \int_{V_1}^{V_2}\left(\frac{RT}{V - b} - \frac{a}{TV^2}\right)dV.$$

Since R, T, a, and b are all constants in this case,

$$W = RT \ln\left(\frac{V_2 - b}{V_1 - b}\right) + \left(\frac{a}{TV_2} - \frac{a}{TV_1}\right).$$

57. For an adiabatic change, $T_1 p_1^{(1-\gamma)/\gamma} = T_2 p_2^{(1-\gamma)/\gamma}$.

$$\therefore \quad \log\frac{T_2}{T_1} = \frac{1-\gamma}{\gamma}\log\left(\frac{p_1}{p_2}\right) = -\frac{0.40}{1.40}\log(1.03) = -0.0037 = \bar{1}.9963.$$

$$\therefore \quad T_2 = 0.9915 T_1 = 0.9915 \times 290°\text{K} = 287.5°\text{K} = 14.5°\text{C}.$$

58. The maximum rate of working will be produced by the operation of a reversible heat engine between the hot water from the spring and the lake. The engine must work in a series of infinitesimal cycles so that, in any one of the cycles, the temperature T of the hot water will decrease by only an infinitesimal amount dT. This means that the extraction of heat from the hot water will be a reversible isothermal process. In the complete series of Carnot cycles the temperature of the hot water will be reduced from T_1, the temperature of the spring, to a value only infinitesimally different from T_0, the temperature of the lake.

Consider a mass of hot water of heat capacity C. The quantity of heat extracted in the general cycle is $-C\, dT$. The amount of work delivered in the cycle is then $dW = -C\, dt[1 - (T_0/T)]$. Thus the total quantity of work delivered when this mass of hot water is reduced in temperature to T_0 is

$$W = \int_{T_1}^{T_2} -C\, dT\left(1 - \frac{T_0}{T}\right) = C\left[(T_1 - T_0) - T_0 \ln\left(\frac{T_1}{T_0}\right)\right].$$

The rate of working is determined by the rate at which hot water can be made available to the engine. If m is the mass of water which can be obtained per second from the spring and c is the specific heat capacity of water, the maximum power available from the engine is

$$P = mc\left[(T_1 - T_0) - T_0 \ln\left(\frac{T_1}{T_0}\right)\right] = \frac{10^5}{60} \text{ g} \cdot \text{s}^{-1} \times 4.18 \text{ J} \cdot \text{g}^{-1} \cdot \text{K deg}^{-1}\left[42 \text{ K deg} - 287 \text{ K deg} \times \ln\left(\frac{329}{287}\right)\right]$$

$$= \frac{10^5}{60} \times 4.18 \text{ J} \cdot \text{s}^{-1} \cdot \text{K deg}^{-1} (42 - 39.2) \text{ K deg} = 19.5 \text{ kW}.$$

Note that this result can also be obtained from a consideration of entropy. From the first law of thermodynamics, we know that the heat Q rejected to the lake per second must be $Q = mc(T_1 - T_0) - W$. From the second law of thermodynamics, for a reversible cycle, $\Delta s = 0$. But the entropy change of the hot water is $mc \ln(T_0/T_1)$, and of the lake is

$$\frac{mc(T_1 - T_0) - W}{T_0}. \qquad \therefore \qquad \frac{mc(T_1 - T_0) - W}{T_0} = mc \ln \frac{T_1}{T_0},$$

from which the previous expression for W is obtained.

59. Since the piston is pushed in rapidly, the change taking place is an adiabatic one. Hence pV^γ is a constant, where γ is the ratio of the specific heats for air, 1.40. Hence

$$\frac{V_2}{V_1} = \left(\frac{p_1}{p_2}\right)^{1/\gamma} = \left(\frac{1}{1.25}\right)^{1/\gamma} \qquad \text{or} \qquad V_2 = \left(\frac{1}{1.25}\right)^{1/1.40} V_1 = 0.853\,V_1.$$

Since the cross-sectional area is constant, the length of tube containing air when the cork is ejected is

$$h_2 = 0.853 \times 15 \text{ cm} = 12.8 \text{ cm}.$$

When the cork is ejected, pressure waves tend to run up and down the tube. Since the length is 12.8 cm at that time, the fundamental note emitted due to the pressure movements up and down the tube will have a pressure node at the piston and an antinode at the free end. Thus 12.8 cm $= \lambda/4$ and $\lambda = 51.2$ cm. But the speed of sound in air is 344 m·s^{-1}. Thus

$$f = \frac{c}{\lambda} = \frac{34400 \text{ cm} \cdot \text{s}^{-1}}{51.2 \text{ cm}} = 671.9 \text{ cycles} \cdot \text{s}^{-1}.$$

If the piston is pushed in slowly, the change is not adiabatic. If the change were done very slowly indeed, the change would be isothermal and V_2/V_1 would be equal to $p_1/p_2 = 0.8$. With a slow movement the ratio V_2/V_1 is likely to be somewhere betweeen the two values. Thus λ will be smaller than the value given above and the frequency of the pop correspondingly greater.

60. Young's modulus is given by the formula, in the usual notation,

$$Y = \frac{S/A}{\Delta l/l_0}.$$

$$\therefore \qquad S = YA\frac{\Delta l}{l_0} = 9.6 \times 10^{11} \text{ dynes} \cdot \text{cm}^{-2} \times \pi \times 10^{-4} \text{ cm}^2 \times \frac{0.05 \text{ cm}}{100 \text{ cm}} = 1.508 \times 10^5 \text{ dynes},$$

and this is the tension in the wire. Further, the mass per unit length is

$$\mu = \rho A = 8.5 \text{ g} \cdot \text{cm}^{-3} \times 10^{-4}\pi \text{ cm}^2 = 2.670 \times 10^{-3} \text{ g} \cdot \text{cm}^{-1}.$$

Thus the frequency of the fundamental transverse vibration emitted by the wire is

$$f_1 = \frac{1}{2L}\sqrt{\frac{S}{\mu}} = \frac{1}{200 \text{ cm}}\sqrt{\frac{1.508 \times 10^5 \text{ dynes}}{2.670 \times 10^{-3} \text{ g} \cdot \text{cm}^{-1}}} = 37.6 \text{ cycles} \cdot \text{s}^{-1}.$$

61. For each wire, $f = (1/2L)\sqrt{S/\mu}$, and thus

$$\frac{f_1}{f_2} = \frac{L_2}{L_1} = \frac{116 \text{ cm}}{112 \text{ cm}} = \frac{29}{28}.$$

If f_0 is the frequency of the tuning fork, since it gives 5 beats with each of the vibrating strings and $f_1 > f_2$, then f_1 must be $(f_0 + 5 \text{ cycles} \cdot \text{s}^{-1})$ and f_2 be $(f_0 - 5 \text{ cycles} \cdot \text{s}^{-1})$. Thus

$$\frac{f_0 + 5 \text{ cycles} \cdot \text{s}^{-1}}{f_0 - 5 \text{ cycles} \cdot \text{s}^{-1}} = \frac{29}{28}.$$

$$\therefore \qquad 28f_0 + 140 \text{ cycles} \cdot \text{s}^{-1} = 29f_0 - 145 \text{ cycles} \cdot \text{s}^{-1}. \qquad \therefore \qquad f_0 = 285 \text{ cycles} \cdot \text{s}^{-1}.$$

62. Since the sources are stationary, the general expression for the frequency heard when observer and source are moving reduces to

$$\frac{f_L}{u + v_L} = \frac{f_S}{u}.$$

In this case the observer is moving toward one source and away from the other. Hence the frequencies heard are

$$f_L = f_s \frac{u \pm v_L}{u}. \qquad \therefore \qquad \frac{u + v_L}{u} = \frac{9}{8} \frac{u - v_L}{u}.$$

$$\therefore \qquad \frac{17}{8} v_L = \frac{1}{8} u \qquad \text{or} \qquad v_L = \frac{340 \text{ m} \cdot \text{s}^{-1}}{17} = 20 \text{ m} \cdot \text{s}^{-1}.$$

63. The potential a distance r from a point charge of magnitude Q is $V = Q/4\pi\epsilon_0 r$.

At a distance of 1 m from a charge of 50 μC,

$$V_1 = \frac{50 \times 10^{-6} \text{ C} \times 9 \times 10^9 \text{ N} \cdot \text{m}^2 \cdot \text{C}^{-2}}{1 \text{ m}} = 4.5 \times 10^5 \text{ V},$$

and at a distance of 1 cm from it,

$$V_2 = \frac{50 \times 10^{-6} \text{ C} \times 9 \times 10^9 \text{ N} \cdot \text{m}^2 \cdot \text{C}^{-2}}{0.01 \text{ m}} = 4.5 \times 10^7 \text{ V}. \qquad \therefore \qquad V_2 - V_1 = 4.455 \times 10^7 \text{ V}.$$

The work done in moving a charge of 10 pC through the potential difference $V_2 - V_1$ is

$$W = 10 \times 10^{-12} \text{ C} \times 4.455 \times 10^7 \text{ V} = 4.455 \times 10^{-4} \text{ J}.$$

64. The fixed plate and the piston together form a parallel-plate capacitor. When a potential V is applied between piston and plate, the energy stored in the capacitor is

$$W = \frac{1}{2} CV^2 = \frac{\epsilon_0 A V^2}{2d},$$

where C is the capacitance, A the area of the plates, and d their separation. Thus if d changes by a small amount Δd,

$$\Delta W = -\frac{\epsilon_0 A V^2 \Delta d}{2d^2}.$$

But if the force of attraction between the plates due to the charges is $\mathbf{F}$, then

$$\Delta W = \mathbf{F} \cdot \Delta \mathbf{d} = -F \Delta d = -\frac{\epsilon_0 A V^2 \Delta d}{2d^2}. \qquad \therefore \qquad F = \frac{\epsilon_0 A V^2}{2d^2}.$$

This force of attraction due to the charges causes the piston to move toward the fixed plate until the compression of the air in the cylinder produces a force equal and opposite to the electrostatic one.

The gas obeys Boyle's law. If p_0 is the initial pressure of the air and p the final pressure of the air once equilibrium has been achieved, then $p_0 v_0 = pv$ or $p_0 Ad = pA(d - \Delta d)$.

$$\therefore \qquad p = p_0 \frac{d}{d - \Delta d}. \qquad \therefore \qquad p - p_0 = p_0 \left(\frac{\Delta d}{d - \Delta d} \right).$$

But $p - p_0$ is the extra pressure produced by the compression. Therefore $F = (p - p_0)A$.

$$\therefore \qquad \frac{\epsilon_0 V^2}{2d^2} = \frac{p_0 \Delta d}{d - \Delta d} \qquad \text{or} \qquad V = \sqrt{\frac{2p_0 d^2 \Delta d}{\epsilon_0 (d - \Delta d)}} \approx \sqrt{\frac{2p_0 d \Delta d}{\epsilon_0}}$$

$$= \sqrt{\frac{2 \times 50 \text{ N} \cdot \text{m}^{-2} \times 0.15 \text{ m} \times 0.0002 \text{ m}}{8.85 \times 10^{-12} \text{ C}^2 \cdot \text{N}^{-1} \cdot \text{m}^{-2}}} = 1.84 \times 10^4 \text{ V}.$$

65. The dipole moment p of a dipole consisting of two charges of $\pm q$ separated by distance l is given by $p = ql$.

$$\therefore \qquad l = \frac{p}{q} = \frac{6.1 \times 10^{-30} \text{ C} \cdot \text{m}}{1.6 \times 10^{-19} \text{ C}} = 3.81 \times 10^{-11} \text{ m}.$$

Along the perpendicular bisector of the dipole, the value of the electric intensity is

$$E = E_0 = \frac{p}{4\pi\epsilon_0 r^3}.$$

In the problem therefore,

$$E = \frac{6.1 \times 10^{-30} \text{ C} \cdot \text{m}}{4\pi \times 8.85 \times 10^{-12} \text{ C}^2 \cdot \text{N}^{-1} \cdot \text{m}^{-2} \times (0.1)^3 \text{ m}^3} = 5.48 \times 10^{-17} \text{ V} \cdot \text{m}^{-1}.$$

66. From Problem 26.2, it is known that the potential existing at any point between two spherical conducting shells, the inner of radius a, which is charged, and the outer, of radius b, which is grounded, is

$$V = \frac{Q}{4\pi\epsilon_0}\left(\frac{1}{r} - \frac{1}{b}\right).$$

In particular the potential of the inner sphere, where $r = a$, will be

$$V = \frac{Q}{4\pi\epsilon_0}\left(\frac{1}{a} - \frac{1}{b}\right).$$

Before the grounded shell is introduced, each sphere, so far away as not to influence the other, has a charge such that $V = q/4\pi\epsilon_0 a$.

$$\therefore \quad q = 4\pi\epsilon_0 aV = \frac{0.03 \text{ m} \times 50 \text{ V}}{9 \times 10^9 \text{ N} \cdot \text{m}^2 \cdot \text{C}^{-2}} = \frac{1}{6} \times 10^{-9} \text{ C}.$$

At all times therefore the total charge on the two conductors together must be $\frac{1}{3} \times 10^{-9}$ C. Because of the connecting wire, the two spheres must stay always at the same potential. When the grounded shell is introduced, charge will flow from one sphere to the other to keep the potential constant. Charges q_1 and q_2 will be left on the spheres such that

$$\frac{q_1}{4\pi\epsilon_0 a} = V_0 = \frac{q_2}{4\pi\epsilon_0}\left(\frac{1}{a} - \frac{1}{b}\right),$$

where $q_1 + q_2 = \frac{1}{3} \times 10^{-9}$ C. Therefore

$$\frac{\frac{1}{3} \times 10^{-9} \text{ C} - q_2}{a} = q_2\left(\frac{1}{a} - \frac{1}{b}\right). \quad \therefore \quad q_2 = \frac{\frac{1}{3} \times 10^{-9} \text{ C}}{2 - (a/b)} = \frac{\frac{1}{3} \times 10^{-9} \text{ C}}{2 - \frac{3}{4}} = \frac{4}{15} \times 10^{-9} \text{ C}.$$

$$\therefore \quad q_1 = \frac{1}{15} \times 10^{-9} \text{ C}. \quad \therefore \quad V_0 = \frac{\frac{1}{15} \times 10^{-9} \text{ C}}{0.03 \text{ m}} \times 9 \times 10^9 \text{ N} \cdot \text{m}^2 \cdot \text{C}^{-2} = 20 \text{ V}.$$

67. When the first capacitor is initially charged, it possesses a charge given by the equation

$$Q = C_1 V_1 = 5 \times 10^{-9} \text{ F} \times 80 \text{ V} = 0.4 \text{ } \mu\text{C}.$$

Later this is shared by the electrometer of capacitance C_2 connected in parallel, and thus $Q = (C_1 + C_2)V_2$.

$$\therefore \quad C_2 = \frac{Q}{V_2} - C_1 = \frac{0.4 \times 10^{-6} \text{ C}}{75 \text{ V}} - 5 \times 10^{-9} \text{ F} = \frac{1}{3} \times 10^{-9} \text{ F}.$$

The charge is further shared with the capacitor of capacitance C_3, no charge being lost at any time. Hence $Q = (C_1 + C_2 + C_3)V_3$, or

$$C_3 = \frac{Q}{V_3} - C_1 - C_2 = \frac{0.4 \times 10^{-6} \text{ C}}{40 \text{ V}} - 5\frac{1}{3} \times 10^{-9} \text{ F} = 4\frac{2}{3} \times 10^{-9} \text{ F}.$$

68. If the radiator has a resistance of 125 Ω when 50 V are dropped across it, the power consumed is

$$\frac{V^2}{R} = \frac{50^2 \text{ V}^2}{125 \text{ }\Omega} = 20 \text{ W}.$$

If this is all assumed radiated away, then $20 \text{ W} = \beta T^4$ W. Further,

$$125 \text{ }\Omega = (50 + \alpha T^2) \text{ }\Omega \text{ or } 75 = \alpha T^2. \quad \therefore \quad \frac{\alpha^2}{\beta} = \frac{75^2}{20}.$$

When the radiator is emitting 980 W, then

$$980 \text{ W} = \beta T_1^4 \text{ W} = \frac{20 \alpha^2}{75^2} T_1^4 \text{ W}. \quad \therefore \quad \alpha T_1^2 = \sqrt{\frac{75^2 \times 980}{20}} = 525.$$

Thus the resistance of the radiator is now $(50 + \alpha T_1^2) \text{ }\Omega = 575 \text{ }\Omega$. But the power, the resistance, and the current are related by $P = I^2 R$.

$$\therefore \quad I = \sqrt{\frac{980 \text{ W}}{575 \text{ }\Omega}} = 1.3 \text{ A}.$$

69. The film projector has a resistance R given by $P = V^2/R$.

$$\therefore \quad R = \frac{115^2 \text{ V}^2}{500 \text{ W}} = 26.45 \text{ }\Omega.$$

The current it takes is obtained from the equation

$$I = \frac{P}{V} = \frac{500\ W}{115\ V} = 4.35\ A.$$

When the supply voltage is 230 V, an additional resistance X is inserted in series to give the same current. Thus

$$R + X = \frac{230\ V}{4.35\ A} = 52.9\ \Omega. \qquad \therefore \qquad X = 26.45\ \Omega.$$

The energy dissipated in the added resistance is

$$I^2 X = 4.35^2\ A^2 \times 26.45\ \Omega = 500\ W.$$

This is more easily seen in the following way. If the same current is to be drawn from a supply with a voltage twice that used previously, $P = IV$ will now be twice as great as before. The extra 500 W will be dissipated in the added resistance, which must have the same resistance as the projector, since each dissipates the same power.

70. The heat gained by the calorimeter and contents must be equal to the heat supplied by the electrical energy. Thus if c is the specific heat capacity of the liquid and S the heat capacity of the calorimeter, then

$$S \times 10\ C\ deg + 400\ g \times c \times 10\ C\ deg = \frac{1}{4.2\ J \cdot cal^{-1}} \times 2^2\ A^2 \times 8.4\ \Omega \times 3 \times 60\ s,$$

if we convert the electrical energy from joules to calories. Similarly,

$$S \times 10\ C\ deg + 560\ g \times c \times 10\ C\ deg = \frac{1}{4.2\ J \cdot cal^{-1}} \times 2^2\ A^2 \times 8.4\ \Omega \times 4 \times 60\ s.$$

$$\therefore \quad (560 - 400)\ g \times c \times 10\ C\ deg = \frac{1}{4.2\ J \cdot cal^{-1}} \times 2^2\ A^2 \times 8.4\ \Omega \times 60(4 - 3)\ s.$$

$$\therefore \quad c = \frac{2^2 \times 8.4 \times 60}{4.2 \times 160 \times 10}\ cal \cdot g^{-1} \cdot C\ deg^{-1} = 0.3\ cal \cdot g^{-1} \cdot C\ deg^{-1}.$$

Hence, reverting to the first equation, we have

$$10S\ C\ deg + 400\ g \times 0.3\ cal \cdot g^{-1} \cdot C\ deg^{-1} \times 10\ C\ deg = 8 \times 3 \times 60\ cal.$$

$$\therefore \quad S = \frac{(1440 - 1200)\ cal}{10\ C\ deg} = 24\ cal \cdot C\ deg^{-1}.$$

71. Let the resistances of resistor and ammeter be R and r, respectively. The first connection is shown in diagram (a). Because there is no accumulation of charge at any point,

$$I_1 + I_2 = 0.55\ A.$$

Further,

$$V_{xy} = I_1 R = I_2 \times 10^3\ \Omega = 50.0\ V.$$

$$\therefore \quad I_2 = \frac{50\ V}{1000\ \Omega} = \frac{1}{20}\ A$$

and

$$I_1 = (0.55 - 0.05)\ A = 0.5\ A. \qquad \therefore \qquad R = \frac{50\ V}{0.5\ A} = 100\ \Omega.$$

The second method of connection is shown in diagram (b). Here 54.3 V = 0.54 A $\times$ (R + r).

$$\therefore \quad r = \frac{51.3\ V}{0.54\ A} - R = (100.56 - 100)\ \Omega = 0.56\ \Omega.$$

72. All points in the diagram have been labeled, and currents inserted in each branch. Applying Kirchhoff's first law to the points A, F, and D, we have

$$I_1 = I_2 + I_3, \qquad I_3 + I_5 = I_6, \qquad I_2 = I_4 + I_5.$$

Applying Kirchhoff's second law to circuits $ACDB$, $BAEF$, and

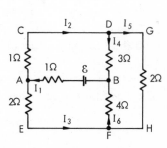

DGHF, we have

$$\mathcal{E} = I_1 \times 1\,\Omega + I_2 \times 1\,\Omega + I_4 \times 3\,\Omega,$$
$$\mathcal{E} = I_1 \times 1\,\Omega + I_3 \times 2\,\Omega + I_6 \times 4\,\Omega,$$
$$0 = I_5 \times 2\,\Omega + I_6 \times 4\,\Omega - I_4 \times 3\,\Omega.$$

Solving these six equations simultaneously leads to the following solutions in terms of $\mathcal{E}$:

$$I_1 = \frac{41\,\mathcal{E}}{139\,\Omega}, \qquad I_2 = \frac{26\,\mathcal{E}}{139\,\Omega}, \qquad I_3 = \frac{15\,\mathcal{E}}{139\,\Omega}, \qquad I_4 = \frac{24\,\mathcal{E}}{139\,\Omega}, \qquad I_5 = \frac{2\,\mathcal{E}}{139\,\Omega}, \qquad \text{and} \qquad I_6 = \frac{17\,\mathcal{E}}{139\,\Omega}.$$

The power dissipated in a resistor R_r through which current I_r passes is $P_r = I_r^2 R_r$. Applying this to all the elements in the diagram, we have

$$P_{AB} = \frac{1681\,\mathcal{E}^2}{(139)^2\,\Omega}, \qquad P_{AC} = \frac{676\,\mathcal{E}^2}{(139)^2\,\Omega}, \qquad P_{AE} = \frac{450\,\mathcal{E}^2}{(139)^2\,\Omega},$$

$$P_{DB} = \frac{1728\,\mathcal{E}^2}{(139)^2\,\Omega}, \qquad P_{GH} = \frac{8\,\mathcal{E}^2}{(139)^2\,\Omega}, \qquad \text{and} \qquad P_{BF} = \frac{1156\,\mathcal{E}^2}{(139)^2\,\Omega}.$$

It is clear that the greatest power is dissipated in the resistor between points *B* and *D*. To fulfill the conditions of the problem, P_{DB} is 1 W for maximum value of the emf $\mathcal{E}$. Thus

$$\frac{1728\,\mathcal{E}^2}{(139)^2\,\Omega} = 1\ \text{W}. \qquad \therefore \quad \mathcal{E}^2 = \frac{(139)^2}{1728}\ \text{V}^2 \qquad \text{or} \qquad \mathcal{E} = \frac{139}{24\sqrt{3}}\ \text{V} = 3.34\ \text{V}.$$

73. Since charge cannot accumulate, $I_1 + I_2 = 5$ A when the galvanometer is used as an ammeter, as in part (a) of the diagram. Further, the potential drops across ammeter and shunt must be equal. Thus

$$9.9\,\Omega \times I_1 = 0.1\,\Omega \times I_2.$$

$$\therefore \quad \frac{I_1}{I_2} = \frac{1}{99} \qquad \text{or} \qquad \frac{I_1}{I_1 + I_2} = \frac{1}{100}.$$

$$\therefore \quad I_1 = \frac{5\ \text{A}}{100} = 50\ \text{mA}.$$

The galvanometer must have a resistor in series with it, as in part (b) of the diagram, when it is used as a voltmeter. At full-scale deflection 50 mA flows through the galvanometer, as calculated in the first part of the problem. The potential dropped across the galvanometer must therefore be

$$V = IR = 50 \times 10^{-3}\ \text{A} \times 9.9\,\Omega = 0.495\ \text{V}.$$

But 50 V is dropped across *R* and the galvanometer. Thus 49.505 V is dropped across the series resistor. It therefore has a resistance

$$R = \frac{49.505\ \text{V}}{50 \times 10^{-3}\,\text{A}} = 990.1\,\Omega.$$

74. In the magnetic field the magnetic force acting on the ions supplies the centripetal force necessary to keep them traversing a circle. Hence $mv^2/R = qvB$.

$$\therefore \quad v = \frac{qRB}{m} \qquad \text{or} \qquad \frac{1}{2}mv^2 = \frac{q^2 R^2 B^2}{2m}.$$

But this kinetic energy is acquired by passing through a potential difference *V*.

$$\therefore \quad qV = \frac{1}{2}mv^2 = \frac{q^2 R^2 B^2}{2m} \qquad \text{or} \qquad V = \frac{qR^2 B^2}{2m}.$$

For both ions, *q*, *R*, and *B* are the same. Therefore $V_1 = k/m_1$ and $V_2 = k/m_2$.

$$\therefore \quad \frac{V_2}{V_1} = \frac{m_1}{m_2} \qquad \text{or} \qquad V_2 = \frac{6}{7} \times 1000\ \text{V} = 857\ \text{V}.$$

75. The magnitude of the torque acting on a single turn of the coil is, in the usual notation,

$$\Gamma = AIB \sin\theta.$$

When the coil has *n* turns,

$$\Gamma = nAIB \sin\theta = 500 \times 0.02\ \text{m} \times 0.01\ \text{m} \times 10^{-8}\ \text{A} \times 0.05\ \text{Wb·m}^{-2} \times 1 = 5 \times 10^{-11}\ \text{N·m}.$$

76. The horizontal component of the earth's magnetic field at M.I.T. is 1.7×10^{-5} Wb·m^{-2}. The magnetic effect due to the vertical wire must be less than $\frac{1}{100}$th of this in order that its effect will be negligible to the accuracy of a compass needle. Thus if r is the minimum distance by which the two experiments should be separated,

$$1.7 \times 10^{-7} \text{ Wb·m}^{-2} = B = \frac{\mu_0}{2\pi} \frac{I}{r}. \qquad \therefore \qquad r = \frac{2 \times 10^{-7} \text{ Wb·A}^{-1} \cdot \text{m}^{-1} \times 50 \text{ A}}{1.7 \times 10^{-7} \text{ Wb·m}^{-2}} = 58.8 \text{ m}.$$

77. From Problem 32.3, it is to be seen that the magnetic induction at the center of a square of side a is

$$B_1 = \frac{2\sqrt{2}\,\mu_0 I}{\pi a}.$$

Here if the length of the current-carrying wire is $4L$, then $a = L$ and thus

$$B_1 = \frac{2\sqrt{2}\,\mu_0 I}{\pi L}.$$

The magnetic induction at the center of a coil of radius r is

$$B_2 = \frac{\mu_0}{2} \frac{I}{r}.$$

Here $2\pi r = 4L$, and thus $r = 2L/\pi$ or $B_2 = \mu_0 \pi I/4L$. Therefore

$$B_2 - B_1 = \frac{\mu_0 I}{L}\left(\frac{\pi}{4} - \frac{2\sqrt{2}}{\pi}\right) = \frac{\mu_0 I}{L}(0.785 - 0.900) < 0.$$

Thus the field due to a square coil is greater than that due to a circular coil.

78. The first student is using an alternating current whose instantaneous value is $i = I_0 \sin \omega t$.

$$\therefore \qquad \frac{di}{dt} = I_0 \omega \cos \omega t \qquad \text{or} \qquad \left(\frac{di}{dt}\right)_{\text{max}} = I_0 \omega.$$

The value of the magnetic induction at any time a distance r from the wire is

$$B = \frac{\mu_0}{2\pi} \frac{i}{r},$$

and the maximum flux passing through the second student's coil when it is correctly oriented is thus

$$\phi = nBA = \frac{\mu_0 An}{2\pi} \frac{i}{r},$$

where A is the area and n the number of turns of the coil, and the distance r is considered great enough so that B may be considered constant over the coil. The induced emf in the coil is

$$\frac{d\phi}{dt} = \frac{\mu_0 An}{2\pi r} \frac{di}{dt},$$

which has a maximum value

$$\left(\frac{d\phi}{dt}\right)_{\text{max}} = \frac{\mu_0 An}{2\pi r} I_0 \omega,$$

which must not exceed 10^{-3} V. The minimum distance r for this to be so is

$$r_{\text{min}} = \frac{\mu_0 A I_0 \omega n}{2\pi \times 10^{-3} \text{ V}} = \mu_0 A I_0 fn \times 10^3 \text{ V}^{-1}$$

$$= 4\pi \times 10^{-7} \text{ Wb·A}^{-1} \cdot \text{m}^{-1} \times 0.25 \text{ m}^2 \times 1 \text{ A} \times 10^3 \text{ s}^{-1} \times 50 \times 10^3 \text{ V}^{-1}$$

$$= 15.7 \text{ m}.$$

79. The current at any time in the circuit is $i = I_f[1 - \exp(-Rt/L)]$. When $i = \frac{1}{2}I_f$, $\exp(-Rt/L) = \frac{1}{2}$. But

$$\frac{di}{dt} = \frac{RI_f}{L} \exp\left(-\frac{Rt}{L}\right).$$

Thus, when $i = \frac{1}{2}I_f$, then

$$\frac{di}{dt} = \frac{RI_f}{2L} = \frac{R}{2L} \times \frac{V}{R} = \frac{V}{2L} = \frac{25\ V}{2 \times 1\ H} = 12.5\ A \cdot s^{-1}.$$

When $i = \frac{9}{10}I_f$, then $\exp(-Rt/L) = \frac{1}{10}$.

$$\therefore \quad t = \frac{L}{R}\ln 10 = \frac{1\ H}{50\ \Omega} \times 2.303 = 0.046\ s.$$

The final current is
$$I_f = \frac{V}{R} = \frac{25\ V}{50\ \Omega} = 0.5\ A.$$

The energy finally stored in the inductor is

$$W = \frac{1}{2}LI_f^2 = \frac{1}{2} \times 1\ H \times 0.5^2\ A^2 = 0.125\ J.$$

80. Since the lamp is rated at 24 V and 36 W, the current it takes is

$$I = \frac{W}{V} = \frac{36\ W}{24\ V} = 1\frac{1}{2}\ A.$$

The added resistor needed must thus pass $1\frac{1}{2}$ A and drop $(220 - 24)\ V = 196\ V$. Its resistance is thus

$$R = \frac{V}{I} = \frac{196\ V}{1.5\ A} = 130\frac{2}{3}\ \Omega.$$

The resistor dissipates a power of
$$IV = 196\ V \times 1.5\ A = 294\ W,$$

while the lamp only uses 36 W. This is very wasteful, and it would be much better to use a transformer to drop the 220 V to 24 V. The losses in the transformer would be negligible in comparison with the 294 W used up in the added resistor.

81. The equation relating the current and the voltage in the coil is $V/I = \sqrt{R^2 + \omega^2 L^2}$.

$$\therefore \quad R^2 + \omega^2 L^2 = \frac{(100\ V)^2}{(2.5\ A)^2} = 1600\ \Omega^2.$$

$$\therefore \quad \omega^2 L^2 = (1600 - 700)\ \Omega^2 \quad \text{or} \quad \omega L = 30\ \Omega.$$

$$\therefore \quad L = \frac{30\ \Omega}{2\pi \times 50\ s^{-1}} = 9.55 \times 10^{-2}\ H.$$

The current in the coil is $I = I_0 \sin \omega t$.

$$\therefore \quad \frac{dI}{dt} = I_0 \omega \cos \omega t.$$

The rms value of dI/dt is

$$\left(\frac{dI}{dt}\right)_{rms} = \frac{I_0 \omega}{\sqrt{2}} = I_{rms}\,\omega.$$

The rms value of the emf induced in the second coil is given by the equation

$$\mathscr{E}_2 = -M_{21}\left(\frac{dI_1}{dt}\right)_{rms}.$$

$$\therefore \quad M_{21} = \frac{-\mathscr{E}_2}{(dI_1/dt)_{rms}} = \frac{-\mathscr{E}_2}{I_{rms}\,\omega} = \frac{50\ V}{2.5\ A \times 2\pi \times 50\ s^{-1}} = \frac{1}{5\pi}\ H = 6.36 \times 10^{-2}\ H.$$

82. The incident light strikes first a water–glass interface at an angle θ to the normal, is refracted into the glass at a smaller angle ϕ to the normal, and, since the glass is a parallel-sided slab, strikes the glass–air interface at angle ϕ to the normal also. When ϕ is the critical angle for a glass–air interface, the light proceeds no further through the cell.
Applying Snell's law of refraction at each interface in turn gives

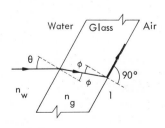

$$n_w \sin \theta = n_g \sin \phi, \quad n_g \sin \phi = 1 \sin 90° = 1. \quad \therefore \quad \sin \theta = \frac{1}{n_w},$$

and θ is thus the critical angle for a water–air interface.

It is necessary to prove also that no previous total internal reflection occurs at the other side of the cell. The second diagram shows the situation there for any arbitrary angle of first incidence α. Total internal reflection is assumed to be occurring at the second interface. (It cannot, of course, occur at the first.)

Applying Snell's law again gives

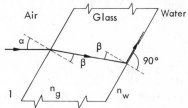

$$1 \sin \alpha = n_g \sin \beta, \quad n_g \sin \beta = n_w \sin 90°. \qquad \therefore \qquad \sin \alpha = n_w.$$

But n_w is greater than 1. It is therefore impossible for any angle of incidence on the first interface to produce total internal reflection at the second. The light stops coming through the cell when total internal reflection occurs at the first face and the angle θ through which the cell is rotated to produce this effect is the critical angle for a water–air interface.

83. Consider the cube in plan. A light ray from the flaw will strike any surface and be totally internally reflected if the angle of incidence on the surface is greater than θ, the critical angle. Therefore we can say that

$$\sin \theta = \frac{1}{n} = \frac{1}{1.6}. \qquad \therefore \qquad \theta = 38.7°.$$

But

$$\tan \theta = \frac{x}{\frac{1}{2}\,\text{in.}} = 0.801. \qquad \therefore \qquad x = 0.400 \text{ in.}$$

Since the reasoning above holds for any light ray from the flaw, each face of the cube must be covered by a circular portion of the setting of radius x. This ensures that no light from the flaw can come directly from the stone, since all rays which would emerge are being blanked off by the setting.

Thus the fraction of the surface which must be covered by the setting is

$$\frac{6 \times \pi x^2}{6 \times 1^2 \,\text{in}^2} = \pi \times (0.400)^2 = 0.503,$$

i.e., almost exactly half the surface of the stone.

84. The image in a plane mirror is the same size as the object. The driver must therefore see an image of width 30 ft in a plane mirror of width x. The object is 40 yd behind the driver, that is, 41 yd from the mirror. The image is thus 41 yd behind the mirror, that is, it is 42 yd from the driver.

All this information is detailed in the diagram, in which AB is the mirror width, CD the image width and OEF the perpendicular from the driver to the plane of the mirror.

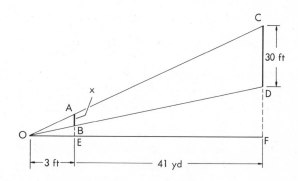

Considering similar triangles OEA and OFC and similar triangles OEB and OFD, we have

$$\frac{AE}{CF} = \frac{OE}{OF} \qquad \text{and} \qquad \frac{BE}{DF} = \frac{OE}{OF}.$$

$$\therefore \qquad AE = \frac{OE}{OF} CF \qquad \text{and} \qquad BE = \frac{OE}{OF} DF.$$

$$\therefore \qquad (AE - BE) = \frac{OE}{OF}(CF - DF). \qquad \therefore \qquad x = \frac{1 \text{ yd}}{42 \text{ yd}} \times 30 \text{ ft} = \frac{5}{7} \text{ ft} = 8\frac{4}{7} \text{ in.}$$

85. The image produced by the object in the first mirror must coincide with the image produced in the second mirror. Otherwise one would obtain a series of images, each image in one mirror acting as object for the production of a further image in the other mirror, *ad infinitum*, or until images at some stage coincided.

Further, since no other real image is formed, the convergent beam of rays produced by reflection at the first mirror must never converge to a point image. Rays must meet the second mirror before

they have formed a point image, and reflection at this surface must cause the rays to converge to the position of the object (consult the diagram).

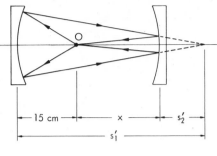

This tells us that the object is closer to the second mirror than its focal point, since reversing the rays discussed in the last paragraph must cause them to retrace their paths. That is, rays from the object are diverged by the second mirror, and since it is concave, the only way this can occur is for the object distance to be less than the focal length.

Applying the mirror formula to the first mirror, we find that

$$\frac{1}{15 \text{ cm}} + \frac{1}{s_1'} = \frac{1}{12 \text{ cm}} .$$

$$\therefore \quad \frac{1}{s_1'} = \frac{1}{12 \text{ cm}} - \frac{1}{15 \text{ cm}} = \frac{1}{60 \text{ cm}} . \qquad \therefore \quad s_1' = 60 \text{ cm}.$$

For the second mirror a real object at distance x from the vertex must produce a virtual image at distance $(15 \text{ cm} + x - 60 \text{ cm})$. Thus

$$\frac{1}{x} - \frac{1}{(45 \text{ cm} - x)} = \frac{1}{14 \text{ cm}} .$$

$$\therefore \quad 45x \text{ cm} - x^2 = 14 \text{ cm} \times (45 \text{ cm} - 2x). \qquad \therefore \quad x^2 - 73x \text{ cm} + 630 \text{ cm}^2 = 0.$$

$$\therefore \quad (x - 63 \text{ cm})(x - 10 \text{ cm}) = 0. \qquad \therefore \quad x = 10 \text{ cm or } 63 \text{ cm}.$$

The solution $x = 63 \text{ cm}$ is clearly inadmissible. This would correspond to the two mirrors each forming in addition a real image, other than the object, at a point between them. The separation of the mirrors in this problem is thus $(15 + 10) \text{ cm} = 25 \text{ cm}$.

86. If the lens is viewed through the top surface in the diagram, the image of the point O on the bottom surface is the point I; AI therefore appears to be the thickness of the lens.

Applying the formula for refraction at a spherical surface,

$$\frac{n}{AO} - \frac{1}{AI} = \frac{1 - n}{-R_1} ,$$

when the top surface has radius of curvature -10 cm, we obtain

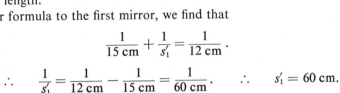

$$\frac{1.5}{3 \text{ cm}} - \frac{1}{AI} = \frac{0.5}{10 \text{ cm}} .$$

$$\therefore \quad -\frac{1}{AI} = \frac{1}{20 \text{ cm}} - \frac{1}{2 \text{ cm}} .$$

That is,

$$AI = \frac{20 \text{ cm}}{9} = 2\frac{2}{9} \text{ cm}.$$

Similarly, when the top surface has radius of curvature -15 cm, the apparent thickness $A'I'$ is obtained from

$$\frac{1.5}{3 \text{ cm}} - \frac{1}{A'I'} = \frac{0.5}{15 \text{ cm}} .$$

$$\therefore \quad -\frac{1}{A'I'} = \frac{1}{30 \text{ cm}} - \frac{1}{2 \text{ cm}} . \qquad \therefore \quad A'I' = \frac{30 \text{ cm}}{14} = 2\frac{1}{7} \text{ cm}.$$

Thus the difference in apparent thickness is

$$AI - A'I' = \left(2\frac{2}{9} - 2\frac{1}{7} \right) \text{ cm} = \frac{5}{63} \text{ cm}.$$

87. To determine the formula for such a lens in a medium of refractive index n, with the radii of curvature being R_1 and R_2, an object is placed at O, producing by refraction in the first surface alone an intermediate image at X which acts as a virtual object for the second surface, producing a final image at I. Then

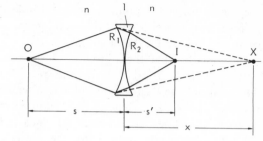

$$\frac{n}{s} + \frac{1}{x} = \frac{1-n}{R_1} \quad \text{and} \quad -\frac{1}{x} + \frac{n}{s'} = \frac{n-1}{R_2}.$$

$$\therefore \quad \frac{n}{s} + \frac{n}{s'} = (1-n)\left(\frac{1}{R_1} - \frac{1}{R_2}\right)$$

or

$$\frac{1}{s} + \frac{1}{s'} = \left(\frac{1}{n} - 1\right)\left(\frac{1}{R_1} - \frac{1}{R_2}\right),$$

which is the normal lens formula with $1/n$ in place of n. If $s = \infty$, then $s' = f$; or if $s = f$, then $s' = \infty$. Hence

$$\frac{1}{f} = \left(\frac{1}{n} - 1\right)\left(\frac{1}{R_1} - \frac{1}{R_2}\right).$$

In this particular problem,

$$\frac{1}{f} = \left(\frac{1}{\frac{4}{3}} - 1\right)\left(\frac{1}{-10 \text{ cm}} - \frac{1}{+10 \text{ cm}}\right) = \frac{1}{4} \times \frac{2}{10 \text{ cm}} = \frac{1}{20 \text{ cm}}.$$

Thus the lens is converging and of focal length 20 cm.

The magnification will be the same as for a thin lens in air (cf. the derivation of this quantity in any basic text), since the end media are the same. Therefore $m = -s'/s = 4$. Hence

$$\frac{1}{s} - \frac{1}{4s} = \frac{1}{f} = \frac{1}{20 \text{ cm}}.$$

$$\therefore \quad \frac{3}{4s} = \frac{1}{20 \text{ cm}}. \quad \therefore \quad s = \frac{60 \text{ cm}}{4} = 15 \text{ cm}.$$

88. The telescope objective lens produces an image of the rod in the first focal plane of the eyepiece. The graticule already there, plus the image, are then viewed together through the eyepiece. The distance from the objective lens to the graticule, s', is such that $1/s + 1/s' = 1/f$. That is,

$$\frac{1}{1000 \text{ cm}} + \frac{1}{s'} = \frac{1}{25 \text{ cm}}.$$

$$\therefore \quad \frac{1}{s'} = \frac{1}{25 \text{ cm}} - \frac{1}{1000 \text{ cm}} = \frac{39}{1000 \text{ cm}}.$$

$$\therefore \quad s' = \frac{1000}{39} \text{ cm}.$$

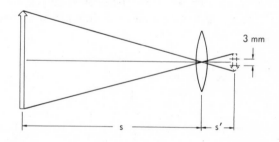

The magnification produced by the objective is

$$m = -\frac{s'}{s} = -\frac{1000 \text{ cm}}{39 \times 1000 \text{ cm}} = -\frac{1}{39}.$$

The part of the image of the rod between the lines of the graticule has a length of 3 mm. The corresponding part of the object, the rod itself, must have a length of $3 \times 39 \text{ mm} = 11.7 \text{ cm}$.

89. The distance from the central fringe to the mth bright fringe of an interference fringe system produced by Young's slits is $y_m = mR\lambda/d$.

Each wavelength produces its own independent fringe system, the two systems overlapping when the mth bright fringe of the system due to wavelength λ coincides with the nth bright fringe due to wavelength λ'.

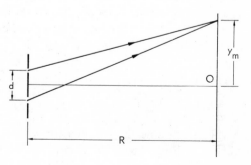

$$\therefore \quad \frac{mR\lambda}{d} = y_m = y'_n = \frac{nR\lambda'}{d}.$$

$$\therefore \quad m\lambda = n\lambda'.$$

$$\therefore \quad \frac{m}{n} = \frac{\lambda'}{\lambda} = \frac{567 \text{ nm}}{486 \text{ nm}} = \frac{7}{6}.$$

The first position for which overlap occurs is therefore where the 7th fringe of the system due to wavelength 486 nm, or the 6th fringe of the system due to wavelength 567 nm, lies. The distance required is

$$y_7 = y_6' = \frac{7 \times 1.50 \text{ m} \times 486 \times 10^{-9} \text{ m}}{10^{-3} \text{ m}} = 5.103 \times 10^{-3} \text{ m} = 5.103 \text{ mm}.$$

90. If d is the grating spacing, then the mth maximum due to wavelength λ occurs at an angle θ given by $\sin \theta = m\lambda/d$. If at the same angle the nth maximum due to wavelength λ' occurs, then $\sin \theta = n\lambda'/d$.

$$\therefore \quad \frac{m}{n} = \frac{\lambda'}{\lambda} = \frac{7}{6}.$$

The first, and only, coincidence occurs for

$$\sin \theta = \frac{7 \times 486 \times 10^{-9} \text{ m}}{d}.$$

But if there are 2000 lines per centimeter, the separation of the lines is

$$\frac{1}{2 \times 10^3} \text{ cm} = \frac{10^{-5}}{2} \text{ m}.$$

$$\therefore \quad \sin \theta = 7 \times 486 \times 10^{-9} \text{ m} \times 2 \times 10^5 \text{ m}^{-1} = 0.680.$$

$$\therefore \quad \theta = 42.9°.$$

This is the only coincidence, since the next one would occur for $m = 14$, $n = 12$. But this would give $\sin \theta = 1.360$, which is impossible.

91. If the work function of the potassium is 2 V, the minimum energy necessary to emit an electron is $2 \text{ eV} = 3.2 \times 10^{-19} \text{ J}$. When radiation of wavelength 1.60×10^{-7} m falls on the plate, the maximum energy of the emitted photoelectrons is

$$W = h\frac{c}{\lambda} - W_0 = \frac{6.6 \times 10^{-34} \text{ J} \cdot \text{s} \times 3.0 \times 10^8 \text{ m} \cdot \text{s}^{-1}}{1.6 \times 10^{-7} \text{ m}} - 3.2 \times 10^{-19} \text{ J}$$

$$= (12.38 - 3.2) \times 10^{-19} \text{ J} = 9.18 \times 10^{-19} \text{ J}.$$

In the magnetic field the electrons traverse a circular path, the necessary centripetal force being supplied by the magnetic force. Thus, in the usual notation, $Bev = mv^2/R$ or $v = BeR/m$.

$$\therefore \quad \frac{1}{2}mv^2 = \frac{B^2 e^2 R^2}{2m}.$$

In this case $\frac{1}{2}mv^2$ is known to be 9.18×10^{-19} J. Thus

$$R = \frac{\sqrt{2 \text{ m} \times 9.18 \times 10^{-19} \text{ J}}}{Be} = \frac{\sqrt{2 \times 9.1 \times 10^{-31} \text{ kg} \times 9.18 \times 10^{-19} \text{ J}}}{5 \times 10^{-5} \text{ Wb} \cdot \text{m}^{-2} \times 1.6 \times 10^{-19} \text{ C}} = 0.1616 \text{ m} = 16.16 \text{ cm}.$$

92. The radiation emitted from a hydrogen atom always has a wavelength given by

$$\frac{1}{\lambda} = R \left(\frac{1}{n_1^2} - \frac{1}{n_2^2} \right).$$

The Lyman, Balmer, Paschen, Brackett, and Pfund series arise when n_1 has the values 1, 2, 3, 4, and 5, respectively, and the short-wavelength limit in each case arises when n_2 has the value infinity, since this gives the smallest possible value for λ. The lines in each series crowd closer and closer to the short-wavelength limit as n_2 increases.

Thus the short-wavelength limits are:

(a) Lyman: $\quad \lambda_{\min} = \frac{1}{R} = \frac{1}{1.09678 \times 10^7} = 91.176 \text{ nm}$,

(b) Balmer: $\quad \lambda_{\min} = \frac{2^2}{R} = 364.703 \text{ nm}$,

(c) Paschen: $\quad \lambda_{\min} = \frac{3^2}{R} = 820.584 \text{ nm}$,

(d) Brackett: $\lambda_{\text{min}} = \dfrac{4^2}{R} = 1458.82$ nm,   (e) Pfund: $\lambda_{\text{min}} = \dfrac{5^2}{R} = 2279.40$ nm.

93. One cubic meter of rock salt has a mass of

$$2.164 \times 10^6 \text{ g} = \frac{2.164 \times 10^6}{58.45} \text{ moles.}$$

The number of atoms it contains is thus

$$n = \frac{2.164 \times 10^6}{58.45} \times 6.023 \times 10^{23} \times 2,$$

since each molecule of rock salt contains two atoms. The volume occupied by one atom is thus $v = 1/n$, and the separation of the principal planes, d, will be

$$d = v^{1/3} = \sqrt[3]{\frac{58.45}{2.164 \times 12.046 \times 10^{29}}} \text{ m} = 2.820 \times 10^{-10} \text{ m.}$$

Bragg's law relates d to the glancing angle for diffraction maxima by the relation $2d \sin \theta = m\lambda$.

$$\therefore \quad \sin \theta = \frac{1.5405 \times 10^{-10} \text{ m}}{2 \times 2.820 \times 10^{-10} \text{m}} = 0.2731. \quad \therefore \quad \theta = 15°51'.$$

94. The electrons are moving quite slowly and thus relativistic effects do not enter. The energy of the electrons is $500 \text{ eV} = 500 \times 1.602 \times 10^{-19} \text{ J} = 8.10 \times 10^{-17} \text{ J}$. But the momentum p is related to the energy E by the relation $p^2 = 2mE$. Thus

$$p = \sqrt{2 \times 9.107 \times 10^{-31} \text{ kg} \times 8.10 \times 10^{-17} \text{ J}}$$
$$= 1.215 \times 10^{-23} \text{ kg} \cdot \text{m} \cdot \text{s}^{-1}.$$

But the wavelength associated with the electron is given by

$$\lambda = \frac{h}{p} = \frac{6.625 \times 10^{-34} \text{ J} \cdot \text{s}}{1.215 \times 10^{-23} \text{ kg} \cdot \text{m} \cdot \text{s}^{-1}} = 5.455 \times 10^{-11} \text{ m.}$$

Bragg's law relates the glancing angle for diffraction maxima and the wavelength by the relation $2d \sin \theta = m\lambda$.

$$\therefore \quad \sin \theta = \frac{2 \times 5.455 \times 10^{-11} \text{ m}}{2 \times 2.86 \times 10^{-10} \text{ m}} = 0.1907. \quad \therefore \quad \theta = 11°.$$

95. The intensity of the radiation after passage through a thickness x of absorber is

$$I = I_0 \, e^{-\mu x} = I_0 \, e^{-\mu_m \rho x}$$

$$\therefore \quad x = \frac{1}{\mu_m \rho} \ln \frac{I_0}{I} = \frac{1}{4.2 \times 10^{-3} \text{ m}^2 \cdot \text{kg}^{-1} \times 1.13 \times 10^4 \text{ kg} \cdot \text{m}^{-3}} \ln 10 = 0.0485 \text{ m} = 4.85 \text{ cm.}$$

96. Radium-226 is a member of the uranium series and the radium has long since achieved secular equilibrium with the other members of the chain. In particular it has achieved secular equilibrium with the parent uranium. Thus, assuming that λ_0 and λ are the decay constants of uranium and radium, respectively, and that N_0 and N are the corresponding number of atoms of each present at any time, then $\lambda_0 N_0 = \lambda N$. Thus

$$N = \frac{\lambda_0}{\lambda} N_0.$$

The ratio λ_0/λ is fixed, and thus N varies directly as N_0. Since the uranium is constantly disintegrating, the quantity N diminishes continuously also. After 1000 years there would be much less radium than there is at present.

97. To obtain the maximum mass of Po^{210} present, use may be made of the argument of Problem 48.2. There it was shown that the maximum mass was present at a time given by the equation

$$t = \frac{1}{\lambda_2 - \lambda_1} \ln \frac{\lambda_2}{\lambda_1}.$$

In this case we may rewrite the equation as

$$t = \frac{\tau_1 \tau_2}{\ln 2(\tau_1 - \tau_2)} \ln \frac{\tau_1}{\tau_2},$$

where τ_1 and τ_2 are the respective half-life periods. Thus

$$t = \frac{5 \times 140 \times 24^2 \times 60^4 \, \text{s}^2}{\ln 2 \times (5 - 140) \times 24 \times 60^2 \, \text{s}} \ln \frac{5}{140} = 2.155 \times 10^6 \, \text{s}.$$

Thus the maximum mass of Po^{210} present is

$$N = \frac{N_0 \lambda_1}{\lambda_2 - \lambda_1}(e^{-\lambda_1 t} - e^{-\lambda_2 t}) = \frac{N_0 \tau_2}{\tau_2 - \tau_1}\left[\exp\left(-\frac{t \ln 2}{\tau_2}\right) - \exp\left(\frac{-t \ln 2}{\tau_1}\right)\right] = \frac{140}{135} \times 0.8523 \, N_0$$

$$= 0.884 \, N_0.$$

Dividing both sides by Avogadro's number will give masses in moles on both sides.

$$\therefore \quad M = 0.884 \, M_0 = \frac{0.884 \times 10^{-10}}{210} \, \text{moles} = 0.884 \times 10^{-10} \, \text{g of } Po^{210}.$$

The activity of this maximum mass is

$$A = \lambda_2 N = 0.884 \lambda_2 N_0 = \frac{0.884 \ln 2}{\tau_2} N_0.$$

$$\therefore \quad A = \frac{0.884 \times 0.6923}{140 \times 24 \times 60 \times 60 \, \text{s}} \times \frac{10^{-10}}{210} \times 6.02 \times 10^{23} = 1.45 \times 10^4 \, \text{dis} \cdot \text{s}^{-1}.$$

98. The Q-value of the reaction is $+0.55$ MeV. This is equivalent to a decrease of mass in the reaction of $0.55/931 = 0.00059$ amu. The combined mass of the initial particles is $14.00752 + 1.00899 = 15.01651$ amu. The combined mass of the final particles must thus be $15.01651 - 0.00059 = 15.01592$ amu. But the mass of the proton is 1.00819 amu. Thus the mass of the carbon isotope formed is

$$15.01592 - 1.00819 = 14.00773 \text{ amu}.$$

99. The rocket acquires a final speed of $11.3 \times 10^3 \, \text{m} \cdot \text{s}^{-1}$ and thus acquires a final energy of

$$E = \frac{1}{2} mv^2 = \frac{1}{2} \times 5 \times 10^4 \, \text{kg} \times 11.3^2 \times 10^6 \, \text{m}^2 \cdot \text{s}^{-2} = 3.192 \times 10^{12} \, \text{J}.$$

If the amount of uranium-235 used up is $y \, \text{g} = y/235$ moles, the number of atoms consumed is $y N_0/235$, where N_0 is Avogadro's number. Each fission produces

$$180 \text{ MeV} = 180 \times 1.60 \times 10^{-13} \, \text{J} = 2.88 \times 10^{-11} \, \text{J}$$

and the conversion is only 5% efficient. Hence

$$2.88 \times 10^{-11} \, \text{J} \times \frac{y N_0}{235} = 20 \times 3.192 \times 10^{12} \, \text{J} \quad \text{or} \quad y = \frac{235 \times 20 \times 3.192 \times 10^{12}}{2.88 \times 10^{-11} \times 6.02 \times 10^{23}} = 865.$$

The mass of uranium used is thus 865 g.

100. If two deuterons combine to give one α-particle, the mass decrease is

$$\Delta m = (2 \times 2.0147 - 4.0039) \text{ amu} = 0.0255 \text{ amu} = 0.0255 \times 931 \text{ MeV}$$

$$= 23.74 \times 1.6 \times 10^{-13} \, \text{J} = 3.80 \times 10^{-12} \, \text{J}.$$

Two grams of deuterium contain 6.02×10^{23} deuterons. One gram of deuterium thus contains $(6.02/4) \times 10^{23}$ pairs of deuterons. Thus the total energy released when every pair fuses is

$$E = \frac{6.02}{4} \times 10^{23} \times 3.80 \times 10^{-12} \, \text{J} = 5.72 \times 10^{11} \, \text{J}.$$

101. In S and in S' let the y- and y'-axes be at right angles to the common x-axis in the plane containing the x-axis and the rod.

To an observer in S the coordinates of the endpoints of the rod are (x_1, y_1) and (x_2, y_2). To an observer in S', the corresponding coordinates are (x_1', y_1') and (x_2', y_2'). By the Lorentz transformation equations,

$$x_2' - x_1' = (x_2' - x_1')\sqrt{1 - (v^2/c^2)} \quad \text{and} \quad y_2' - y_1' = y_2' - y_1'.$$

Thus we may write

$$x_2' - x_1' = 10 \cos 30° \sqrt{1 - 0.95^2} \text{ cm} = 2.704 \text{ cm},$$

$$y_2' - y_1' = 10 \sin 30° = 5.000 \text{ cm}.$$

The length of the rod in the S' system is thus

$$\sqrt{2.704^2 + 5.000^2} \text{ cm} = 5.684 \text{ cm},$$

and it is inclined to the x-axis at an angle $\tan^{-1} (5.000/2.704)$, that is, at an angle of $61°36'$.

SECTION III

This section consists of supplementary problems only. No worked-out solutions are given. However, at the end of the section there are answers to all problems.

Supplementary Problems

1. A nonuniform plank of length 15 ft is being used as a seesaw by two children weighing 55 lb and 65 lb. If they sit at the ends of the plank in one way the fulcrum is central, but if they exchange places, the fulcrum has to be displaced 9 in. for balance. What is the weight of the plank and the position of its center of gravity?

2. A uniform shelf of weight 12 lb is hinged to a vertical wall at the center of one edge, and is held in a horizontal position by a chain from the wall to the center of the other edge. If the chain is inclined at 45° to the horizontal, find the tension in the chain and the horizontal and vertical components of the reaction at the hinge.

3. A uniform ladder of weight 144 lb and length 26 ft rests with one end against a smooth vertical wall and the other pegged to the ground to prevent slipping. If the lower end of the ladder is 10 ft from the wall, what are the reactions at wall and peg?

4. A square is cut from a uniform circular disk, one corner of the square coinciding with the center of the disk and the opposite corner lying on the circumference. Where is the center of mass of the remainder of the disk?

5. A man is in his bedroom which has a window 4 ft high and sees a ball shoot vertically upward past his window and a little later fall back again. If the ball is in sight for 0.25 s on each occasion, how far above the top of the window does the ball rise?

6. A boy is playing a game in which he drops a stone from a bridge 144 ft high and then picks up another stone and throws it after the first. The object of the game is to strike the first stone with the second before it has reached the ground. There is a delay of 1 s before the second stone is launched, and the best the boy can do is to make the two stones hit just as the first reaches the ground. What is the maximum speed with which he can launch the second stone?

7. A car accelerates uniformly from rest and travels a distance of 120 ft while accelerating from 20 ft·s⁻¹ to 40 ft·s⁻¹. How long did it take to achieve the speed of 20 ft·s⁻¹, and what will be the speed after a further 90 ft?

8. An aircraft is being observed by two men traveling in trains moving in opposite directions on parallel tracks at 40 mph. To the observer in one train the airplane appears to cross the track at right angles; while to the observer on the other train the angle appears to be 45°. At what angle does the airplane actually cross the track and what is its speed relative to the ground?

9. A body slides from rest down a plane of length 1 meter inclined at 30° to the horizontal, and then along a horizontal plane of the same material. If the coefficient of kinetic friction between the body and the plane is 0.35, how far along the horizontal plane will the body travel?

10. A block slides from rest down a 45° inclined plane in twice the time it takes to slide from rest down a frictionless 45° incline. Find the coefficient of kinetic friction between block and plane.

11. A body is projected up a plane inclined at 60° to the horizontal with an initial speed of 32 ft·s⁻¹. The coefficient of kinetic friction between plane and body is 0.25. How far up the plane will the body travel, and how long does it take to come to rest?

12. Assume that the orbits of the moon around the earth and the earth around the sun are circular, and that the ratio of the radii of the orbits is 390 to 1. Compare the masses of the sun and the earth. The moon makes 13 revolutions round the earth in a year.

13. The value of *g* is experimentally determined at the foot of a mine shaft 500 m deep and is found to be greater than the value measured at the surface by 1 in 10^5. Suppose that the earth is a sphere of radius 6.00×10^6 m and that the mean density of the earth below a depth of 500 m is known to be 5.50 g·cm⁻³. What is the mean density of the crust to a depth of 500 m?

14. Masses of 200 g and 100 g are joined by a light rod and allowed to slide down a plane inclined at 30° to the horizontal, one behind the other. The coefficients of kinetic friction between the plane and the two masses are 0.35 and 0.25, respectively. Find the common acceleration down the plane and the tension in the rod when the larger mass is in front and when the smaller mass is in front.

15. Masses of 60 g and 50 g are connected by a light, inextensible cord which passes over a pulley mounted on horizontal frictionless bearings. When released from rest, each mass moves 64 cm in the first 4 s of motion. The pulley has a radius of 4 cm. What is its moment of inertia?

16. A crate whose base is 2 ft square and whose center of gravity is centrally located 2 ft above its base is standing on the back of a truck with four of its edges parallel to the sides. The truck suddenly accelerates forward and the crate topples over. What is the minimum acceleration that the truck can have?

17. An Arctic explorer weighing 160 lb is pulling a sled weighing 800 lb along a horizontal snow slope when a crevice opens beneath his feet. With what acceleration does he fall? The coefficient of kinetic friction between snow and sled is 0.10.

  Suppose that his companions throw themselves on to the sled and stop it from being pulled into the crevice. What is the minimum value of their combined weight? The coefficient of static friction is 0.12.

18. A block of mass 0.3 slug stands on the horizontal top of a trolley of mass 1 slug which can run on wheels that have negligible friction at the bearings. The coefficient of static friction between block and trolley is 0.40. A string attached to the trolley runs horizontally to a pulley and supports a hanging body at its other end. What is the greatest possible mass of this body if the block does not slip?

19. A body weighing 10 lb, projected with a velocity of 24 ft·s⁻¹ up a rough plane inclined at 30° to the horizontal, travels a distance of 16 ft before coming to rest. Calculate the work done against friction.

  Suppose that the body is started down the plane again from rest. Calculate how much more time it takes to travel down the plane than it did to travel up.

20. A body of mass 20 g is placed on a wedge of mass 1 kg, as in the diagram. All surfaces are frictionless. With what acceleration does the wedge move to the left? What acceleration must be given to the wedge if the block is to remain stationary relative to the wedge?

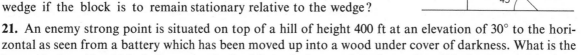

21. An enemy strong point is situated on top of a hill of height 400 ft at an elevation of 30° to the horizontal as seen from a battery which has been moved up into a wood under cover of darkness. What is the least velocity with which shells need to be fired from the battery in order to demolish the strong point?

22. Secret agent 008 has the arch-fiend in the telescopic sights of his rifle. He is 400 ft from his target, his rifle has a muzzle velocity of 2000 ft·s⁻¹, and the axis of the sight is horizontal. At what angle to the horizontal is the barrel of the rifle inclined?

23. A mass of 0.25 kg is rotating in a circle of radius 50 cm with a speed of 5 m·s⁻¹ on the surface of a smooth table. The mass is kept in the circular path by a string which passes through a hole in the table at the position of the center of the circle. Suppose that the string is pulled through the hole until the radius of the circle is reduced to 30 cm. By what factor has the tension in the string increased and what work has been done on the rotating mass?

24. A box is resting on the floor of a railway carriage which is moving at constant speed around a circular portion of track of radius 500 m. The coefficient of static friction between box and floor is 0.25. What is the maximum possible speed the train can have and yet not make the box begin to slide?

25. A car weighing 2500 lb is powered by an engine of 30 hp. If the car uses 10 hp in order to maintain a speed of 30 mph on the level, what is the steepest incline it can climb at this speed, frictional forces being assumed the same?

26. In a laboratory a small body of mass 1 kg is suspended from the ceiling by a light elastic cord of unstretched length 1 m, which extends 1 cm when a force of 1 N is applied to it. The body executes uniform circular motion in a horizontal plane while the cord makes an angle of 30° with the vertical. What is the tension in the string and the angular speed of the body?

27. A cowboy fires his gun and the 10-g bullet, while traveling horizontally at 250 m·s⁻¹, strikes a piece of wood of mass 490 g which is standing on top of a fence 1 m high. The bullet remains embedded in the wood. How far from the fence does the wood hit the ground?

28. A bullet of mass 5 g is fired into, and becomes embedded in, a wooden block of mass 5 kg which is initially at rest on a horizontal surface. The block moves backward a distance of 20 cm before coming to rest. The coefficient of sliding friction between block and surface is known to be 0.25. What was the speed of the bullet before it struck the block?

29. A hoop weighing 5 lb is propelled by a horizontal force directed through its center of mass. The coefficient of static friction between hoop and road is 0.40. What is the maximum force that can be applied without causing the hoop to slide?

30. An electric motor is delivering 2 hp when the current to the motor is cut off without disconnecting the load. The moment of inertia of the rotor assembly is 1 slug·ft², and the motor was originally turning at 1800 rpm. How many revolutions does the motor make before coming to rest?

31. A cable drum of weight W consists of a circular cylinder of radius r terminating symmetrically in two circular ends of radius R. The drum is placed on an inclined plane making an angle θ with the horizontal and the cable is pulled off the drum from the bottom and up the slope. Show that the drum rolls up the plane without slipping if the force applied has a magnitude greater than $W \sin \theta \times R/(R - r)$.

32. A merry-go-round in a children's playground has a mass of 20 slugs, a radius of 5 ft, and a radius of gyration of 3 ft. When it is turning with an angular speed of 3 rad·s⁻¹, a child of mass 2 slugs runs at a speed of 8 ft·s⁻¹ tangentially to the rim and jumps aboard. What is now the angular speed of the merry-go-round?

33. A horizontal rod 100 cm long and of negligible weight is suspended at its ends on vertical wires of equal length, the wires having cross-sectional areas of 1 mm² and 2 mm². Young's moduli for the wires are 3.0×10^{12} dynes·cm⁻² and 2.0×10^{12} dynes·cm⁻², respectively. At what points should a weight be hung from the rod to produce in the wires (1) equal stresses and (2) equal strains?

34. A very keen student performs experiments while commuting by train to his university. On one occasion he sets up a pendulum in the railroad car and finds that it oscillates 120 times per minute when the train is traveling at constant speed on a straight portion of track; but that it oscillates 121 times per minute when the train is traveling at 60 mph around a circular portion of the track. What is the radius of curvature of this part of the track? By how much should the track be banked if trains normally take the curve at this speed?

35. A bullet of mass 20 g is fired vertically at a speed of 200 m·s⁻¹ into a wooden block of mass 5 kg which is hanging from a spring with a force constant of 200 N·m⁻¹. The bullet comes to rest inside the block. What is the amplitude of the resultant simple harmonic motion?

36. A seesaw consists of a uniform plank of negligible thickness and of length 5.0 m resting symmetrically on a round cylindrical log of diameter 1.0 m. Show that in use the seesaw executes simple harmonic motion and determine its period.

37. A cylinder of wood is floating in water with one end protruding 20 cm above the surface. Oil of density 0.75 g·cm⁻³ is poured onto the water until it forms a layer 2 cm deep. What length of wood will be left protruding above the oil?

38. The bulb and immersed portions of a common hydrometer up to the zero mark on the stem have a volume of 3 times that of the portion of the stem from the zero to the one hundred mark. The hydrometer sinks to the twenty mark in water. What is the density of a liquid in which it sinks to the seventy-five mark?

39. A surfboard of mass 1200 g and density 0.75 g·cm⁻³ is just submerged in fresh water when a lead weight of density 11.3 g·cm⁻³ is added to it. What mass of lead is required if it is placed on top of the board and what mass if it is suspended beneath the board?

40. A balloon of volume 1000 m³ is filled with helium. The combined mass of skin, basket, and load is 1000 kg. What is the net upward force on the balloon and its initial acceleration when released? The molecular weights of helium and air are 4 and 29, respectively, and the density of air is 1.29 kg·m⁻³.

41. In a clean glass U-tube the diameters of the limbs are 1 mm and 8 mm, respectively. Find the difference in the water levels in the two limbs. The surface tension of water is 0.0728 N·m⁻¹.

42. Spherical particles of radius 1.00 × 10⁻⁴ cm and density 3.20 g·cm⁻³ are shaken up in water. The height of the water column is 4.75 cm. What proportion of the particles are still in suspension 2 hr after the mixture has been left to stand in a vertical position? The viscosity of water is 0.01 poise.

43. A tank standing on a level surface contains water to a depth of 30 cm. At what height should a hole be punched in the side so that the water stream emerging will strike the surface as far from the tank as possible?

44. At what temperature do a Fahrenheit and a Kelvin thermometer read the same value?

45. A mercury thermometer is made up of a glass bulb of capacity 0.25 cm³ at 0°C and a capillary tube on which the 0°C and 100°C divisions are 25 cm apart. The coefficient of linear expansion of glass is 1.0 × 10⁻⁵ C deg⁻¹ and the coefficient of volume expansion of mercury is 1.8 × 10⁻⁴ C deg⁻¹. What is the radius of the capillary tube?

46. A spherical wooden ball has a density of 0.90 g·cm⁻³ at 0°C and floats in a liquid of density 0.92 g·cm⁻³ at 0°C. The ball is made from wood which has a coefficient of linear expansion of 0.4 × 10⁻⁵ C deg⁻¹ along the grain and a coefficient of linear expansion of 1.8 × 10⁻⁵ C deg⁻¹ perpendicular to the grain. The coefficient of cubical expansion of the liquid is 1.5 × 10⁻³ C deg⁻¹. Determine the temperature at which the ball just sinks.

47. A steel hoop just slips onto the wheel of a cart after it has been heated to 420°C. Calculate the stress in this metal tire when it has cooled to 20°C. Young's modulus for steel is 2.0 × 10¹¹ N·m⁻² and its coefficient of linear expansion is 1.2 × 10⁻⁵ C deg⁻¹.

48. How much heat is required to raise from 1°K to 4°K the temperature of 5 g of aluminum? The specific heat of aluminum in this temperature region is 12 T^3 erg·g⁻¹·K deg⁻¹, where T°K is the absolute temperature. What is the mean specific heat of aluminum over the range stated?

49. Our inquiring physics student takes two bodies of different materials which have similar surfaces. He finds that they cool from 75°C to 30°C in 9 min and 12 min under the same conditions. The masses of the bodies are 30 g and 80 g, respectively. What ratio does he calculate for their specific heat capacities?

50. On a calm, clear night when convection and conduction in the air can be considered negligible, the water in a large pond is at 0°C. For what thickness of ice will the temperature of the exposed ice surface stabilize at −5°C? The thermal conductivity of ice is 0.0042 cal·cm⁻¹·C deg⁻¹·s⁻¹ and its emissivity is 0.3.

51. Heat is conducted through a compound wall consisting of parallel layers of substances of thermal conductivities 0.32 and 0.14 cal·s⁻¹·cm⁻¹·C deg⁻¹ and thicknesses 3.6 cm and 4.2 cm, respectively. The temperatures of the outer faces of the wall are maintained at 24°C and 2°C. Find the rate of transfer of heat per unit area across the wall when equilibrium has been reached.

52. A small blackened metal sphere of radius 0.25 cm is placed in an enclosure maintained at 77°C. When the temperature of the sphere is 27°C, its temperature rises at the rate of 0.135 C deg·s⁻¹. All the heating is due to radiation. Obtain a value for the Stefan-Boltzmann constant. The density and specific heat capacity of the metal are 8.90 g·cm⁻³ and 0.093 cal·g⁻¹·C deg⁻¹, respectively.

53. On a day when the barometric height is 76 cm of mercury, a diver is working in salt water of density 1.026 g·cm⁻³ at a depth of 25 m. The density at the surface is 11.8 × 10⁻⁴ g·cm⁻³, and the temperature at a depth of 25 m is the same as at the surface. What is the density of the air in the diver's suit?

54. A quantity of gas is contained in two bulbs of equal volume connected by a tube of negligible volume. The pressure of the gas is 60 cm of mercury when the temperature of both bulbs is 27°C. What is the pressure when one bulb is immersed in melting ice and the other in boiling water?

55. Two flasks, one containing 1 liter of hydrogen at 2 atm and the other ¾ liter of helium at 1 atm, are joined so that the gases mix. The temperature remains constant. What is the final pressure of the mixture?

56. In an air-conditioning plant, air at 10°C and 90% relative humidity is passed through a spray of water to cool it to 5°C and is then heated to 20°C before being passed into a room. The saturation vapor pressures of water in millimeters of mercury at 5°C, 10°C, and 20°C are 6.51, 8.94, and 17.5, respectively. What percentage of water vapor has been removed from the air and what is the relative humidity of the air in the room?

57. An ideal gas at a pressure of 10^6 dynes·cm^{-2} is contained in a cylinder of volume 1 liter. The gas is heated at constant volume until its pressure is doubled, then kept at constant pressure while the volume is doubled, then kept at constant volume while the pressure is returned to its original value, and finally kept at constant pressure while the volume is returned to its original value.

What is the work done by the gas in the cycle and the total quantities of heat entering and leaving the cylinder during the cycle? The specific heat of the gas at constant volume is 21.4 J·$mole^{-1}$·K deg^{-1} and R has the value 8.31 J·$mole^{-1}$·K deg^{-1}?

58. An ideal heat engine takes in heat at a rate of 700 W at a temperature of 500°K and rejects heat at a temperature of 300°K. What mechanical power does it produce?

Suppose that the engine is now used as a refrigerator which consumes 100 W of mechanical power and operates between the temperatures of 17°C and −13°C. At what rate can it remove heat from the low-temperature reservoir?

59. A standing wave in bromine gas at 300°K has nodes 7.39 cm apart when the frequency is 1000 cycles·s^{-1}. Is bromine monatomic or diatomic?

60. A uniform tube of length 25.6 cm, closed at one end, resonates when a tuning fork of frequency 330 cycles·s^{-1} is held above it. The length of the tube is then gradually decreased. When the length is 15.7 cm, a tuning fork of frequency 528 cycles·s^{-1} causes resonance. Find the velocity of sound in air and the end correction of the tube.

61. A wire 1 m long is stretched to a tension of 50 N. When a bridge is placed 48 cm from one end and the two sections of the wire are plucked, 8 beats are heard every second. What is the linear density of the wire?

62. Two whistles, one stationary, the other moving away with a speed of 100 ft·s^{-1}, are each sounding with a frequency of 440 cycles·s^{-1}. An observer is moving away from the stationary whistle with a speed of 57 ft·s^{-1} in the direction of the other whistle. How many beats per second does the observer hear? The velocity of sound in air is 1140 ft·s^{-1}?

63. The H_γ line emitted by hydrogen atoms in the laboratory has a wavelength of 434 nm. When the spectrum of a distant galaxy is examined, the H_γ line is found to have a wavelength of 589 nm due to the red shift. What is the speed of this galaxy along the line joining it to the earth? Is it approaching or receding?

64. Two small identical balls of mass 0.1 g are suspended from the same point by strings of length 1 m. A charge of 0.2 μC is shared equally between them. What is the angle between the strings when the balls come to rest?

65. A charge Q is spread uniformly along an insulating bar of length $2x$. Show that the magnitude of the electric intensity at a point on the perpendicular bisector of the bar a distance y from the bar is

$$\frac{Q}{4\pi\epsilon_0 y} \cdot \frac{1}{\sqrt{x^2 + y^2}}.$$

66. A drop which carries 6 electronic charges and has a mass of 1.6×10^{-12} g is falling with terminal velocity between plates 1.8 cm apart. What voltage should be applied between the plates to make the drop move upward with the same speed as it was formerly moving downward?

67. A proton having an energy of 100 eV is fired along the perpendicular to a very large metal plate which has a surface density of charge of 10^{-7} C·m^{-2}. How far away does the proton start if it just fails to reach the plate?

68. Two capacitors of capacitance 2 μF and 4 μF are each charged from a 100-V battery. They are then joined together in both possible ways. What are the charge, voltage, and energy of each capacitor in each case?

69. A neon tube is connected across a capacitor of capacitance 25 μF which is being charged continuously through a resistance of 0.5 MΩ from a 2500-V supply. A flash of negligible duration completely discharges the capacitor when the potential across the neon tube reaches 2000 V. How many flashes occur per minute and how much energy is dissipated in each discharge?

70. An electron, after accelerating through a potential difference, is found to have a mass 5% greater than its rest mass. What was the magnitude of the potential difference? If the accelerated particle had been a proton, what potential difference would have been necessary?

71. The charge on a parallel-plate capacitor has fallen to 95% of its original value after one day due to leakage through the dielectric. Given that ρ is the resistivity and ϵ the permittivity of the dielectric, what is the magnitude of $\rho\epsilon$?

72. A battery of emf 4.5 V and internal resistance 0.3 Ω is connected in parallel with a second battery of emf 4.0 V and internal resistance 0.7 Ω. The joint system provides current for an external resistance of 10 Ω. What is the potential difference across the external resistance and the current drawn from each battery?

73. Find the single resistance equivalent to the network shown in the diagram.

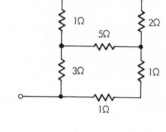

74. A water-cooled magnet in a laboratory is powered from 220-V dc transmission lines and takes 50 A. Water enters it at 12°C and must not leave at a temperature higher than 72°C. What is the minimum rate of flow of the cooling water?

75. The filament of an electric lamp consists of 12 cm of tungsten wire of diameter 2×10^{-3} cm. Tungsten has a resistivity of 5.5×10^{-8} $\Omega \cdot$m at 20°C and a mean temperature coefficient of resistivity of 5.0×10^{-3} C deg^{-1} over the temperature range of the problem. The working temperature of the filament is 2020°C. What is the resistance of the filament and its wattage when it is used on a 230-V supply?

76. A beam of singly ionized carbon atoms is accelerated through a potential difference of 4000 V and then passed through a slit into a magnetic induction of 0.250 Wb$\cdot$m^{-2} directed at right angles to their motion. What is the separation of the traces of C^{12} and C^{13} atoms on a photographic plate lying in the same plane as the slit?

77. A conducting bar of mass 50 g rests on, and at right angles to, two horizontal rails 10 cm apart. A current of 20 A passes through the bar from one rail to the other. The coefficient of static friction between bar and rails is 0.30. What is the smallest magnetic induction at right angles to the plane of bar and rails which will cause the bar to move over the rails?

78. Show that, if the current in an inductive circuit continued to increase at its initial rate, it would reach its equilibrium value in a time equal to the time constant of the circuit.

79. A mutual inductor consists of a long solenoid of radius 5 cm having 200 turns per centimeter. On the center of the solenoid is wound a secondary coil of 200 turns. A ballistic galvanometer of sensitivity 7 cm per μC is connected to the secondary coil, giving it a total resistance of 400 Ω. What is the deflection produced on the galvanometer when a current of 1 mA is reversed in the solenoid?

80. A lamp is placed in series with a 5-μF capacitor and an alternating supply of 60 cycles$\cdot$s^{-1}. The lamp takes 0.333 A and the voltage across it is 123.2 V. What are the supply voltage, the power factor, and the phase angle?

81. A coil is in series with a noninductive resistor and a 230-V 50-cycle$\cdot$s^{-1} supply. Potential differences of 110 V and 170 V are set up across the coil and resistor, respectively, and 1.7 A flows through the circuit. What are the inductance and resistance of the coil?

82. When a 50-V battery of negligible internal resistance is connected into a circuit, the current flowing is found to be 1 A. It is still 1 A when the battery is replaced by a 130-V 60-cycle$\cdot$s^{-1} ac supply. What elements are in the circuit? What is the value of the current if a 110-V, 120-cycle$\cdot$s^{-1} generator is substituted for the other ac supply?

Fundamental Constants

Constant	Symbol	Value
Velocity of light	c	2.9979×10^8 m s^{-1}
Elementary charge	e	1.6021×10^{-19} C
Electron rest mass	m_e	9.1091×10^{-31} kg
Proton rest mass	m_p	1.6725×10^{-27} kg
Neutron rest mass	m_n	1.6748×10^{-27} kg
Planck constant	h	6.6256×10^{-34} J s
	$\hbar = h/2\pi$	1.0545×10^{-34} J s
Charge-to-mass ratio for electron	e/m_e	1.7588×10^{11} kg^{-1} C
Quantum charge ratio	h/e	4.1356×10^{-15} J s C^{-1}
Bohr radius	a_0	5.2917×10^{-11} m
Compton wavelength:		
of electron	$\lambda_{C,e}$	2.4262×10^{-12} m
of proton	$\lambda_{C,p}$	1.3214×10^{-15} m
Rydberg constant	R	1.0974×10^7 m^{-1}
Bohr magneton	μ_B	9.2732×10^{-24} J T^{-1}
Avogadro constant	N_A	6.0225×10^{23} mol^{-1}
Boltzmann constant	k	1.3805×10^{-23} J °K^{-1}
Gas constant	R	8.3143 J °K^{-1} mol^{-1}
Ideal gas normal volume (STP)	V_0	2.2414×10^{-2} m^3 mol^{-1}
Faraday constant	F	9.6487×10^4 C mol^{-1}
Coulomb constant	K_e	8.9874×10^9 N m^2 C^{-2}
Vacuum permittivity	ϵ_0	8.8544×10^{-12} N^{-1} m^{-2} C^2
Magnetic constant	K_m	1.0000×10^{-7} m kg C^{-2}
Vacuum permeability	μ_0	1.3566×10^{-6} m kg C^{-2}
Gravitational constant	γ	6.670×10^{-11} N m^2 kg^{-2}
Acceleration of gravity at sea level and at equator	g	9.7805 m s^{-2}

Numerical constants: $\pi = 3.1416$; $e = 2.7183$; $\sqrt{2} = 1.4142$; $\sqrt{3} = 1.7320$

Four-Place Logarithms of Numbers

N	0	1	2	3	4	5	6	7	8	9
10	0000	0043	0086	0128	0170	0212	0253	0294	0334	0374
11	0414	0453	0492	0531	0569	0607	0645	0682	0719	0755
12	0792	0828	0864	0899	0934	0969	1004	1038	1072	1106
13	1139	1173	1206	1239	1271	1303	1335	1367	1399	1430
14	1461	1492	1523	1553	1584	1614	1644	1673	1703	1732
15	1761	1790	1818	1847	1875	1903	1931	1959	1987	2014
16	2041	2068	2095	2122	2148	2175	2201	2227	2253	2279
17	2304	2330	2355	2380	2405	2430	2455	2480	2504	2529
18	2553	2577	2601	2625	2648	2672	2695	2718	2742	2765
19	2788	2810	2833	2856	2878	2900	2923	2945	2967	2989
20	3010	3032	3054	3075	3096	3118	3139	3160	3181	3201
21	3222	3243	3263	3284	3304	3324	3345	3365	3385	3404
22	3424	3444	3464	3483	3502	3522	3541	3560	3579	3598
23	3617	3636	3655	3674	3692	3711	3729	3747	3766	3784
24	3802	3820	3838	3856	3874	3892	3909	3927	3945	3962
25	3979	3997	4014	4031	4048	4065	4082	4099	4116	4133
26	4150	4166	4183	4200	4216	4232	4249	4265	4281	4298
27	4314	4330	4346	4362	4378	4393	4409	4425	4440	4456
28	4472	4487	4502	4518	4533	4548	4564	4579	4594	4609
29	4624	4639	4654	4669	4683	4698	4713	4728	4742	4757
30	4771	4786	4800	4814	4829	4843	4857	4871	4886	4900
31	4914	4928	4942	4955	4969	4983	4997	5011	5024	5038
32	5051	5065	5079	5092	5105	5119	5132	5145	5159	5172
33	5185	5198	5211	5224	5237	5250	5263	5276	5289	5302
34	5315	5328	5340	5353	5366	5378	5391	5403	5416	5428
35	5441	5453	5465	5478	5490	5502	5514	5527	5539	5551
36	5563	5575	5587	5599	5611	5623	5635	5647	5658	5670
37	5682	5694	5705	5717	5729	5740	5752	5763	5775	5786
38	5798	5809	5821	5832	5843	5855	5866	5877	5888	5899
39	5911	5922	5933	5944	5955	5966	5977	5988	5999	6010
40	6021	6031	6042	6053	6064	6075	6085	6096	6107	6117
41	6128	6138	6149	6160	6170	6180	6191	6201	6212	6222
42	6232	6243	6253	6263	6274	6284	6294	6304	6314	6325
43	6335	6345	6355	6365	6375	6385	6395	6405	6415	6425
44	6435	6444	6454	6464	6474	6484	6493	6503	6513	6522
45	6532	6542	6551	6561	6571	6580	6590	6599	6609	6618
46	6628	6637	6646	6656	6665	6675	6684	6693	6702	6712
47	6721	6730	6739	6749	6758	6767	6776	6785	6794	6803
48	6812	6821	6830	6839	6848	6857	6866	6875	6884	6893
49	6902	6911	6920	6928	6937	6946	6955	6964	6972	6981
50	6990	6998	7007	7016	7024	7033	7042	7050	7059	7067
51	7076	7084	7093	7101	7110	7118	7126	7135	7143	7152
52	7160	7168	7177	7185	7193	7202	7210	7218	7226	7235
53	7243	7251	7259	7267	7275	7284	7292	7300	7308	7316
54	7324	7332	7340	7348	7356	7364	7372	7380	7388	7396

Four-Place Logarithms of Numbers

N	0	1	2	3	4	5	6	7	8	9
55	7404	7412	7419	7427	7435	7443	7451	7459	7466	7474
56	7482	7490	7497	7505	7513	7520	7528	7536	7543	7551
57	7559	7566	7574	7582	7589	7597	7604	7612	7619	7627
58	7634	7642	7649	7657	7664	7672	7679	7686	7694	7701
59	7709	7716	7723	7731	7738	7745	7752	7760	7767	7774
60	7782	7789	7796	7803	7810	7818	7825	7832	7839	7846
61	7853	7860	7868	7875	7882	7889	7896	7903	7910	7917
62	7924	7931	7938	7945	7952	7959	7966	7973	7980	7987
63	7993	8000	8007	8014	8021	8028	8035	8041	8048	8055
64	8062	8069	8075	8082	8089	8096	8102	8109	8116	8122
65	8129	8136	8142	8149	8156	8162	8169	8176	8182	8189
66	8195	8202	8209	8215	8222	8228	8235	8241	8248	8254
67	8261	8267	8274	8280	8287	8293	8299	8306	8312	8319
68	8325	8331	8338	8344	8351	8357	8363	8370	8376	8382
69	8388	8395	8401	8407	8414	8420	8426	8432	8439	8445
70	8451	8457	8463	8470	8476	8482	8488	8494	8500	8506
71	8513	8519	8525	8531	8537	8543	8549	8555	8561	8567
72	8573	8579	8585	8591	8597	8603	8609	8615	8621	8627
73	8633	8639	8645	8651	8657	8663	8669	8675	8681	8686
74	8692	8698	8704	8710	8716	8722	8727	8733	8739	8745
75	8751	8756	8762	8768	8774	8779	8785	8791	8797	8802
76	8808	8814	8820	8825	8831	8837	8842	8848	8854	8859
77	8865	8871	8876	8882	8887	8893	8899	8904	8910	8915
78	8921	8927	8932	8938	8943	8949	8954	8960	8965	8971
79	8976	8982	8987	8993	8998	9004	9009	9015	9020	9025
80	9031	9036	9042	9047	9053	9058	9063	9069	9074	9079
81	9085	9090	9096	9101	9106	9112	9117	9122	9128	9133
82	9138	9143	9149	9154	9159	9165	9170	9175	9180	9186
83	9191	9196	9201	9206	9212	9217	9222	9227	9232	9238
84	9243	9248	9253	9258	9263	9269	9274	9279	9284	9289
85	9294	9299	9304	9309	9315	9320	9325	9330	9335	9340
86	9345	9350	9355	9360	9365	9370	9375	9380	9385	9390
87	9395	9400	9405	9410	9415	9420	9425	9430	9435	9440
88	9445	9450	9455	9460	9465	9469	9474	9479	9484	9489
89	9494	9499	9504	9509	9513	9518	9523	9528	9533	9538
90	9542	9547	9552	9557	9652	9566	9571	9576	9581	9586
91	9590	9595	9600	9605	9609	9614	9619	9624	9628	9633
92	9638	9643	9647	9652	9657	9661	9666	9671	9675	9680
93	9685	9689	9694	9699	9703	9708	9713	9717	9722	9727
94	9731	9736	9741	9745	9750	9754	9759	9763	9768	9773
95	9777	9782	9786	9791	9795	9800	9805	9809	9814	9818
96	9823	9827	9832	9836	9841	9845	9850	9854	9859	9863
97	9868	9872	9877	9881	9886	9890	9894	9899	9903	9908
98	9912	9917	9921	9926	9930	9934	9939	9943	9948	9952
99	9956	9961	9965	9969	9974	9978	9983	9987	9991	9996

Four-Place Values of Trigonometric Ratios and Radians

Degrees	Radians	Sin	Cos	Tan	Cot	Sec	Csc		
0° 00′	.0000	.0000	1.0000	.0000	——	1.000	——	1.5708	90° 00′
10	029	029	000	029	343.8	000	343.8	679	50
20	058	058	000	058	171.9	000	171.9	650	40
30	.0087	.0087	1.0000	.0087	114.6	1.000	114.6	1.5621	30
40	116	116	.9999	116	85.94	000	85.95	592	20
50	145	145	999	145	68.75	000	68.76	563	10
1° 00′	.0175	.0175	.9998	.0175	57.29	1.000	57.30	1.5533	89° 00′
10	204	204	998	204	49.10	000	49.11	504	50
20	233	233	997	233	42.96	000	42.98	475	40
30	.0262	.0262	.9997	.0262	38.19	1.000	38.20	1.5446	30
40	291	291	996	291	34.37	000	34.38	417	20
50	320	320	995	320	31.24	001	31.26	388	10
2° 00′	.0349	.0349	.9994	.0349	28.64	1.001	28.65	1.5359	88° 00′
10	378	378	993	378	26.43	001	26.45	330	50
20	407	407	992	407	24.54	001	24.56	301	40
30	.0436	.0436	.9990	.0437	22.90	1.001	22.93	1.5272	30
40	465	465	989	466	21.47	001	21.49	243	20
50	495	494	988	495	20.21	001	20.23	213	10
3° 00′	.0524	.0523	.9986	.0524	19.08	1.001	19.11	1.5184	87° 00′
10	553	552	985	553	18.07	002	18.10	155	50
20	582	581	983	582	17.17	002	17.20	126	40
30	.0611	.0610	.9981	.0612	16.35	1.002	16.38	1.5097	30
40	640	640	980	641	15.60	002	15.64	068	20
50	669	669	978	670	14.92	002	14.96	039	10
4° 00′	.0698	.0698	.9976	.0699	14.30	1.002	14.34	1.5010	86° 00′
10	727	727	974	729	13.73	003	13.76	981	50
20	756	756	971	758	13.20	003	13.23	952	40
30	.0785	.0785	.9969	.0787	12.71	1.003	12.75	1.4923	30
40	814	814	967	816	12.25	003	12.29	893	20
50	844	843	964	846	11.83	004	11.87	864	10
5° 00′	.0873	.0872	.9962	.0875	11.43	1.004	11.47	1.4835	85° 00′
10	902	901	959	904	11.06	004	11.10	806	50
20	931	929	957	934	10.71	004	10.76	777	40
30	.0960	.0958	.9954	.0963	10.39	1.005	10.43	1.4748	30
40	989	987	951	992	10.08	005	10.13	719	20
50	.1018	.1016	948	.1022	9.788	005	9.839	690	10
6° 00′	.1047	.1045	.9945	.1051	9.514	1.006	9.567	1.4661	84° 00′
10	076	074	942	080	9.255	006	9.309	632	50
20	105	103	939	110	9.010	006	9.065	603	40
30	.1134	.1132	.9936	.1139	8.777	1.006	8.834	1.4573	30
40	164	161	932	169	8.556	007	8.614	544	20
50	193	190	929	198	8.345	007	8.405	515	10
7° 00′	.1222	.1219	.9925	.1228	8.144	1.008	8.206	1.4486	83° 00′
10	251	248	922	257	7.953	008	8.016	457	50
20	280	276	918	287	7.770	008	7.834	428	40
30	.1309	.1305	.9914	.1317	7.596	1.009	7.661	1.4399	30
40	338	334	911	346	7.429	009	7.496	370	20
50	367	363	907	376	7.269	009	7.337	341	10
8° 00′	.1396	.1392	.9903	.1405	7.115	1.010	7.185	1.4312	82° 00′
10	425	421	899	435	6.968	010	7.040	283	50
20	454	449	894	465	6.827	011	6.900	254	40
30	.1484	.1478	.9890	.1495	6.691	1.011	6.765	1.4224	30
40	513	507	886	524	6.561	012	6.636	195	20
50	542	536	881	554	6.435	012	6.512	166	10
9° 00′	.1571	.1564	.9877	.1584	6.314	1.012	6.392	1.4137	81° 00′
		Cos	Sin	Cot	Tan	Csc	Sec	Radians	Degrees

83. The angle of incidence of a ray of light on a prism made of glass of refractive index 1.50 is gradually increased, and it is found that, when the angle is 4°47′, the ray just fails to pass through the prism. What is the refracting angle of the prism?

84. A luminous object is moved along the axis of a spherical mirror. At distances of 9 cm and 12 cm from the pole of the mirror, it is found that the images are of the same size. What type of mirror is being used and what is its focal length?

85. A glass marble made of material of refractive index 1.50 contains an air bubble lying on a diameter *AB*. When viewed from *A*, it seems to be $\frac{4}{5}$ cm from it; but when viewed from *B*, it seems to be 4 cm from *B*. What are the true position of the bubble and the radius of the marble?

86. A drop of a transparent liquid is placed on the surface of a horizontal plane mirror. An equiconvex lens with radii of curvature 25 cm and made of glass of refractive index 1.50 is placed on the drop. When a luminous object is moved along the axis of the system, it is found to be coincident with its image when 35 cm from the lens. What is the refractive index of the liquid?

87. A small object is placed 30 cm in front of a thin diverging lens of focal length −15 cm. Light refracted by the lens falls on a concave spherical mirror of radius of curvature 30 cm, and a real image of the object is formed by reflection 20 cm from the mirror. What is the distance between lens and mirror?

88. Our intelligent physics student constructs a rudimentary microscope from a solid transparent rod of length 36 cm and refractive index 1.48 by making the ends spherical and convex and of radius of curvature 3 cm. One end acts as objective and the other as eyepiece. How far from one end should an object be placed to produce a final image at infinity and what will be the magnifying power of the microscope?

89. An astronomical telescope consists of two thin converging lenses and gives an angular magnification of 10 when in normal adjustment, with the lenses 55 cm apart. An object 2 m away from the objective lens is viewed through the telescope. Through what distance should the eye lens be moved in order that the final image may be viewed at infinity?

90. The diameter of the tenth bright ring viewed by reflection in a Newton's-rings apparatus changes from 1.50 cm to 1.32 cm when liquid is introduced between the lens and the plate. Given that the lens is in contact with the plate at its center, what is the refractive index of the liquid? If the diameters are correct to ±0.1 mm, how accurate is the result?

91. A diffraction grating with 2000 lines per centimeter produces a strong diffraction maximum at 30° when illuminated normally with a monochromatic beam of visible light. What are the possible wavelengths of the incident light? Suppose that there is also a strong maximum at 22°1′. Which of these wavelengths is the correct one?

92. A blue lamp emits light of mean wavelength 4500 Å. The lamp is rated at 150 W and 8% of the energy appears as emitted light. How many quanta are emitted by the lamp per second?

93. The work function of potassium is 2.0 eV. What is the maximum velocity of electrons emitted from a clean potassium surface when light of wavelength 4000 Å falls on it?

94. The mass absorption coefficient in aluminum-27 for x-rays of wavelength 0.70 Å is 5.0 cm²·g⁻¹. The density of aluminum is 2.7 g·cm⁻³. What thickness of aluminum is required to reduce the intensity to one-tenth of its incident value? What is the atomic collision cross section for this process?

95. The K absorption edge of rhodium occurs at a wavelength of 0.533 Å. One of the K_α lines emitted from a rhodium target has a wavelength of 0.612 Å. How many electron volts of energy must an incoming particle possess if it is to eject an electron from the appropriate L level of rhodium?

96. X-rays are reflected from the principal planes of a cubic crystal at a minimum glancing angle of 12.5°. If the crystal has a density of 3.12 g·cm⁻³ and a molecular weight of 62.4, the molecule being composed of two atoms, what is the wavelength of the x-rays? At what other angles will reflections be obtained from these planes?

97. A narrow beam of electrons of energy 200 eV passes through a thin polycrystalline foil. Calculate the angle through which the electrons are diffracted in the second order from the crystal planes with interplanar spacing 2.15 Å.

98. What is the mass of 1 Ci of Th^{232} which has a half-life of 1.39×10^{10} yr?

99. When B^{11} is bombarded by protons, α-particles are given off, the atom left being Be^8. The α-particles emitted at right angles to the incident beam have an energy of 11.5 MeV. What is the energy of the incident protons? In amu, the masses of proton, α-particle, Be^8, and B^{11} are 1.00814, 4.00387, 8.00785, and 11.01279.

100. How much electrical energy is obtained from a nuclear power station when 5 g of Pu^{239} are used up? The conversion efficiency is 18% and the fission of each Pu^{239} atom releases 180 MeV of energy.

Answers to Supplementary Problems

1. 80 lb; $11\frac{1}{4}$ in.
2. 8.5 lb; 6 lb; 6 lb
3. 30 lb; 147.1 lb at 78°14′ to the ground
4. 0.095r from center
5. 2.25 ft
6. 40 ft·s⁻¹
7. 4 s; 50 ft·s⁻¹
8. 63°26′; 89.4 mph
9. 56.3 cm
10. 0.75
11. 16.14 ft; 1.01 s
12. 3.51×10^5 to 1
13. 3.45 g·cm⁻³
14. 2.21 m·s⁻²; ±0.057 N
15. 17,840 g·cm²
16. $g/2$
17. 2.67 ft·s⁻²; 533 lb
18. 0.87 slug
19. 10 ft·lb; 0.18 s
20. $g/100$; g
21. 196 ft·s⁻¹
22. 0.0917°
23. 4.63; 5.56 J
24. 35 m·s⁻¹
25. 1 in 10
26. 11.32 N; 0.51 rev·s⁻¹.
27. 2.26 m
28. 991 m·s⁻¹
29. 4 lb
30. 484.5 rev
32. 2.7 rad·s⁻¹
33. 66.7 cm; 57.1 cm
34. 1325 m; 10°21′
35. 12.6 cm
36. 4.1 s
37. 19.5 cm
38. 0.853 g·cm⁻³
39. 400 g; 439 g
40. 1098 N; 0.932 m·s⁻¹
41. 2.6 cm
42. 27%
43. 15 cm
44. 574.25°
45. 0.69×10^{-2} cm
46. 15.2°C
47. 9.6×10^8 N·m²
48. 3825 erg; 255 erg·g⁻¹
49. 2 to 1
50. 10.05 cm
51. 0.533 cal·s⁻¹·cm⁻²
52. 5.65×10^{-5} erg·cm⁻²·K deg⁻⁴·s⁻¹
53. 4.11×10^{-3} g·cm⁻³
54. 63.06 cm
55. 11/7 atm
56. 19.1%; 37.2%
57. 100 J; 972.5 J; 872.5 J
58. 280 W; 867 W
59. Diatomic
60. 348.5 m·s⁻¹; 0.80 cm
61. 5.02 g·m⁻¹
62. 6.74
63. $5c/14$; receding
64. 32°34′
66. 588 V
67. 8.85 mm
68. 2×10^{-4} C; 100 V; 10^{-2} J; 4×10^{-4} C; 100 V; 2×10^{-2} J; 0.67×10^4 C; 33.3 V; 1.1×10^{-3} J; 1.33×10^{-4} C; 33.3 V; 2.2×10^{-3} J
69. 3; 50 J
70. 2.56×10^4 V; 4.70×10^7 V
71. 1.68×10^6 Ω F
72. 4.26 V; 0.978 A; −0.372 A
73. 2.27 Ω
74. 2.63 liter·min⁻¹
75. 231 Ω; 229 W
76. 1.04 cm
77. 0.0735 Wb·m⁻²
79. 1.38 cm
80. 215.5 V; 0.5716; 55°8′
81. 0.195 H; 20.58 Ω
82. 0.318 H; 50 Ω; 0.449 A
83. 45°
84. Concave; 10.5 cm
85. 1 cm; 2 cm
86. 1.286
87. 50 cm
88. 9.55 cm; −7.4
89. 16.67 cm
90. 1.29 ± 0.04
91. 8.333×10^{-5} cm; 6.250×10^{-5} cm; 5.000×10^{-5} cm; 4.167×10^{-5} cm; 6.250×10^{-5} cm
92. 2.72×10^{19}
93. 6.214×10^5 m·s⁻¹
94. 0.1706 cm; 87.9 barn
95. 3.01 keV
96. 1.104 Å; 25°39′; 40°29′; 59°57′
97. 23°47′
98. 9.01×10^6 cm
99. 7.81 MeV
100. 1.82×10^4 kW·hr

Appendix

CONVERSION FACTORS
UNITS AND SYMBOLS
FUNDAMENTAL CONSTANTS
FOUR-PLACE LOGARITHMS OF NUMBERS
FOUR-PLACE VALUES OF TRIGONOMETRIC RATIOS AND RADIANS

Time:

$1\text{ s} = 1.667 \times 10^{-2}\text{ min} = 2.778 \times 10^{-4}\text{ hr}$
$\quad = 3.169 \times 10^{-8}\text{ yr}$
$1\text{ min} = 60\text{ s} = 1.667 \times 10^{-2}\text{ hr}$
$\quad = 1.901 \times 10^{-6}\text{ yr}$
$1\text{ hr} = 3600\text{ s} = 60\text{ min} = 1.141 \times 10^{-4}\text{ yr}$
$1\text{ yr} = 3.156 \times 10^{7}\text{ s} = 5.259 \times 10^{5}\text{ min}$
$\quad = 8.766 \times 10^{3}\text{ hr}$

Length:

$1\text{ m} = 10^{2}\text{ cm} = 39.37\text{ in.} = 6.214 \times 10^{-4}\text{ mi}$
$1\text{ mi} = 5280\text{ ft} = 1.609\text{ km}$
$1\text{ in.} = 2.540\text{ cm}$
$1\text{ Å (angstrom)} = 10^{-8}\text{ cm} = 10^{-10}\text{ m}$
$\quad = 10^{-4}\,\mu\text{ (micron)}$
$1\,\mu\text{ (micron)} = 10^{-6}\text{ m}$
$1\text{ AU (astronomical unit)} = 1.496 \times 10^{11}\text{ m}$
$1\text{ light year} = 9.46 \times 10^{15}\text{ m}$
$1\text{ parsec} = 3.084 \times 10^{16}\text{ m}$

Angle:

$1\text{ radian} = 57.3°$
$1° = 1.74 \times 10^{-2}\text{ rad}$
$1' = 2.91 \times 10^{-4}\text{ rad}$
$1'' = 4.85 \times 10^{-6}\text{ rad}$

Area:

$1\text{ m}^2 = 10^{4}\text{ cm}^2 = 1.55 \times 10^{-5}\text{ in}^2$
$\quad = 10.76\text{ ft}^2$
$1\text{ in}^2 = 6.452\text{ cm}^2$
$1\text{ ft}^2 = 144\text{ in}^2 = 9.29 \times 10^{-2}\text{ m}^2$

Volume:

$1\text{ m}^3 = 10^{6}\text{ cm}^3 = 10^{3}\text{ liters}$
$\quad = 35.3\text{ ft}^3 = 6.1 \times 10^{4}\text{ in}^3$
$1\text{ ft}^3 = 2.83 \times 10^{-2}\text{ m}^3 = 28.32\text{ liters}$
$1\text{ in}^3 = 16.39\text{ cm}^3$

Velocity:

$1\text{ m s}^{-1} = 10^{2}\text{ cm s}^{-1} = 3.281\text{ ft s}^{-1}$
$1\text{ ft s}^{-1} = 30.48\text{ cm s}^{-1}$
$1\text{ mi min}^{-1} = 60\text{ mi hr}^{-1} = 88\text{ ft s}^{-1}$

Acceleration:

$1\text{ m s}^{-2} = 10^{2}\text{ cm s}^{-2} = 3.281\text{ ft s}^{-2}$
$1\text{ ft s}^{-2} = 30.48\text{ cm s}^{-2}$

Mass:

$1\text{ kg} = 10^{3}\text{ g} = 2.205\text{ lb}$
$1\text{ lb} = 453.6\text{ g} = 0.4536\text{ kg}$
$1\text{ amu} = 1.6604 \times 10^{-27}\text{ kg}$

Force:

$1\text{ N} = 10^{5}\text{ dyn} = 0.2248\text{ lbf} = 0.102\text{ kgf}$
$1\text{ dyn} = 10^{-5}\text{ N} = 2.248 \times 10^{-6}\text{ lbf}$
$1\text{ lbf} = 4.448\text{ N} = 4.448 \times 10^{5}\text{ dyn}$
$1\text{ kgf} = 9.81\text{ N}$

Pressure:

$1\text{ N m}^{-2} = 9.265 \times 10^{-6}\text{ atm}$
$\quad = 1.450 \times 10^{-4}\text{ lbf in}^{-2}$
$\quad = 10\text{ dyn cm}^{-2}$
$1\text{ atm} = 14.7\text{ lbf in}^{-2} = 1.013 \times 10^{5}\text{ N m}^{-2}$
$1\text{ bar} = 10^{6}\text{ dyn cm}^{-2}$

Energy:

$1\text{ J} = 10^{7}\text{ ergs} = 0.239\text{ cal}$
$\quad = 6.242 \times 10^{18}\text{ eV}$
$1\text{ eV} = 10^{-6}\text{ MeV} = 1.60 \times 10^{-12}\text{ erg}$
$\quad = 1.07 \times 10^{-9}\text{ amu}$
$1\text{ cal} = 4.186\text{ J} = 2.613 \times 10^{19}\text{ eV}$
$\quad = 2.807 \times 10^{10}\text{ amu}$
$1\text{ amu} = 1.492 \times 10^{-10}\text{ J}$
$\quad = 3.564 \times 10^{-11}\text{ cal} = 931.0\text{ MeV}$

Temperature:

$°K = 273.1 + °C$
$°C = \frac{5}{9}(°F - 32)$
$°F = \frac{9}{5}°C + 32$

Power:

$1\text{ W} = 1.341 \times 10^{-3}\text{ hp}$
$1\text{ hp} = 745.7\text{ W}$

Electric Charge:*

$1\text{ C} = 3 \times 10^{9}\text{ stC}$
$1\text{ stC} = \frac{1}{3} \times 10^{-9}\text{ C}$

Current:*

$1\text{ A} = 3 \times 10^{9}\text{ stA}$
$1\text{ stA} = \frac{1}{3} \times 10^{-9}\text{ A}$
$1\,\mu\text{A} = 10^{-6}\text{ A},\ 1\text{ mA} = 10^{-3}\text{ A}$

Electric Field:*

$1\text{ N C}^{-1} = 1\text{ V m}^{-1} = 10^{-2}\text{ V cm}^{-1}$
$\quad = \frac{1}{3} \times 10^{-4}\text{ stV cm}^{-1}$

Electric Potential:*

$1\text{ V} = \frac{1}{3} \times 10^{-2}\text{ stV}$
$1\text{ stV} = 3 \times 10^{2}\text{ V}$

Resistance:

$1\,\Omega = 10^{6}\mu\Omega$
$1\text{ M}\Omega = 10^{6}\Omega$

Capacity:*

$1\text{ F} = 9 \times 10^{11}\text{ stF}$
$1\text{ stF} = \frac{1}{9} \times 10^{-11}\text{ F}$
$1\,\mu\text{F} = 10^{-6}\text{ F},\ 1\text{ pF} = 10^{-12}\text{ F}$

Magnetic Field:

$1\text{ T} = 10^{4}\text{ gauss},\ 1\text{ gauss} = 10^{-4}\text{ T}$

Magnetic Flux:

$1\text{ Wb} = 10^{8}\text{ maxwell},\ 1\text{ maxwell} = 10^{-8}\text{ Wb}$

Magnetizing Field:

$1\text{ A m}^{-1} = 4\pi \times 10^{-3}\text{ oersted}$
$1\text{ oersted} = 1/4\pi \times 10^{3}\text{ A m}^{-1}$

*In all cases, 3 actually means 2.998 and 9 means 8.987.

Units and Symbols

Quantity	Symbol	Name of unit	Relation to fundamental units	
			MKSC	MKSA
Length	l, s	meter	m	
Mass	m	kilogram	kg	
Time	t	second	s	
Velocity	v		$\mathrm{m\ s^{-1}}$	
Acceleration	a		$\mathrm{m\ s^{-2}}$	
Angular velocity	ω		$\mathrm{s^{-1}}$	
Angular frequency	ω		$\mathrm{s^{-1}}$	
Frequency	ν	hertz (Hz)	$\mathrm{s^{-1}}$	
Momentum	p		$\mathrm{m\ kg\ s^{-1}}$	
Force	F	newton (N)	$\mathrm{m\ kg\ s^{-2}}$	
Angular momentum	L		$\mathrm{m^2\ kg\ s^{-1}}$	
Torque	τ		$\mathrm{m^2\ kg\ s^{-2}}$	
Work	W	joule (J)	$\mathrm{m^2\ kg\ s^{-2}}$	
Power	P	watt (W)	$\mathrm{m^2\ kg\ s^{-3}}$	
Energy	E_k, E_p, U, E	joule (J)	$\mathrm{m^2\ kg\ s^{-2}}$	
Temperature	T	°K	$\mathrm{m^2\ kg\ s^{-2}/particle}$	
Coefficient of diffusion	D		$\mathrm{m^2\ s^{-1}}$	
Coefficient of thermal conductivity	K		$\mathrm{m\ kg\ s^{-3}\ {}^{\circ}K^{-1}}$	
Coefficient of viscosity	η		$\mathrm{m^{-1}\ kg\ s^{-1}}$	
Young's modulus	Y		$\mathrm{m^{-1}\ kg\ s^{-2}}$	
Bulk modulus	κ		$\mathrm{m^{-1}\ kg\ s^{-2}}$	
Shear modulus	G		$\mathrm{m^{-1}\ kg\ s^{-2}}$	
Moment of inertia	I		$\mathrm{m^2\ kg}$	
Gravitational field	$\mathcal{G}$		$\mathrm{m\ s^{-2}}$	
Gravitational potential	$V_\mathcal{G}$		$\mathrm{m^2\ s^{-2}}$	
Charge	q, Q	coulomb	C	A s
Electric current	I	ampere	$\mathrm{s^{-1}\ C}$	A
Electric field	$\mathcal{E}$		$\mathrm{m\ kg\ s^{-2}\ C^{-1}}$	$\mathrm{m\ kg\ s^{-3}\ A^{-1}}$
Electric potential	V	volt (V)	$\mathrm{m^2\ kg\ s^{-2}\ C^{-1}}$	$\mathrm{m^2\ kg\ s^{-3}\ A^{-1}}$
Current density	j		$\mathrm{m^{-2}\ s^{-1}\ C}$	$\mathrm{m^{-2}\ A}$
Electric resistance	R	ohm (Ω)	$\mathrm{m^2\ kg\ s^{-1}\ C^{-2}}$	$\mathrm{m^2\ kg\ s^{-3}\ A^{-2}}$
Inductance	L	henry (H)	$\mathrm{m^2\ kg\ C^{-2}}$	$\mathrm{m^2\ kg\ s^{-2}\ A^{-2}}$
Electric permittivity	ϵ_0		$\mathrm{m^{-3}\ kg^{-1}\ s^2\ C^2}$	$\mathrm{m^{-3}\ kg^{-1}\ s\ A^2}$
Polarization	$\mathcal{P}$		$\mathrm{m^{-2}\ C}$	$\mathrm{m^{-2}\ s\ A}$
Dielectric displacement	$\mathcal{D}$		$\mathrm{m^{-2}\ C}$	$\mathrm{m^{-2}\ s\ A}$
Magnetic field	$\mathcal{B}$	tesla (T)	$\mathrm{kg\ s^{-1}\ C^{-1}}$	$\mathrm{kg\ s^{-2}\ A^{-1}}$
Magnetic permeability	μ_0		$\mathrm{m\ kg\ C^{-2}}$	$\mathrm{m\ kg\ s^{-2}\ A^{-2}}$
Magnetization	$\mathcal{M}$		$\mathrm{m^{-1}\ s^{-1}\ C}$	$\mathrm{m^{-1}\ A}$
Magnetizing field	$\mathcal{H}$		$\mathrm{m^{-1}\ s^{-1}\ C}$	$\mathrm{m^{-1}\ A}$
Magnetic flux	$\Phi_\mathcal{B}$	weber (Wb)	$\mathrm{m^2\ kg\ s^{-1}\ C^{-1}}$	$\mathrm{m^2\ kg\ s^{-2}\ A^{-1}}$
Electric dipole moment	p		$\mathrm{m\ C}$	$\mathrm{m\ s\ A}$
Electric quadrupole moment	Q		$\mathrm{m^2\ C}$	$\mathrm{m^2\ s\ A}$
Magnetic dipole moment	M		$\mathrm{m^2\ s^{-1}\ C}$	$\mathrm{m^2\ A}$
Magnetic quadrupole moment	Q		$\mathrm{m^3\ s^{-1}\ C}$	$\mathrm{m^3\ A}$
Capacity	C	farad (F)	$\mathrm{m^{-2}\ kg^{-1}\ s^2\ C^2}$	$\mathrm{m^{-2}\ kg^{-1}\ s^4\ A^2}$

Four-Place Values of Trigonometric Ratios and Radians

Degrees	Radians	Sin	Cos	Tan	Cot	Sec	Csc		
9° 00'	.1571	.1564	.9877	.1584	6.314	1.012	6.392	1.4137	**81° 00'**
10	600	593	872	614	197	013	277	108	50
20	629	622	868	644	084	013	166	079	40
30	.1658	.1650	.9863	.1673	5.976	1.014	6.059	1.4050	30
40	687	679	858	703	871	014	5.955	1.4021	20
50	716	708	853	733	769	015	855	992	10
10° 00'	.1745	.1736	.9848	.1763	5.671	1.015	5.759	1.3963	**80° 00'**
10	774	765	843	793	576	016	665	934	50
20	804	794	838	823	485	016	575	904	40
30	.1833	.1822	.9833	.1853	5.396	1.017	5.487	1.3875	30
40	862	851	827	883	309	018	403	846	20
50	891	880	822	914	226	018	320	817	10
11° 00'	.1920	.1908	.9816	.1944	5.145	1.019	5.241	1.3788	**79° 00'**
10	949	937	811	974	066	019	164	759	50
20	978	965	805	.2004	4.989	020	089	730	40
30	.2007	.1994	.9799	.2035	4.915	1.020	5.016	1.3701	30
40	036	.2022	793	065	843	021	4.945	672	20
50	065	051	787	095	773	022	876	643	10
12° 00'	.2094	.2079	.9781	.2126	4.705	1.022	4.810	1.3614	**78° 00'**
10	123	108	775	156	638	023	745	584	50
20	153	136	769	186	574	024	682	555	40
30	.2182	.2164	.9763	.2217	4.511	1.024	4.620	1.3526	30
40	211	193	757	247	449	025	560	497	20
50	240	221	750	278	390	026	502	468	10
13° 00'	.2269	.2250	.9744	.2309	4.331	1.026	4.445	1.3439	**77° 00'**
10	298	278	737	339	275	027	390	410	50
20	327	306	730	370	219	028	336	381	40
30	.2356	.2334	.9724	.2401	4.165	1.028	4.284	1.3352	30
40	385	363	717	432	113	029	232	323	20
50	414	391	710	462	061	030	182	294	10
14° 00'	.2443	.2419	.9703	.2493	4.011	1.031	4.134	1.3265	**76° 00'**
10	473	447	696	524	3.962	031	086	235	50
20	502	476	689	555	914	032	039	206	40
30	.2531	.2504	.9681	.2586	3.867	1.033	3.994	1.3177	30
40	560	532	674	617	821	034	950	148	20
50	589	560	667	648	776	034	906	119	10
15° 00'	.2618	.2588	.9659	.2679	3.732	1.035	3.864	1.3090	**75° 00'**
10	647	616	652	711	689	036	822	061	50
20	676	644	644	742	647	037	782	032	40
30	.2705	.2672	.9636	.2773	3.606	1.038	3.742	1.3003	30
40	734	700	628	805	566	039	703	974	20
50	763	728	621	836	526	039	665	945	10
16° 00'	.2793	.2756	.9613	.2867	3.487	1.040	3.628	1.2915	**74° 00'**
10	822	784	605	899	450	041	592	886	50
20	851	812	596	931	412	042	556	857	40
30	.2880	.2840	.9588	.2962	3.376	1.043	3.521	1.2828	30
40	909	868	580	994	340	044	487	799	20
50	938	896	572	.3026	305	045	453	770	10
17° 00'	.2967	.2924	.9563	.3057	3.271	1.046	3.420	1.2741	**73° 00'**
10	996	952	555	089	237	047	388	712	50
20	.3025	979	546	121	204	048	356	683	40
30	.3054	.3007	.9537	.3153	3.172	1.049	3.326	1.2654	30
40	083	035	528	185	140	049	295	625	20
50	113	062	520	217	108	050	265	595	10
18° 00'	.3142	.3090	.9511	.3249	3.078	1.051	3.236	1.2566	**72° 00'**
		Cos	Sin	Cot	Tan	Csc	Sec	Radians	Degrees

(Continued)

270

Four-Place Values of Trigonometric Ratios and Radians

Degrees	Radians	Sin	Cos	Tan	Cot	Sec	Csc		
18° 00′	.3142	.3090	.9511	.3249	3.078	1.051	3.236	1.2566	72° 00′
10	171	118	502	281	047	052	207	537	50
20	200	145	492	314	018	053	179	508	40
30	.3229	.3173	.9483	.3346	2.989	1.054	3.152	1.2479	30
40	258	201	474	378	960	056	124	450	20
50	287	228	465	411	932	057	098	421	10
19° 00′	.3316	.3256	.9455	.3443	2.904	1.058	3.072	1.2392	71° 00′
10	345	283	446	476	877	059	046	363	50
20	374	311	436	508	850	060	021	334	40
30	.3403	.3338	.9426	.3541	2.824	1.061	2.996	1.2305	30
40	432	365	417	574	798	062	971	275	20
50	462	393	407	607	773	063	947	246	10
20° 00′	.3491	.3420	.9397	.3640	2.747	1.064	2.924	1.2217	70° 00′
10	520	448	387	673	723	065	901	188	50
20	549	475	377	706	699	066	878	159	40
30	.3578	.3502	.9367	.3739	2.675	1.068	2.855	1.2130	30
40	607	529	356	772	651	069	833	101	20
50	636	557	346	805	628	070	812	072	10
21° 00′	.3665	.3584	.9336	.3839	2.605	1.071	2.790	1.2043	69° 00′
10	694	611	325	872	583	072	769	1.2014	50
20	723	638	315	906	560	074	749	985	40
30	.3752	.3665	.9304	.3939	2.539	1.075	2.729	1.1956	30
40	782	692	293	973	517	076	709	926	20
50	811	719	283	.4006	496	077	689	897	10
22° 00′	.3840	.3746	.9272	.4040	2.475	1.079	2.669	1.1868	68° 00′
10	869	773	261	074	455	080	650	839	50
20	898	800	250	108	434	081	632	810	40
30	.3927	.3827	.9239	.4142	2.414	1.082	2.613	1.1781	30
40	956	854	228	176	394	084	595	752	20
50	985	881	216	210	375	085	577	723	10
23° 00′	.4014	.3907	.9205	.4245	2.356	1.086	2.559	1.1694	67° 00′
10	043	934	194	279	337	088	542	665	50
20	072	961	182	314	318	089	525	636	40
30	.4102	.3987	.9171	.4348	2.300	1.090	2.508	1.1606	30
40	131	.4014	159	383	282	092	491	577	20
50	160	041	147	417	264	093	475	548	10
24° 00′	.4189	.4067	.9135	.4452	2.246	1.095	2.459	1.1519	66° 00′
10	218	094	124	487	229	096	443	490	50
20	247	120	112	522	211	097	427	461	40
30	.4276	.4147	.9100	.4557	2.194	1.099	2.411	1.1432	30
40	305	173	088	592	177	100	396	403	20
50	334	200	075	628	161	102	381	374	10
25° 00′	.4363	.4226	.9063	.4663	2.145	1.103	2.366	1.1345	65° 00′
10	392	253	051	699	128	105	352	316	50
20	422	279	038	734	112	106	337	286	40
30	.4451	.4305	.9026	.4770	2.097	1.108	2.323	1.1257	30
40	480	331	013	806	081	109	309	228	20
50	509	358	001	841	066	111	295	199	10
26° 00′	.4538	.4384	.8988	.4877	2.050	1.113	2.281	1.1170	64° 00′
10	567	410	975	913	035	114	268	141	50
20	596	436	962	950	020	116	254	112	40
30	.4625	.4462	.8949	.4986	2.006	1.117	2.241	1.1083	30
40	654	488	936	.5022	1.991	119	228	054	20
50	683	514	923	059	977	121	215	1.1025	10
27° 00′	.4712	.4540	.8910	.5095	1.963	1.122	2.203	1.0996	63° 00′
		Cos	Sin	Cot	Tan	Csc	Sec	Radians	Degrees

Four-Place Values of Trigonometric Ratios and Radians

Degrees	Radians	Sin	Cos	Tan	Cot	Sec	Csc		
27° 00'	.4712	.4540	.8910	.5095	1.963	1.122	2.203	1.0996	**63° 00'**
10	741	566	897	132	949	124	190	966	50
20	771	592	884	169	935	126	178	937	40
30	.4800	.4617	.8870	.5206	1.921	1.127	2.166	1.0908	30
40	829	643	857	243	907	129	154	879	20
50	858	669	843	280	894	131	142	850	10
28° 00'	.4887	.4695	.8829	.5317	1.881	1.133	2.130	1.0821	**62° 00'**
10	916	720	816	354	868	134	118	792	50
20	945	746	802	392	855	136	107	763	40
30	.4974	.4772	.8788	.5430	1.842	1.138	2.096	1.0734	30
40	.5003	797	774	467	829	140	085	705	20
50	032	823	760	505	816	142	074	676	10
29° 00'	.5061	.4848	.8746	.5543	1.804	1.143	2.063	1.0647	**61° 00'**
10	091	874	732	581	792	145	052	617	50
20	120	899	718	619	780	147	041	588	40
30	.5149	.4924	.8704	.5658	1.767	1.149	2.031	1.0559	30
40	178	950	689	696	756	151	020	530	20
50	207	975	675	735	744	153	010	501	10
30° 00'	.5236	.5000	.8660	.5774	1.732	1.155	2.000	1.0472	**60° 00'**
10	265	025	646	812	720	157	1.990	443	50
20	294	050	631	851	709	159	980	414	40
30	.5323	.5075	.8616	.5890	1.698	1.161	1.970	1.0385	30
40	352	100	601	930	686	163	961	356	20
50	381	125	587	969	675	165	951	327	10
31° 00'	.5411	.5150	.8572	.6009	1.664	1.167	1.942	1.0297	**59° 00'**
10	440	175	557	048	653	169	932	268	50
20	469	200	542	088	643	171	923	239	40
30	.5498	.5225	.8526	.6128	1.632	1.173	1.914	1.0210	30
40	527	250	511	168	621	175	905	181	20
50	556	275	496	208	611	177	896	152	10
32° 00'	.5585	.5299	.8480	.6249	1.600	1.179	1.887	1.0123	**58° 00'**
10	614	324	465	289	590	181	878	094	50
20	643	348	450	330	580	184	870	065	40
30	.5672	.5373	.8434	.6371	1.570	1.186	1.861	1.0036	30
40	701	398	418	412	560	188	853	1.0007	20
50	730	422	403	453	550	190	844	977	10
33° 00'	.5760	.5446	.8387	.6494	1.540	1.192	1.836	.9948	**57° 00'**
10	789	471	371	536	530	195	828	919	50
20	818	495	355	577	520	197	820	890	40
30	.5847	.5519	.8339	.6619	1.511	1.199	1.812	.9861	30
40	876	544	323	661	501	202	804	832	20
50	905	568	307	703	1.492	204	796	803	10
34° 00'	.5934	.5592	.8290	.6745	1.483	1.206	1.788	.9774	**56° 00'**
10	963	616	274	787	473	209	781	745	50
20	992	640	258	830	464	211	773	716	40
30	.6021	.5664	.8241	.6873	1.455	1.213	1.766	.9687	30
40	050	688	225	916	446	216	758	657	20
50	080	712	208	959	437	218	751	628	10
35° 00'	.6109	.5736	.8192	.7002	1.428	1.221	1.743	.9599	**55° 00'**
10	138	760	175	046	419	223	736	570	50
20	167	783	158	089	411	226	729	541	40
30	.6196	.5807	.8141	.7133	1.402	1.228	1.722	.9512	30
40	225	831	124	177	393	231	715	483	20
50	254	854	107	221	385	233	708	454	10
36° 00'	.6283	.5878	.8090	.7265	1.376	1.236	1.701	.9425	**54° 00'**
		Cos	Sin	Cot	Tan	Csc	Sec	Radians	Degrees

(Continued)

Four-Place Values of Trigonometric Ratios and Radians

Degrees	Radians	Sin	Cos	Tan	Cot	Sec	Csc		
36° 00′	.6283	.5878	.8090	.7265	1.376	1.236	1.701	.9425	**54° 00′**
10	312	901	073	310	368	239	695	396	50
20	341	925	056	355	360	241	688	367	40
30	.6370	.5948	.8039	.7400	1.351	1.244	1.681	.9338	30
40	400	972	021	445	343	247	675	308	20
50	429	995	004	490	335	249	668	279	10
37° 00′	.6458	.6018	.7986	.7536	1.327	1.252	1.662	.9250	**53° 00′**
10	487	041	969	581	319	255	655	221	50
20	516	065	951	627	311	258	649	192	40
30	.6545	.6088	.7934	.7673	1.303	1.260	1.643	.9163	30
40	574	111	916	720	295	263	636	134	20
50	603	134	898	766	288	266	630	105	10
38° 00′	.6632	.6157	.7880	.7813	1.280	1.269	1.624	.9076	**52° 00′**
10	661	180	862	860	272	272	618	047	50
20	690	202	844	907	265	275	612	.9018	40
30	.6720	.6225	.7826	.7954	1.257	1.278	1.606	.8988	30
40	749	248	808	.8002	250	281	601	959	20
50	778	271	790	050	242	284	595	930	10
39° 00′	.6807	.6293	.7771	.8098	1.235	1.287	1.589	.8901	**51° 00′**
10	836	316	753	146	228	290	583	872	50
20	865	338	735	195	220	293	578	843	40
30	.6894	.6361	.7716	.8243	1.213	1.296	1.572	.8814	30
40	923	383	698	292	206	299	567	785	20
50	952	406	679	342	199	302	561	756	10
40° 00′	.6981	.6428	.7660	.8391	1.192	1.305	1.556	.8727	**50° 00′**
10	.7010	450	642	441	185	309	550	698	50
20	039	472	623	491	178	312	545	668	40
30	.7069	.6494	.7604	.8541	1.171	1.315	1.540	.8639	30
40	098	517	585	591	164	318	535	610	20
50	127	539	566	642	157	322	529	581	10
41° 00′	.7156	.6561	.7547	.8693	1.150	1.325	1.524	.8552	**49° 00′**
10	185	583	528	744	144	328	519	523	50
20	214	604	509	796	137	332	514	494	40
30	.7243	.6626	.7490	.8847	1.130	1.335	1.509	.8465	30
40	272	648	470	899	124	339	504	436	20
50	301	670	451	952	117	342	499	407	10
42° 00′	.7330	.6691	.7431	.9004	1.111	1.346	1.494	.8378	**48° 00′**
10	359	713	412	057	104	349	490	348	50
20	389	734	392	110	098	353	485	319	40
30	.7418	.6756	.7373	.9163	1.091	1.356	1.480	.8290	30
40	447	777	353	217	085	360	476	261	20
50	476	799	333	271	079	364	471	232	10
43° 00′	.7505	.6820	.7314	.9325	1.072	1.367	1.466	.8203	**47° 00′**
10	534	841	294	380	066	371	462	174	50
20	563	862	274	435	060	375	457	145	40
30	.7592	.6884	.7254	.9490	1.054	1.379	1.453	.8116	30
40	621	905	234	545	048	382	448	087	20
50	650	926	214	601	042	386	444	058	10
44° 00′	.7679	.6947	.7193	.9657	1.036	1.390	1.440	.8029	**46° 00′**
10	709	967	173	713	030	394	435	999	50
20	738	988	153	770	024	398	431	970	40
30	.7767	.7009	.7133	.9827	1.018	1.402	1.427	.7941	30
40	796	030	112	884	012	406	423	912	20
50	825	050	092	942	006	410	418	883	10
45° 00′	.7854	.7071	.7071	1.000	1.000	1.414	1.414	.7854	**45° 00′**
		Cos	Sin	Cot	Tan	Csc	Sec	Radians	Degrees

Index

Topics are listed by chapter and question numbers if in Section I, and by section and question numbers if in Sections II or III.